SEPUP

Science

INDIANA EDITION ▶ GRADE 6

SEPUP

Science

INDIANA EDITION ▶ GRADE 6

SCIENCE
EDUCATION FOR
PUBLIC
UNDERSTANDING
PROGRAM

SEPUP

UNIVERSITY OF CALIFORNIA AT BERKELEY

LAWRENCE HALL OF SCIENCE LHS

LaB-aiDS

RONKONKOMA, NEW YORK

This book is a compilation of the following SEPUP publications:

Issues and Life Science

Studying People Scientifically
Ecology

Issues and Earth Science

The Earth in Space
Exploring the Solar System

Issues and Physical Science

Energy

This project was supported, in part, by the
National Science Foundation
Opinions expressed are those of the authors
and not necessarily those of the Foundation.

3 4 5 6 7 8 9   11 12 13 14 15
©2010 The Regents of the University of California
ISBN: 1-60301-368-7
978-1-60301-368-0

SEPUP
Lawrence Hall of Science
University of California at Berkeley
Berkeley CA 94720-5200

e-mail: sepup@berkeley.edu
Website: www.sepuplhs.org

Published by:

LaB-aiDS

17 Colt Court
Ronkonkoma NY 11779
Website: www.lab-aids.com

A Letter to 6th Grade Indiana Science Students,

As you examine the activities in this book, you may wonder, "Why does this book look so different from other science books I've seen?" The reason is simple: it is a different kind of science program, and only some of what you will learn can be seen by leafing through this book!

This program uses several kinds of activities to teach life, earth and physical science concepts. For example, you will design and conduct an experiment to investigate human responses. You will investigate how introduced species impact ecosystems. A solar cell activity will help you to explain the reason for Indiana's seasons. And you will play the roles of council members and scientists to decide to fund one space exploration mission. You will also design and conduct investigations to explore energy transfer. A combination of experiments, readings, models, debates, role plays, and projects will help you uncover the nature of science and the relevance of science to your interests.

You will find that important scientific ideas come up again and again in different activities. You will be expected to do more than just memorize these concepts: you will be asked to explain and apply them. In particular, you will improve your decision-making skills, using evidence and weighing outcomes to decide what you think should be done about scientific issues facing society.

How do we know that this is a good way for you to learn? In general, research on science education supports it. In particular, the activities in this book were tested by hundreds of students and their teachers, and they were modified on the basis of their feedback. In a sense, this entire book is the result of an investigation: we had people test our ideas, we interpreted the results, and we revised our ideas! We believe the result will show you that learning more about science is important, enjoyable, and relevant to your life.

This student book is a compilation of SEPUP publications, customized to align to the Indiana Core Content Expectations, for Science Grade 6. The sequence of units provided below indicates the order that they appear in this publication. Please note that due to the nature of this compilation, "Unit" lettering may appear discontiguous.

Contents

LAB-AIDS Correlation to
INDIANA CORE CONTENT EXPECTATIONS FOR SCIENCE
Grade 6

This document illustrates how curricula from LAB-AIDS are used to address the Indiana Core Content Expectations for Science, Grade 6, Science. Each heading tells the unit (s) that aligns to that particular content. The formative analysis question numbering in the last column shows that the student response addresses the Core Content Expectation.

Note: SEPUP lessons come in several types including Investigations, View and Reflect, Reading, Laboratory, Talking it Over, Role Play, Modeling, Project

Grade 6 RECOMMENDED SCOPE AND SEQUENCE

ISSUES & LIFE SCIENCE (IALS) UNITS

Studying People Scientifically (20 days)

Ecology (40 days)

ISSUES & EARTH SCIENCE (IAES) UNITS

The Earth in Space (25 days)

Exploring the Solar System (25 days)

ISSUES & PHYSICAL SCIENCE (IAPS) UNIT

Energy (40 days)

For a total of 150 days

GRADE 6 - CORE STANDARD 1 - PHYSICAL SCIENCE

Core Standard: Explain that all objects and substances in the natural world are composed of matter in different states with different properties. *This group of expectations all map to the "Energy" (E) SEPUP Unit . . . the issue of home energy efficiency provides context*

Core Standard: Understand that there are different forms of energy with unique characteristics

INDIANA INDICATOR	UNIT TITLE — ACTIVITY NUMBER(S)	INDIANA ASSESSMENT BLUEPRINT
6.1.1 Understand that the properties and behavior of matter can be explained by a model which depicts particles representing atoms or molecules in motion.	IAPS: E - 59, 60, 61, 63	59 AQ 3 60 AQ 2-3 and Teacher Extension 61 AQ 3-4 and Teacher Extension 63 AQ 2
6.1.2 Explain the properties of solids, liquids and gases using drawings and models that represent matter as particles in motion whose state can be represented by the relative positions and movement of the particles.	IAPS: E - 58A	58A All AQ
6.1.3 Using a model in which matter is composed of particles in motion, investigate that when substances undergo a change in state, mass is conserved.	IAPS: E - 58A	58A All AQ
6.1.4 Recognize that objects in motion have kinetic energy and objects at rest have potential energy.	IAPS: E - 54, 56, 57, 58	54 AQ 2, 5 56 AQ 3-4 57 AQ 1-5 58 AQ 1-2
6.1.5 Describe with examples that potential energy exists in several different forms (gravitational potential energy, elastic potential energy, and chemical potential energy, among others).	IAPS: E - 58, 65	58 Procedure, AQ 1-3 65 AQ 2, 3, 5 IB 1
6.1.6 Compare and contrast potential and kinetic energy and how they can be transformed within a system from one form to another.	IAPS: E - 54, 55, 58	54 Procedure (DI), AQ 5 55 AQ 1, 3 58 Procedure, AQ 1-2
6.1.7 Explain that energy may be manifested as heat, light, electricity, mechanical motion, and sound and is often associated with chemical reactions.	IAPS: E - 55, 56, 57, 58, 63, 65, 66 67	55 AQ 3 56 AQ 4 58 Procedure, AQ 1-2 63 AQ 2 65 AQ 1, 3, 4 66 AQ 2 67 AQ 3, 5 IB 4, 13

GRADE 6 - CORE STANDARD 2 - EARTH AND SPACE SCIENCE

Core Standard: Understand the relationships between celestial bodies and the force that keeps them in regular and predictable motion. *This group of indicators all map to both the "Earth in Space" (ES) and the "Exploring the Solar System" (EX) SEPUP Unit . . .context is provided by the issue of how the Earth Moon system relates to the ways we measure time and issues related to how space is explored.*

INDIANA INDICATOR	UNIT TITLE— ACTIVITY NUMBER(S)	INDIANA ASSESSMENT BLUEPRINT
6.2.1 Describe and model how the position, size and relative motions of the earth, moon, and sun cause day and night, solar and lunar eclipses and phases of the moon.	IAES: ES - 73, 74, 89, 80, 81, 84	73 Procedure, AQ 1-3 74 AQ2 79 Procedure, AQ 1-5 80 Procedure, AQ 4 81 Procedure, AQ 5 84 AQ 5 IB 1, 6, 9, 12
6.2.2 Recognize that gravity is a force that keeps celestial bodies in regular and predictable motion, holds objects to earth's surface, and is responsible for ocean tides.	IAES: ES - 82, 84 EX - 95, 96	82 Procedure, AQ 3 84 AQ 5 IB 3, 7 95 AQ 1-3 96 Procedure, AQ 2, AQ 3 IB 12
6.2.3 Understand that the sun, an average star where nuclear reactions occur, is the central and largest body in the solar system.	IAES: EX - 92 IAPS: E - 58	92 AQ 1-4 IB 2 58 Reading
6.2.4 Compare and contrast the planets of the solar system with one another and with asteroids and comets with regard to their size, composition, distance from sun, surface features and ability to support life.	IAES: EX - 88, 89, 90, 91, 94	88 Procedure 89 Procedure, AQ 1 90 Procedure 91 Procedure, Extension 94 Procedure, AQ 2 IB 6, 14, 18
6.2.5 Demonstrate that the seasons in both hemispheres are the result of the inclination o f the earth on its axis which in turn causes changes in sunlight intensity and length of day.	IAES: ES - 75, 76, 77, 78, 84	75 Procedure, AQ 4-7 76 Procedure, AQ 7, Extension 77 Procedure, AQ 1-6 78 AQ 1-2, Extension 84 Procedure, AQ 1 IB 10, 11, 12, 14, 15, 16

GRADE 6 - CORE STANDARD 3 - LIFE SCIENCE

Core Standard: Describe that all organisms, including humans, are part of complex systems found in all biomes (freshwater, marine, forest, desert, grassland, tundra). *This group of indicators all map to the "Ecology" (ECO) SEPUP Unit . . . *the issue of introduced species provides context*

INDIANA INDICATOR	UNIT TITLE — ACTIVITY NUMBER(S)	INDIANA ASSESSMENT BLUEPRINT
6.3.1 Describe specific relationships (predator/prey consumer/producer or parasite/host) between organisms and determine whether these relationships are competitive or mutually beneficial.	IALS: ECO - 72, 73, 78-82, 84-88	80 AQ 1, AQ 2 84 AQ 3-6, Extension 85 AQ 1, AQ 3 87 AQ 1 88 Procedure IB 9, 11
6.3.2 Describe how changes caused by organisms in the habitat where they live can be beneficial or detrimental to themselves or the native plants and animals.	IALS: ECO - 72, 81, 82, 85, 87, 88	81 AQ 6 82 AQ 6 85 AQ 1 88 Procedure IB 6, 24, 29, 30, 43, 44, 46b
6.3.3 Describe how certain biotic and abiotic factors, such as predators, quantity of light and water, range of temperatures, and soil composition, can limit the number of organisms that an ecosystem can support.	IALS: ECO - 85, 87, 88	85 AQ 1c (UC) 87 AQ 1 ET 88 AQ 2, AQ 3 (ET), Procedure CS & S1 IB 23, 27, 29, 30, 35, 45
6.3.4 Recognize that plants use energy from the sun to make sugar (glucose) by the process of photosynthesis.	IALS: ECO - 80, 81, 82	80 AQ 3 81 AQ 4, AQ 5 (UC) Procedure Part B DI 82 AQ3a, 3c, 5b, 5c IB 10, 15, 28
6.3.5 Describe how all animals, including humans, meet their energy needs by consuming other organisms, breaking down their structures, and using the materials to grow and function.	IALS: ECO - 78, 79, 80	78 AQ 1, AQ 2, Procedure 79 Stopping to Think 3, 4 80 AQ 2 IB 2
6.3.6 Recognize that food provides the energy for the work that cells do and is a source of the molecular building blocks that can be incorporated into a cell's structure or stored for later use.	IALS: ECO - 81, 82, 82A Spirals into 7th Grade BodyWorks Unit	81 AQ 4, AQ 5 (UC) Procedure Part B DI 82 AQ3a, 3c, 5b, 5c 82A All AQ

GRADE 6 - CORE STANDARD 4 - SCIENCE, ENGINEERING AND TECHNOLOGY

Core Standard: Apply a form of energy to design and construct a simple mechanical device. *This group of expectations all map to the "Energy" (E) SEPUP Unit . . . the issue of home energy efficiency provides context*

INDIANA INDICATOR	UNIT TITLE — ACTIVITY NUMBER(S)	INDIANA ASSESSMENT BLUEPRINT
6.4.1 Understand how to apply potential or kinetic energy to power a simple device.	IAPS: E - 54, 65	54 AQ 2, 3, 5 65 AQ 3-5 IB 4
6.4.2 Construct a simple device that uses potential or kinetic energy to perform work.	IAPS: E - 54, 65, 68	54 AQ 1, 3, 4 65 Procedure 68 Procedure
6.4.3 Describe the transfer of energy amongst energy interactions.	IAPS: E - 54, 55, 58, 66, 69	54 AQ 2, 3, 4, 5 55 AQ 3 58 Procedure, AQ 2 66 AQ 2 69 Extension IB 2, 8

GRADE 6 - PROCESS STANDARDS

The Nature of Science - Students gain scientific knowledge by observing the natural and constructed world, performing and evaluating investigations and communicating their findings. These principles should guide student work and be integrated into the curriculum along with the content standards on a daily basis.

INDIANA INDICATOR	UNIT TITLE	ACTIVITY NUMBERS
A.1 Make predictions and develop testable questions based on research and prior knowledge.	IALS: ED - SPS	5, 8, 9
	ECO	72, 75, 78, 77, 79, 80, 81, 83
	IAES: ES	72, 74, 76, 78, 79, 82
	IAPS: E	53, 54, 60-62, 65-68, 70
A.2 Plan and carry out investigations as a class, in small groups or independently often over a period of several class lessons.	IALS: ED - SPS, SEPUP Throughout	Exemplar - 8
	ECO - SEPUP Throughout	Exemplar - 81
	IAES: ES - SEPUP Throughout	Exemplar - 72
	IAPS: E - SEPUP Throughout	Exemplar - 59

GRADE 6 - PROCESS STANDARDS, CONTINUED

INDIANA INDICATOR	UNIT TITLE	ACTIVITY NUMBERS
A.3 Collect quantitative data with appropriate tools or technologies and use appropriate units to label numerical data.	IALS: ED - SPS ECO IAES: ES EX IAPS: E	 5 80, 81, 86 72, 77 90, 91, 93 54, 56, 59-63, 65-70
A.4 Incorporate variables that can be changed, measured or controlled.	IALS: ED - SPS ECO IAES: ES IAPS: E	 3, 5, 8, 10 81, 83, 85 72, 77 54, 56, 59-63, 65-70, 72
A.5 Use the principles of accuracy and precision when making measurement.	IALS: ED - SPS IAES: ES EX IAPS: E	 5 72, 77 90, 91, 93 56, 61, 63, 67, 68, 70
A.6 Test predictions with multiple trials.	IALS: ED - SPS ECO IAES: ES IAPS: E	 5, 8, 10 81, 83 72 54, 56, 68
A.7 Keep accurate records in a notebook during investigations.	IALS: ED - SPS - SEPUP Throughout ECO - SEPUP Throughout IAES: ES EX - SEPUP Throughout IAPS: E - SE	 Exemplar - 8 Exemplar - 81 Exemplar - 72 Exemplar - 93 Exemplar 68

GRADE 6 - PROCESS STANDARDS, CONTINUED

INDIANA INDICATOR	UNIT TITLE	ACTIVITY NUMBERS
A.8 Analyze data, using appropriate mathematical manipulations as required, and use it to identify patterns and make inferences based on these patterns.	IALS: ED - SPS ECO IAES: ES EX IAPS: E	3, 4, 5, 8 72, 77, 81, 83, 84, 85 71, 72, 75, 76, 79, 82, 83, 84 93, 95 54, 56, 61-70, 72
A.9 Evaluate possible causes for differing results (valid data).	IALS: ED - SPS ECO IAES: ES EX IAPS: E	8, 9, 10 81, 84 72, 77 93 54-56, 58-70, 72
A.10 Compare the results of an experiment with the prediction.	IALS: ED - SPS ECO IAES: ES EX IAPS: E	5, 8, 9 81, 83 72, 77 93 54-56, 58-70, 72
A.11 Communicate findings using graphs, charts, maps and models through oral and written reports.	IALS: ED - SPS ECO IAES: ES EX IAPS: E	8, 9, 10 81, 83, 88 72, 83, 84 86, 93, 95 54, 56, 61, 62, 63, 65, 66, 67, 68, 72

The Design Process - As citizens of the constructed world, students will participate in the design process. Students will learn to use materials and tools safely and employ the basic principles of the engineering design process in order to find solutions to problems.

INDIANA INDICATOR	UNIT TITLE	ACTIVITY NUMBERS
B.1 Identify a need or problem to be solved.	IAPS: E	60, 70
B.2 Brainstorm potential solutions.	IAPS: E	60, 70
B.3 Document the design throughout the entire design process so that it can be replicated in a portfolio/notebook with drawings including labels.	IAPS: E	60, 70
B.4 Select a solution to the need or problem.	IAPS: E	60, 70
B.5 Select the most appropriate materials to develop a solution that will meet the need.	IAPS: E	60, 70
B.6 Create the solution through a prototype.	IAPS: E	60, 70
B.7 Test and evaluate how well the solution meets the goal.	IAPS: E	60, 70
B.8 Evaluate and test the design using measurement.	IAPS: E	60, 70
B.9 Present evidence using mathematical representations (graphs, data tables).	IAPS: E	60, 70
B.10 Communicate the solution including evidence using mathematical representations (graphs, data tables), drawings or prototypes.	IAPS: E	60, 70
B.11 Redesign to improve the solution based on how well the solution meets the need.	IAPS: E	70

KEY SKILLS MATRIX FOR GRADE 6 INDIANA

INQUIRY SKILLS

	Unit A Studying People Scientifically	Unit E Ecology	Unit F The Earth in Space	Unit G Exploring the Solar System	Unit D Energy	Total Opportunities to Practice Skills
Makes observations	1, 3, 5, 8	74-78, 80-84	71, 72, 76, 77, 79–84	86, 93, 94	54, 56, 58-63, 65-71	42
Identifies data	2-5, 7-10	72-81, 83-85, 87, 88	71, 72, 74–84	85, 86, 89, 93, 94	54-56, 58-70, 72	56
Analyzes data	2-5, 7-10	72-81, 83-85, 87, 88	71–84	85, 86, 89, 93, 94	54-56, 58-70, 72	58
Makes/ interprets data tables	3-5, 8, 9	77, 81, 83	72, 79, 83, 84	93–97	54-56, 58, 61-70, 72	33
Makes/ interprets graphs	3	72, 77, 78, 84, 85	75	93, 95		9
Identifies/ controls a variable	2, 3, 5, 8, 10	81, 83, 85	72, 77		54, 56, 59-63, 65-70,72	24
Makes a prediction/ hypothesis	5, 8	72, 75-81, 83	72, 74, 76, 78, 79, 82		54, 60-62, 65-68, 70	26
Designs an investigation	5, 8	81, 83, 84		72	54, 59-60, 65-66, 68, 70	13
Creates/uses models	3	84	72, 73, 76, 77, 80, 81	93	60, 63, 70	12
Evaluates models		84	77, 81		63, 70	5
Makes evidence- based decisions	2, 3, 4, 9, 10	87, 88	73, 82, 84	89–91, 98	53, 64-68, 70-72	23
Revises predictions or explanations based on evidence	2-5, 7, 8	75, 76, 78, 81, 83	72, 73, 76, 77, 80–82	89–91	53, 64-68, 70-72	21
Total Opportunities to Practice Skills	47	71	95	29	80	322

LITERACY AND COMMUNICATION SKILLS

	Unit A Studying People Scientifically	Unit E Ecology	Unit F The Earth in Space	Unit G Exploring the Solar System	Unit D Energy	Total Opportunities To Practice Skills
Reads for information	4, 6, 7, 9, 10	72-76, 79, 85, 87	71, 74, 78, 82–84	85–89, 92, 96–98	53, 55, 57, 64, 71, 72	34
Communicates orally	1, 3, 4, 7-10	72-85, 88	71, 73–75, 77, 78, 80, 82–84	85–89, 94, 96–98	53-72	63
Communicates in writing	1, 2, 4-6, 8-10	72, 74, 79, 81, 83, 87, 88	71–78, 80, 82–84	85–87, 89, 92, 94–98	53-72	48
Describes observations	2, 3, 5, 7-9	74, 78-84	71, 72, 76, 77, 79, 80, 82–84	86, 93, 95	54, 56, 59, 60, 62-63, 65-70	38
Writes explanations	1 thru 10	74-85, 88	71–73, 75–78, 80, 82–84	85–89, 95, 97, 98	54-55, 57-60, 62-72	46
Makes presentations	10	88	84		65, 69-70, 72	7
Uses diagrams or sketches	12, 15-18, 21,	75, 78, 80, 82	71–73, 76–81, 84	90, 91, 93, 98	55-56, 58-59, 61, 63-69	36
Formulates operational definitions	1, 3, 5, 7	75, 78, 84	71, 75–80, 82	88, 91, 93, 98	53, 65, 66	22
Listens to others	1 thru 10	72-85, 88	71–73, 75, 77, 78, 80, 82–84	85, 86, 88–91, 93–95, 97, 98	53-72	66
Works collaboratively	1 thru 10	72-85, 88	71–73, 75–77, 80, 81, 83, 84	85, 86, 88–91, 93–95, 97, 98	53-72	66
Keeps a science journal	1 thru 10	72-85, 87, 88	71–76, 78, 80, 82–84	85–91, 93–95, 98	53-72	68
Total Opportunities to Practice Skills	79	101	98	80	136	494

INFORMATION ORGANIZING AND PROCESSING SKILLS

	Unit A Studying People Scientifically	Unit E Ecology	Unit F The Earth in Space	Unit G Exploring the Solar System	Unit D Energy	Total Opportunities to Practice Skills
Categorizes/ sorts information	2, 3, 5, 7-10	73, 75-82, 84, 88	71, 72, 75, 78, 79-84	85, 86, 88, 89, 94, 98	53, 56, 58, 64-66, 70, 72	38
Sequences information	2, 5, 8	72	79, 80	85	54, 58, 65-66, 68, 70	13
Summarizes information	2 thru 10	72-79, 81-88	72–74, 79-83	87, 89–96, 98	54, 58-60, 62-67, 70, 72	55
Differentiates observations/ inferences	2	72, 74, 76, 78, 83	71	98	63, 65-67, 70	13
Differenti-ates evidence/ opinion	10	75, 87, 88	77	89, 98	62, 70	9
Draws/ ana-lyzes concept maps		86	84			2
Creates/ uses other graphic organizers	2	73, 75, 88	78, 82	85, 87, 88, 91–93	64	13
Total Op-portunities to Practice Skills	22	37	25	26	33	143

LABORATORY/MATH SKILLS

	Unit A Studying People Scientifically	Unit E Ecology	Unit F The Earth in Space	Unit G Exploring the Solar System	Unit D Energy	Total Opportunities to Practice Skills
Uses tools cor-rectly	5	74, 78, 80-83	72, 77	90, 91, 93	54, 56, 59-63, 65-70	25
Uses apprprte. tools to mea-sure			72	90, 91, 93	56, 59-63, 65, 67, 69-70	14
Uses SI mea-surements			72	93	56, 59-63, 65, 67, 69-70	12
Calculates mean, median, mode		77		90, 91		3
Determines a scale	3, 8	77, 84	75	93		6
Uses graphs appropriately	3, 5	77, 84	75	93		6
Follows proce-dures	3, 5, 8	74-81, 83, 84	71–73, 75–84	85–98	54, 56, 58, 60-63, 65-70	56
Total Op-portunities to Practice Skills	8	21	19	25	49	122

COMPUTER SKILLS						
	Unit A Studying People Scientifically	Unit E Ecology	Unit F The Earth in Space	Unit G Exploring the Solar System	Unit D Energy	Total Opportunities to Practice Skills
Gathers information or conducts research	2, 3, 5, 6	72, 73, 79, 87	74–76, 81–83	87, 97, 98		17
Uses a simulation of scientific phenomena	6		76, 81		55, 64, 71-72	7
Total Opportunities to Practice Skills	5	4	8	3	4	24

SEPUP

Issues
& Life Science

EXPERIMENTAL DESIGN:
STUDYING PEOPLE
SCIENTIFICALLY

SCIENCE
EDUCATION FOR
PUBLIC
UNDERSTANDING
PROGRAM

SEPUP

UNIVERSITY OF CALIFORNIA AT BERKELEY

LAWRENCE HALL OF SCIENCE **LHS***

LaB-aiDS®
INCORPORATED

RONKONKOMA, NEW YORK

This book is part of SEPUP's middle school
science course sequence:

Issues and Earth Science

Studying Soils Scientifically
Rocks and Minerals
Erosion and Deposition
Plate Tectonics
Weather and Atmosphere
The Earth in Space
Exploring the Solar System

Issues and Life Science

Experimental Design: Studying People Scientifically
Body Works
Cell Biology and Disease
Genetics
Ecology
Evolution
Bioengineering

Issues and Physical Science

Studying Materials Scientifically
The Chemistry of Materials
Water
Energy
Force and Motion

Additional SEPUP instructional materials include:
CHEM-2 (Chemicals, Health, Environment and Me): Grades 4–6
SEPUP Modules: Grades 7–12
Science and Sustainability: Course for Grades 9–12
Science and Global Issues Biology: Course for Grades 9–12

 This material is based upon work supported by the National Science Foundation
under Grant No. 9554163. Any opinions, findings, and conclusions or recommendations expressed in this material are those of the authors and do not necessarily
reflect the views of the National Science Foundation.

The preferred citation format for this book is
SEPUP. (2009). Issues and Life Science. Lawrence Hall of Science, University of California at Berkeley. Published by Lab-Aids®, Inc., Ronkonkoma, NY

1 2 3 4 5 6 7 8 9   13 12 11 10 09 08
©2009 The Regents of the University of California
ISBN: 978-1-60301-267-6

SEPUP
Lawrence Hall of Science
University of California at Berkeley
Berkeley CA 94720-5200

e-mail: sepup@berkeley.edu
Website: www.sepuplhs.org

Published by:

17 Colt Court
Ronkonkoma NY 11779
Website: www.lab-aids.com

A Letter to *Issues and Life Science* Students

As you examine the activities in this book, you may wonder, "Why does this book look so different from other science books I've seen?" The reason is simple: it is a different kind of science program, and only some of what you will learn can be seen by leafing through this book!

Issues and Life Science, or *IALS,* uses several kinds of activities to teach science. For example, you will design and conduct an experiment to investigate human responses. You will explore a model of how species compete for food. And you will play the roles of scientists learning about the causes of infectious disease. A combination of experiments, readings, models, debates, role plays, and projects will help you uncover the nature of science and the relevance of science to your interests.

You will find that important scientific ideas come up again and again in different activities. You will be expected to do more than just memorize these concepts: you will be asked to explain and apply them. In particular, you will improve your decision-making skills, using evidence and weighing outcomes to decide what you think should be done about scientific issues facing society.

How do we know that this is a good way for you to learn? In general, research on science education supports it. In particular, the activities in this book were tested by hundreds of students and their teachers, and they were modified on the basis of their feedback. In a sense, this entire book is the result of an investigation: we had people test our ideas, we interpreted the results, and we revised our ideas! We believe the result will show you that learning more about science is important, enjoyable, and relevant to your life.

IALS Staff

ISSUES & LIFE SCIENCE PROJECT

Director (2003–2008): Barbara Nagle
Director (1995–2002): Herbert D. Thier

AUTHORS

Barbara Nagle
Manisha Hariani
Donna Markey
Herbert D. Thier
Asher Davison
Susan K. Boudreau
Daniel Seaver
Laura Baumgartner

OTHER CONTRIBUTORS

Sara Dombkowski, Kathaleen Burke, Richard Duquin, Laura Lenz, Raquel Araujo Gomes

CONTENT AND SCIENTIFIC REVIEW

Gary R. Cutter, Director of Biostatistics, AMC Cancer Research, Denver, Colorado
Peter J. Kelly, Emeritus Professor of Education and Senior Visiting Fellow, School of Education, University of Southampton, Southampton, England
Deborah Penry, Assistant Professor, Department of Integrative Biology, University of California at Berkeley, Berkeley, California

RESEARCH ASSISTANCE

Marcelle Siegel, Leif Asper

PRODUCTION

Design and composition: Seventeenth Street Studios
Administrative assistance: Roberta Smith and Anna Vorster

We would also like to thank Miriam Shein and Sylvia Parisotto for their contributions to this publication.

FIELD TEST CENTERS

This course is a revision of *Science and Life Issues*. The following centers participated in field testing the original course or the revised materials. We are extremely grateful to the center directors and teachers who taught the program. These teachers and their students contributed significantly to improving the course.

REGIONAL CENTER, SOUTHERN CALIFORNIA

Donna Markey, *Center Director*
  Kim Blumeyer, Helen Copeland, Pat McLoughlin, Donna Markey,
  Philip Poniktera, Samantha Swann, Miles Vandegrift

REGIONAL CENTER, IOWA

Dr. Robert Yager and Jeanne Bancroft, *Center Directors*
  Rebecca Andresen, Lore Baur, Dan Dvorak, Dan Hill, Mark Kluber, Amy
  Lauer, Lisa Martin, Stephanie Phillips

REGIONAL CENTER, WESTERN NEW YORK

Dr. Robert Horvat, *Center Director*
  Kathaleen Burke, Dick Duquin, Eleanor Falsone, Lillian Gondree, Jason
  Mayle, James Morgan, Valerie Tundo

JEFFERSON COUNTY, KENTUCKY

Pamela Boykin, *Center Director*
  Charlotte Brown, Tara Endris, Sharon Kremer, Karen Niemann,
  Susan Stinebruner, Joan Thieman

LIVERMORE, CALIFORNIA

Scott Vernoy, *Center Director*
  Rick Boster, Ann Ewing, Kathy Gabel, Sharon Schmidt, Denia Segrest,
  Bruce Wolfe

QUEENS, NEW YORK

Pam Wasserman, *Center Director*
  Gina Clemente, Cheryl Dodes, Karen Horowitz, Tricia Hutter, Jean Rogers,
  Mark Schmucker, Christine Wilk

TUCSON, ARIZONA

Jonathan Becker, *Center Director*
  Peggy Herron, Debbie Hobbs, Carol Newhouse, Nancy Webster

INDEPENDENT

Berkeley, California: Robyn McArdle
Fresno, California: Al Brofman
Orinda, California: Sue Boudreau, Janine Orr, Karen Snelson
Tucson, Arizona: Patricia Cadigan, Kevin Finegan

Contents

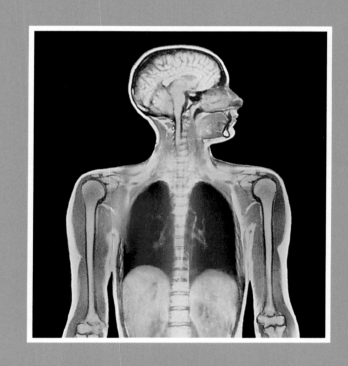

Experimental Design:
Studying People Scientifically

Unit A

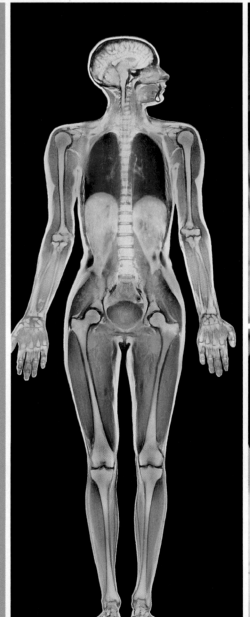

MEDICAL RESEARCH

STUDY PARTICIPANTS NEEDED

Be part of a medical research study and earn up to $
a day. Your participation could help improve the qua
of life for people with various health condit
YOU CAN MAKE A DIFFERENCE! Study partici
who meet the following criteria are eligible:
- 18 to 68 years old
- male or female
- available weekends/weekd
- non-smokers

Experimental Design: Studying People Scientifically

But it's true. I heard about it on the news last night. Broccoli decreases your risk of having cancer," stated Alissa.

Eric rolled his eyes. "They used to say margarine was much better for you than butter, then it was butter is better—who knows what medical researchers are saying today?"

"I don't know, Eric, this sounded pretty convincing," replied Alissa. "They've done scientific studies and everything."

"I'm not going to eat it just because some doctor says I should," said Eric stubbornly.

• • •

What would you do if you were Eric? What factors might influence your view? How do you respond to everyday dilemmas, and on what basis do you make your decisions?

Scientists collect information and do studies to answer such questions. In this unit, you will learn some of the scientific principles and approaches used to study people.

INVESTIGATION

We all solve problems every day—from little problems like what to wear to school, to bigger problems like whether to get a job or go to college. Different kinds of problems require different problem-solving approaches. One problem can often be solved in more than one way. What do you do when you are faced with a problem?

CHALLENGE → **What approaches do you use to solve problems? What approaches do scientists use to solve various kinds of problems?**

MATERIALS

For each pair of students

1	gummy candy life preserver
1	gummy candy worm
1	plastic cup
4	paper clips

For each student

1	Student Sheet 1.1 "Anticipation Guide: Ideas about Experimental Design"

PROCEDURE

1. Complete Student Sheet 1.1 "Anticipation Guide: Ideas about Experimental Design." Complete the "Before" column only.

2. Work with your partner to solve the problem below. A picture of the set-up is on the next page.

Save Fred!

Poor Fred! He was sailing along on a boat (your plastic cup) when a strong wind blew it upside-down. Fred (your candy worm) ended up on top of the upside-down boat. Unfortunately for Fred, his life preserver (your candy life preserver) is still trapped under the boat.

Your job is to place the life preserver firmly around Fred's body, but you must obey three rules:

1. Fred may not fall into the "sea" (onto the table) more than one time; if he does, Fred "drowns."

2. You may not injure him in any way.

3. You may use only the four paper clips to move Fred, the boat, and the life preserver. You may not touch anything except the paper clips.

3. Work with your partner to record in your science notebook exactly what you did to save Fred. Be as specific as possible. For example, did you modify one of the paper clips? How did you avoid hurting Fred? You may wish to draw a picture or a diagram to explain your procedure.

4. Exchange your procedure with your table partners' procedure. Do you think you could follow their procedure? If not, ask them to clarify their descriptions.

ANALYSIS

> ### Key to Analysis Icons
>
> = Answer the question by yourself.
>
> = Discuss with your partner.
>
> = Discuss with your group.
>
> = Discuss the question in class.

 1. You can solve problems in many different ways. In fact, you may use more than one way to solve a single problem. You can

- develop a plan.
- find a pattern.
- draw a picture or a diagram.
- act out the problem.
- make a list.
- guess and test.

- work backward.
- write an equation.
- construct a table or graph.
- simplify the problem.
- use objects to model the problem.

a. Which of these ways did you and your partner use to save Fred?

b. Choose three of these ways and record a problem that could be solved using each method.

 2. As a class, discuss the ways in which various groups of partners saved Fred. How were your problem-solving methods similar? How were they different?

3. Do you think scientists follow only one method to solve problems? Explain.

4. The traditional scientific method includes the following steps for solving problems.

   Step 1. State the problem or question.

   Step 2. Propose an explanation, also known as the hypothesis.

   Step 3. Collect evidence. (Conduct an experiment.)

   Step 4. Analyze data.

   Step 5. Draw conclusions, and, if necessary, revise and repeat the experiment.

   When you saved Fred did you follow all of these steps in this order? Explain.

5. Do you think scientists always follow all of these steps in this order? Explain.

6. Fill in the "After" column for statements 1 and 2 only on Sheet 1.1, "Anticipation Guide: Ideas about Experimental Design." Did your thinking change?

7. **Reflection:** People face problems in their lives every day. What did you learn from this activity that you can use to solve other problems? How do you think this compares with how scientists solve problems?

VIEW AND REFLECT

Although scientists use many methods to solve problems, scientists in the same field frequently use similar approaches. Often these involve doing an experiment. For example, if a botanist (someone who studies plants) wanted to develop plants that resist drought, the botanist would use many plants and follow procedures common to many botanical experiments. A materials scientist working to develop a new type of plastic for an artificial limb would use a different procedure. What kinds of experiments are possible when you study human beings? How can you collect evidence in these situations? Begin to consider these issues as you watch the story of the disease called pellagra (puh-LAY-gra), which affected poor rural families of the South.

Poor families of the South were more likely to develop pellagra.

Whenever you see this icon, it means that you will find more information or a technology extension on this subject on the Issues and Life Science *page of the SEPUP website.*

CHALLENGE ➡ **What are the common elements of all scientific problem-solving methods?**

MATERIALS

For each student

    Student Sheet 1.1, "Anticipation Guide: Ideas about Experimental Design" from Activity 1

1 **Student Sheet 2.2, "Observations and Inferences"**

1 **Student Sheet 2.3, "The Pellagra Story: Dr. Goldberger and the Traditional Scientific Method"**

Dr. Joseph Goldberger

PROCEDURE

1. To prepare to watch the story on the video, first read Analysis Questions 1–4.

2. Your teacher will provide you with a student sheet or ask you to prepare a table like Table 1 to record your notes during the video.

3. Watch the story of Dr. Goldberger and pellagra on the video.

4. Complete Student Sheet 2.2, "Observations and Inferences."

Table 1: Notes on The Pellagra Story

What was the problem of pellagra?

What did people think caused pellagra?
1.
2.
3.
4.

What evidence did Dr. Goldberger observe or collect about pellagra?

What did Dr. Goldberger conclude about the cause of pellagra?

ANALYSIS

1. **a.** What was the first step in Dr. Goldberger's research into pellagra? Explain why this step was important in developing his hypothesis.

   b. During this first step in his research, what evidence did Dr. Goldberger find that suggested that pellagra was not caused by germs?

2. **a.** What was Dr. Goldberger's hypothesis about the cause of pellagra?

   b. What did he do to provide evidence of the relationship between pellagra and nutrition? Be sure to explain *how* his research provided evidence that supported or disproved his hypothesis.

   c. How could he have provided more convincing evidence of the relationship between pellagra and nutrition?

3. Why didn't people believe Dr. Goldberger's conclusion about the cause of pellagra? Give two reasons.

4. Compare the steps of the traditional scientific method to the steps Dr. Goldberger followed to investigate pellagra. How were the steps the same? How were the steps different?

5. Fill in the "After" column for Statements 3 and 4 only on Sheet 1.1, "Anticipation Guide: Ideas about Experimental Design." Did your thinking change?

6. To investigate his hypothesis, Dr. Goldberger had prisoners volunteer to be fed a poor diet; as a result, seven out of 11 prisoners developed pellagra. What do you think about Dr. Goldberger's decision to experiment on people? Support your answer with evidence and identify the trade-offs of your decision.

   Hint: To write a complete answer, first state your opinion. Provide two or more pieces of evidence that support your opinion. Then consider all sides of the issue and identify the trade-offs of your decision.

7. **Reflection:** How do people in different careers solve problems? Scientists, plumbers, engineers, auto mechanics, nurses, teachers, and many other workers solve problems. Choose two careers that interest you. Describe the kind of problems you think people face in these careers. Describe how you think they solve them.

EXTENSION

For links to more information about Dr. Joseph Goldberger and his war on pellagra, go to the *Issues and Life Science* page of the SEPUP website.

INVESTIGATION

Collecting evidence is an important part of science. One way to collect evidence is to conduct experiments as Dr. Goldberger did. Products such as medicines are tested by volunteers before they are made available to the public. These tests are known as **clinical trials**.

A Clinical Trial

Imagine that you suffer from severe headaches several times a month. These headaches are so painful that you can't read, listen to music, or watch television. Regular headache medicines don't work very well for you. One day, you complain to your doctor about your headaches. She tells you that the local medical school is conducting clinical trials of a new headache medicine. She asks if you would like to volunteer to be a part of this trial. Hoping for relief, you say yes.

Since medicines cannot be tested in the classroom, you will participate in a simulation of a clinical trial. In this simulation, differences in taste will equal differences in response to the medicine. The illustration on the next page, "Clinical Trial of A Headache Medicine," explains the simulation.

CHALLENGE   **How are medicines tested during a clinical trial?**

MATERIALS

For each group of four students
- 4   small tasting cups (one for each student)
- 1   sample cup of yellow lemon drink
- 1   sample cup of pink lemon drink

For each student
- 1   Student Sheet 3.1, "Analysis of Clinical Trial"

CLINICAL TRIAL OF A HEADACHE MEDICINE

The taste of the yellow lemon drink represents a headache.

The taste of the pink lemon drink represents the medicine taken to treat your headache.

If the pink lemon drink tastes the same as the yellow, there is no change in your headache.

If the pink lemon drink tastes better than the yellow, your headache is gone!

If the pink lemon drink tastes worse than the yellow, your headache is gone, but you experience side effects.

SAFETY

Never taste materials or eat or drink in science class unless specifically told to do so by your teacher. Be sure that your work area is clean and free of any materials not needed for this activity. If you are allergic to lemons or other citrus fruits, juice drinks, or sugar, or if you have any other health issue, such as diabetes, that limits what you can eat, tell your teacher and do not taste the drink samples in this activity.

PROCEDURE

1. Record your group number (found on the sample cups) in your science notebook; this represents the batch of medicine you received.

2. Fill your tasting cup halfway full of yellow lemon drink by carefully pouring from the sample cup into your tasting cup.

3. Taste the yellow lemon drink. Empty the cup.

4. Fill your tasting cup halfway full of pink lemon drink.

5. Taste the pink lemon drink.

6. *Did the pink lemon drink taste the same, better, or worse than the yellow lemon drink?* Record your response in a table like the one below.

Results of Treatment

	Same as yellow lemon drink	Better than yellow lemon drink	Worse than yellow lemon drink
My response (Show with an X)			
My group's response (Show number of each)			

7. Share your results with your group. Summarize your group results in Row 2 of your data table.

8. Have one person from your group report your group's results to your teacher.

9. After a class discussion of the results, record the class's results and create a bar graph of the class's data on Student Sheet 3.1, "Analysis of Clinical Trial."

ANALYSIS

 1. What evidence do you have that the medicine does or does not work to improve headaches?

 2. **a.** What is a placebo?

b. Why is a placebo group included in clinical trials?

 3. In this activity, if a person finds that the drink tastes worse, the headache is gone, but there are side effects.

a. Assume that the side effects are mild, such as a slight stomachache. Explain why this medicine should or should not be sold to people suffering from a headache. Are there any trade-offs involved in your decision?

b. What if the side effects were serious, such as nausea and vomiting? Explain why this medicine should or should not be sold to people suffering from a headache. Are there any trade-offs involved in your decision?

4. In this activity, if a person finds that the medicine tastes better or worse, the headache is gone. Review the results of this simulation. Think about whether the medicine works and how often side effects occur. What would you conclude about the safety and effectiveness of this medicine for treating headaches? Support your conclusion with evidence.

 ## EXTENSION

Ask your teacher to post your class data on the *Issues and Life Science* page of the SEPUP website. Look at the results posted by other students. How do your results compare?

How can we be certain that the foods we eat are safe, that the cosmetics we use won't harm us, and that medical products are effective? In the United States, the Federal Food, Drug, and Cosmetic Act and several other laws protect the public's safety. Before the Federal Food, Drug, and Cosmetic Act was passed in 1938, most products were not regulated.

CHALLENGE

How are medicines, such as over-the-counter and prescription drugs, tested?

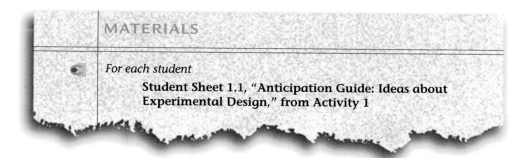

MATERIALS

For each student

Student Sheet 1.1, "Anticipation Guide: Ideas about Experimental Design," from Activity 1

READING

The Role of the FDA

Today, the U.S. Food and Drug Administration (FDA) enforces the laws on medical product safety and effectiveness. The FDA approves medicines that have been proven to be safe and effective for people to use. To be approved, a product must undergo and pass scientific tests. Usually, new medicines are first tested in animals to see whether they cause any harmful side effects. Only then are the medicines tested by volunteers in clinical trials. The results of clinical trials must show that the medicine is both safe and effective before it can be approved for use by the public.

Listen as your teacher reads aloud.

Stop when you see this yellow pencil and close your book.

Write down the main ideas you just heard.

Informed Consent

In clinical trials, volunteers are chosen carefully. They must not be allergic to drugs similar to the one that will be tested. Also, they cannot be taking certain other medications. These things might make it more likely for them to experience harmful side effects. The volunteers must be told about any risks, such as possible side effects. They sign an **informed consent** form. This form states that they have been told (informed) about the risks and that they agree (consent) to participate in the trial.

Treatment and Control Groups

The volunteers are then divided into two groups. One group receives a pill or liquid that contains the medicine being tested. The other group receives a pill or liquid that looks the same but contains only an inactive ingredient, such as sugar. This inactive pill is called a **placebo** (pla-SEE-bo). Neither the patients nor their doctors know who is receiving the medicine and who is receiving the placebo. The placebo is used as a **control**. It helps to prove that any improvement in the patient is due to the medicine and not to other aspects of the medical treatment. For example, just going to see a doctor may result in an improvement in a patient's condition.

The Placebo Effect

Why is it necessary to use placebos in clinical trials? For many years, scientists observed that people in clinical trials who receive placebos were more likely to show an improvement than other patients with the same disease. This improvement in the health of people receiving placebos is known as the **placebo effect**. Scientists give several explanations for the placebo effect. One factor is the regular, and often better, medical care that patients receive in a clinical trial. Another factor is the psychological effect of participating in a clinical trial. A patient who is getting regular medical attention and a pill may have a more positive attitude toward his or her health. He or she may also be more careful about diet, exercise, or other factors related to the illness. As a result, this person may be more likely to

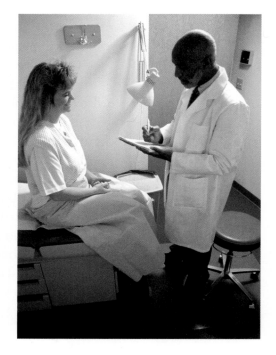

recover because of this positive attitude, and not as a result of anything in the pill. Today, scientists and doctors are studying this connection between a person's mental attitude and his or her physical health to understand how they influence each other.

The placebo effect sometimes makes it difficult to determine if a treatment is effective. For example, the use of vitamin C to treat colds is controversial. Some studies suggest that vitamin C improves cold symptoms. Other studies suggest that vitamin C doesn't work any better than a placebo, and that people who feel better from vitamin C are experiencing a placebo effect. Studies of high blood pressure, asthma, pain, depression, and cough have shown that about 30–40% of patients taking a placebo experience some relief of their symptoms. This relief can sometimes be measured objectively: for example, blood pressure actually drops in some patients taking placebos.

ANALYSIS

1. In clinical trials of medicines, why is one group of volunteers given a placebo? Explain.

2. Activity 3, "Testing Medicines: A Clinical Trial," simulated a clinical trial that investigated whether a headache medicine was effective. A person reporting a better or worse taste with the pink lemon drink (compared with the yellow lemon drink) represented a person feeling better after taking a pill for headache relief. In this simulation:

   a. What represented the medicine?

   b. What represented the placebo?

   c. Look at your data on Student Sheet 3.1, "Analysis of Clinical Trial." How many people experienced the placebo effect?

   d. Look at your data on Student Sheet 3.1. How many people in the placebo group were unaffected by the placebo?

3. What is the purpose of a placebo?

4. In your own words, what is the placebo effect?

5. Complete the "After" column for statements 5–9 on Student Sheet 1.1 "Anticipation Guide: Ideas about Experimental Design."

6. Imagine a clinical trial to test a treatment for serious illnesses, such as heart disease or cancer. What is the trade-off of giving placebos to some people participating in this clinical trial?

Table 1: Clinical Trial of Cold Medicine				
	Feel the same	Feel better	Feel worse	Total number of people in group
Control group (received placebo)	60	35	5	100
Treatment group (received medicine)	10	80	10	100

7. Review the data shown above from a clinical trial of a cold medicine.

   a. Copy and complete a table like the one shown below to compare the number of people who feel better as a result of the medicine vs. the placebo:

   Analysis of Clinical Trial Data

	Number of people who feel better	Total number of people in group	Percent who feel better
Control group (received placebo)			
Treatment group (received medicine)			

   b. Is the medicine effective in a high percentage of the population? Explain your answer.

   c. Compare the percentage of people who feel worse in the placebo group vs. the percentage who feel worse in the treatment group. What difference do you observe? What could explain this difference?

   d. Would you conclude that this medicine is safe and effective for treating colds? Explain the evidence for your conclusion.

Table 2: Clinical Trial of a Stomachache Pill				
	Feel the same	Feel better	Feel worse	Total number of people in group
Control group (received placebo)	50	46	4	100
Treatment group (received medicine)	41	55	4	100

8. Review the data shown above from a clinical trial of a stomachache pill. Think about whether the medicine works and how often side effects occur. Explain why this medicine should or should not be sold. Support your answer with evidence about the safety and effectiveness of this medicine.

9. a. Reflection: What evidence do you use to decide if cold, stomachache, or other over-the-counter medicines work for you?

   b. What effect do you think a positive attitude has on your everyday health? What about when you are sick?

LABORATORY

Useful scientific experiments are often designed to test only a single factor, or **variable.** You may remember that Dr. Goldberger had screens put on the windows during his experiment on prisoners. He also had bedsheets and clothes washed regularly. One strength of Dr. Goldberger's experiment was his effort to reduce all the other variables—such as the presence of insects or variations in cleanliness—that could affect his results. His goal was to make diet the only factor that was being changed. In this case, diet was the variable being tested.

Scientists are interested in how people respond to the environment. People use their senses—touch, sight, hearing, smell, and taste—to get information about their surroundings. This information travels through nerves to the human brain. In this activity you will investigate your sense of touch. Can you identify all of the variables that might affect your results? What can you do to try to keep all of these variables the same? How can you control those variables to measure the smallest distance apart at which you can feel two points?

CHALLENGE

What is the smallest distance apart at which you can still feel two points? How do you compare with other people in your class?

MATERIALS

For each pair of students

1   **2-point sensor**
6   **plastic toothpicks**
1   **Student Sheet 5.1, "Touch-test Data"**
1   **Student Sheet 5.2, "Sensitivity to Two Points: Class Results"**

Student Sheet 1.1 "Anticipation Guide: Ideas about Experimental Design," from Activity 1

 SAFETY

Be careful when doing the touch tests. Press gently when testing, making sure to only slightly depress the skin surface.

PROCEDURE

Part A

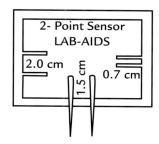

1. 1. Slide 2 plastic toothpicks into the 2-point sensor on the side marked "1.5 cm."

2. With your eyes open, investigate your sense of touch by touching the skin of your fingers, palm of your hand, and forearm with the point of just one toothpick.

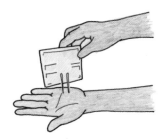

3. With your eyes open, touch your fingers, palm, and forearm with the points of both toothpicks. Notice what the points look like as they touch your skin and compare that to how it feels.

4. Record your observations in your science notebook while your partner investigates his or her own sense of touch.

5. Have your partner close his or her eyes while you touch the skin on his or her fingers with either one or two toothpick points. Touch just hard enough to see that the points are barely pushing down on the skin. Randomly alternate between one and two points. Can your partner tell the difference?

6. Create a larger version of the table shown on the next page. In the table, record your observations about your partner's ability to tell the difference between one and two points on his or her fingers.

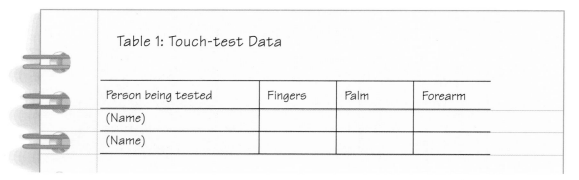

Table 1: Touch-test Data

Person being tested	Fingers	Palm	Forearm
(Name)			
(Name)			

7. Repeat Steps 5 and 6 on your partner's palm and forearm.

8. Switch places and repeat Steps 5–7.

9. Discuss with your partner what you observe when you are lightly touching your partner's skin with the one- or two-point sensor. What does the skin look like when you lightly touch it with the sensor? How far is the skin depressed?

10. Discuss with your partner the variables that were easy to control and the variables that were harder to control. List these in your science notebook. Discuss how you will control the more difficult variables in Part B of the activity.

Part B

11. What is the smallest distance—0.7 cm, 1.5 cm, or 2.0 cm—at which you think you can still feel two points on the palm of your hand? In your science notebook, record your hypothesis. Explain why you made this prediction.

12. Identify your dominant hand. (This is usually the hand you write with.) Throughout the experiment, you will test your dominant hand.

13. Begin completing Student Sheet 5.1, "Touch-test Data." Write your name, and circle which of your hands is dominant. You will begin by testing the palm of your hand, so circle "palm" as the part tested.

14. Since you will test your partner (and vice versa), switch student sheets so you can record the data on his or her sheet.

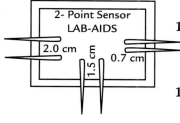

15. Slide two toothpicks into each side of the 2-point sensor as shown on the left. You should end up with toothpicks on three sides, with the toothpick points 0.7 cm apart, 1.5 cm apart, and 2.0 cm apart.

16. Practice using the 2-point sensor so that you can safely and easily test using any of the three sides.

17. As the experimenter, you will use the 2-point sensor to test your partner. Record your partner's responses on Table 1, "Touch-test Data," on Student Sheet 5.1. It is important that you fill in each box in each row before starting the next row.

    For example, when you do Trial 1, you will fill in each box in the first row:

    a. Turn the 2-point sensor to the 0.7 cm side and touch your partner's palm with just one point.

    b. Turn the sensor to the 1.5 cm side and touch your partner's palm with just one point.

    c. Turn the sensor to 2.0 cm and touch your partner's palm with two points.

18. Before starting the touch tests, ask your partner to close his or her eyes. The partner being tested should not try to "guess the right answer." The goal is to report what you really feel—one point or two.

19. Use Table 1, "Touch-test Data," to test your partner. You can start with any row you want, but be sure you complete all the rows. Don't tell your partner which row you are using. Remember to touch just hard enough to see that the points are barely pushing down on the skin. After each touch test, have your partner report whether he or she feels one or two points, and record the response.

20. After you complete all the touch tests in Table 1, have your partner test you by repeating Steps 17-19.

21. Give your partner back his or her original Student Sheet.

22. Complete the rest of Student Sheet 5.1.

22. If you have time, repeat this experiment to test the sensitivity of your fingertips and your forearm.

ANALYSIS

1. **a.** According to your data, what can you conclude about your sensitivity to 2-point touches? How does this conclusion compare with your hypothesis?

   b. Compare your results with those of your partner. How similar or different are your results?

   c. Compare your results with those of another pair of students. How similar or different are your results?

2. Look at the class results on Student Sheet 5.2, "Sensitivity to Two Points: Class Results." Compare the smallest distance at which you could feel two points with the results of the rest of the class. What can you conclude about the sensitivity of different people to touch? Is it possible to make conclusions about people in general?

3. You were able to determine the smallest distance at which you could still feel two points using only the 2-point touch data. The 1-point touches acted as a control. Why would you need a control when experimenting on people?

4. **a.** A good experiment is reproducible. What parts of this experiment are reproducible?

   b. How could this experiment be improved?

5. What factors make scientific study of people difficult? How do scientists deal with these factors in a well-designed investigation?

6. Fill in the "After" column for Statements 10–12 on Student Sheet 1.1, "Anticipation Guide: Ideas about Experimental Design." Did your thinking change?

7. Design an experiment to determine a person's sensitivity to sound. Assume you have a machine that you can set to produce sounds of varying volume (measured in units called decibels). Hint: Think about how you tested your sensitivity to 2-point touches.

EXTENSION

Ask your teacher to post your class data on the *Issues and Life Science* website. Look at the data posted by other students. What can you conclude about the sensitivity of different people to touch? What effect does sample size have on your conclusions? Explain your ideas.

You probably found that some parts of your arm were more sensitive than others. In this reading you will learn about some of the reasons for these differences.

CHALLENGE ➤ **Why do different parts of your body have different sensitivities to touch?**

READING

You use your senses to gather information about your environment. Your senses include sight, hearing, taste, smell, and touch. To understand how you feel objects you touch, you need to know a little about your nervous system. Your **nervous system** includes your brain, spinal cord, and nerves. The diagram below shows how these parts of your nervous system are connected. Nerves are made up of nerve cells or **neurons** and are found throughout your body.

Your nerves take in information from the world. For example, your nerves have helped you collect information about the weight of your backpack when you pick it up and think, "It's heavy!" The nerves that sense this information are called **sensory neurons.** Sensory neurons do more than just sense pressure; they also sense sound waves in your ear, light waves in your eyes, and chemicals in your nose and on your tongue.

HUMAN NERVOUS SYSTEM

....

STOPPING TO THINK 1

RESPONDING TO THE ENVIRONMENT

a. Why are the nerves that take information from our world called sensory neurons?

b. What kind of information do sensory neurons detect?

....

Information travels from sensory neurons all over your body to your spinal cord before continuing to your brain. There are nerves in your spinal cord and brain called **interneurons** that connect to the sensory neurons. Your brain analyzes all of the information from the interneurons and helps you understand what your sensory neurons have detected. For example, the interneurons help you identify the object at your feet as a dog. Your brain can then provide directions to other neurons called **motor neurons.** Motor neurons send signals to your muscles that cause you to move. For example, they might signal your muscles to reach down and pet the dog. Sometimes there is a need for a reflex action, such as when you touch a hot stove. In this case, the message never reaches the brain. The interneurons in your spinal cord signal the motor neurons of your arm and hand to move your hand away fast.

Signals travel from nerves in your body to your brain. These signals can travel up to several hundred miles per hour!

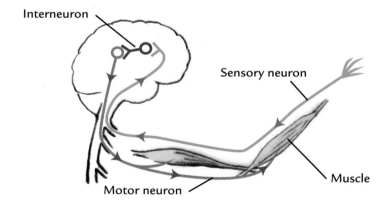

PATH OF A NERVE IMPULSE

....

STOPPING TO THINK 2

a. Someone accidentally bumps into you in the hallway. What part of your body detected the feeling of being bumped?

b. Where in your body is this feeling analyzed?

c. "Inter" means between. Why are the neurons in the spinal cord and brain called interneurons?

....

Sometimes your nervous system responds to messages that you provide and sometimes your nervous system responds to messages from your brain that you are not aware of. For example, you decide to eat a sandwich. Your brain sends signals along nerves to direct your muscles to pick up the sandwich and take a bite. But what happens after you swallow? Do you have to think about directing your body to process the food? Your body automatically moves food through your digestive system and processes it. For this to happen, muscles inside your body must move. These muscles are controlled by the automatic, or involuntary, part of your nervous system. You don't even have to think about it!

STOPPING TO THINK 3

a. Is breathing completely involuntary? Explain.

b. Explain how motor neurons can be part of both the voluntary and the involuntary nervous systems.

Even when you are not consciously thinking about what your body is doing, your brain is controlling your body's movements. Your brain only weighs 3 pounds and is made up mainly of water and fat, and yet it:

- processes information from the world around you through your senses.

- controls and coordinates all of your movements.

- controls basic life processes such as body temperature, blood pressure, heart rate and breathing.

- allows you to think, reason, dream, and experience emotions.

HUMAN BRAIN FUNCTIONS

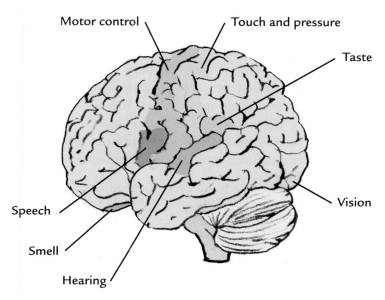

Motor control

Touch and pressure

Taste

Vision

Speech

Smell

Hearing

The parts of your brain have various functions. The largest, wrinkled part of the brain that you see is called the cerebrum. The folds or wrinkles increase the surface area of the brain, allowing more room for neurons and making it more efficient. This is where all of the thinking and reasoning you do takes place. Specific parts of the cerebrum control certain types of thought processes and actions.

The two smaller parts of the brain are the cerebellum and the brain stem. The cerebellum controls the coordination of movement, posture, and balance.

STRUCTURE OF THE
HUMAN BRAIN

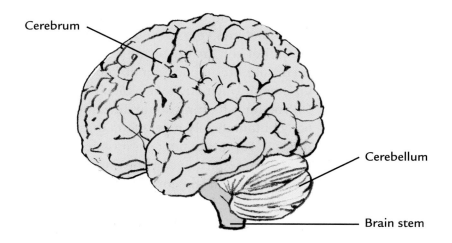

During complex voluntary movements, such as those involved in learning to ride a bike, many parts of your brain work together to perform the sequence of movements necessary to ride the bike successfully. Deep within the brain is the brain stem. This is where the basic life functions such as heartbeat, blood pressure, and breathing are controlled.

STOPPING TO THINK 4

1. When you decide what to wear in the morning, which of the three parts of your brain do you use?

2. What is a benefit of the cerebrum having folds and wrinkles?

3. What part of the brain enables you to breathe, even when you are asleep?

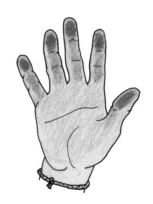

TOUCH RECEPTORS ON
A HUMAN HAND

Now you know how you sense information from the outside world and react to it. But why are some parts of your body more sensitive than others? If you are touched with two closely spaced points, some parts of your body will be able to detect that there are two, while other parts of your body will only be able to detect one point. When something touches your arm, you feel it if it is detected by the nerve endings in your skin. You have nerves in your body that detect pressure, heat, sounds, smells, and light. The nerve endings that detect pressure on your skin are called **touch receptors** (ree-SEP-tors). They help carry a message from your skin to your brain.

Some parts of your body have more touch receptors than others. When two points stimulate the same touch receptors, you feel the points as one touch. When they stimulate different touch receptors, you feel two different touches. The illustration (left) shows the concentration of touch receptors on a hand. Notice that the tip of the finger has more touch receptors than the rest of the finger. When you reach out to touch something, you often use your fingertips. You may have heard of people with limited or no vision reading Braille. Braille is a written language that uses raised dots instead of letters. Braille is read with fingertips. Not surprisingly, you have the greatest number of touch receptors right at your fingertips—just where they are needed.

ANALYSIS

1. **a.** Where would you expect to have more touch receptors: on the palm of your hand or on the back of your hand? Explain your ideas.

   b. Explain how you could test your answer to Question 1a.

2. When your partner touched you with the toothpick points in Activity 5, how did you sense it? Describe or draw the path through the nervous system that enabled you to identify if it was a one- or two-point touch.

3. Review your results from Activity 5, "Can You Feel the Difference?" Based on what you now know, where on your arm—fingers, palm, or forearm—do you have the fewest touch receptors?

4. Describe the structures that make up the nervous system.

EXTENSION

 For links to more information on the human nervous system, go to the *Issues and Life Science* page of the SEPUP website.

READING

Studying people *scientifically* presents some interesting challenges. One challenge is that people react differently to identical events. Think about the results of your experiments on touch sensitivity. You probably discovered that not everyone could feel two points at the same distance. How do you think scientists deal with this type of challenge?

CHALLENGE

How are qualitative and quantitative data used when testing a hypothesis about people?

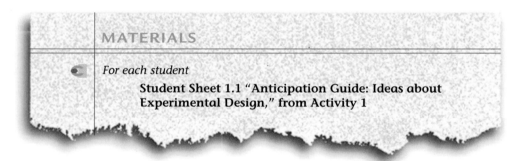

MATERIALS

For each student
Student Sheet 1.1 "Anticipation Guide: Ideas about Experimental Design," from Activity 1

READING

Scientists usually begin with an idea about what they want to investigate. This is also true for scientists who study people. This idea, or hypothesis, is the basis for their study. As you now know, a **hypothesis** (hi-PAH-thuh-sis) is an explanation based on observed facts or on an idea of how things work. For example, Dr. Goldberger hypothesized that there was a relationship between pellagra and diet.

Doctor and patient

In some cases scientists predict the possible outcomes of an experiment. A hypothesis can include a prediction of what might happen. In the last activity, your hypothesis included a prediction about the results. To make sure they don't influence results, scientists studying people often do *not* predict the possible results of their experiments.

After developing a hypothesis, scientists usually plan and conduct experiments. The results of an experiment can provide evidence that supports or contradicts a hypothesis. In some cases, an experiment provides new information. This new information can produce another hypothesis and another experiment. In this way, a hypothesis can be a "work in progress" that is continually revised.

Scientist examining rat brain scan

Doctor and nurse working on computer

The word data *(DAY-tuh) is plural. It refers to a set of information. The singular form is* datum, *one piece of information.*

STOPPING TO THINK 1

You hear your friend Yoshi tell someone that a hypothesis is the same as a guess. Explain whether you agree with Yoshi.

In the case of pellagra, Dr. Goldberger conducted an experiment on prisoners to test his hypothesis. During the experiment, seven of 11 prisoners, or 64%, developed pellagra after six months. Even though all of the prisoners followed the same diet, they did not respond in the same way. Scientists try to account for individual differences by studying a large enough **sample size.**

STOPPING TO THINK 2

Explain whether Dr. Goldberger provided enough evidence to prove that pellagra is not contagious.

In the United States today, government agencies, such as the Food and Drug Administration (FDA), tightly control and review experimentation on humans. After receiving government approval, companies often search for volunteers to participate in clinical trials. Clinical trials test medicines, food, medical procedures, and medical equipment. **Data** collected during these trials provide evidence for making conclusions about a product or treatment. The type of data collected depends on what is being investigated.

For example, imagine a company that is conducting trials of a new hearing aid. The company would like to know how clearly volunteers can hear when using the hearing aid. People will try out the hearing aid and report how clearly they hear sounds, and if they hear any buzzing or other undesired noise from the hearing aid. They may also report whether they find the hearing aid comfortable to wear and attractive in appearance. These are all examples of qualitative data. **Qualitative** (KWAL-i-tay-tiv) **data** describe properties or characteristics (qualities) that are used to identify things. Qualitative data often result from putting things into categories.

STOPPING TO THINK 3

You notice a skateboard for sale on an Internet website. The price is good, but the website provides no picture or other information. What qualitative data would you like to have before you decide if you will buy it?

What if you were interested in buying the hearing aid? You would probably want to know how well it works when compared with other hearing aids. In

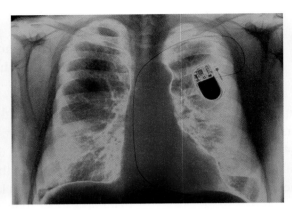

Medical products, such as hearing aids, pacemakers, and contact lenses are tested before being sold to the public.

clinical trials, people with hearing problems might be tested to measure the softest sound they could hear with and without the different hearing aids. The volume of sound (how loud it is) is measured in decibels. The company might report that in clinical tests 90% of the people wearing the hearing aid heard sounds as low as 35 decibels, when only 10% could hear these sounds without the hearing aid. In this case, numerical, or quantitative, data were collected. **Quantitative** (KWAN-ti-tay-tiv) **data** are values that have been measured or counted. The word *quantitative* is related to the word *quantity*, which means "number" or "amount."

Consider an everyday example of qualitative and quantitative information. Imagine you are at a large store with a friend when suddenly you turn around and she's not with you anymore. You look around, but you don't see her anywhere nearby. You ask a store employee if he has seen her. You describe your friend as a tall 13-year-old girl with short brown hair, brown eyes, a red jacket, two braids, and a dimple when she smiles. You have included important qualitative and quantitative information about your friend.

STOPPING TO THINK 4

Reread the description of your friend in the above paragraph. Create a list of each of her characteristics. Identify each characteristic as either qualitative or quantitative.

Both qualitative and quantitative evidence are important in identifying your friend. Qualitative data provide information about important characteristics that are difficult to measure but can be described and categorized. But in some cases quantitative data help give a clearer description. Think about the description of your friend in the previous paragraph. A height that seems tall to you might seem short to the store employee. But if you tell him that your friend is 5 feet 7 inches tall, you will both have a clear idea of how tall she is.

a. What kinds of qualitative data are useful in studying people scientifically? Provide at least two examples.

b. What kinds of quantitative data are useful in studying people scientifically? Provide at least two examples.

ANALYSIS

1. You decide to take a medicine for your upset stomach. You have a choice of two medicines. Both medicines are advertised as safe based on clinical trials. Medicine A was tested on 100 people. Medicine B was tested on 10,000 people.

   a. Which medicine would you take? Explain. Support your answer with evidence.

   b. Was your decision based on qualitative or quantitative information?

2. You're a nurse at a local hospital. While you are there, you read a patient chart containing the data below. Identify each item of patient data as quantitative or qualitative.

3. Imagine conducting a clinical trial of a headache medicine. Based on your research, you hypothesize that the medicine will successfully treat headaches in people. Before the Food and Drug Administration (FDA) will approve your study, you must explain the type of data you will collect to test your hypothesis.

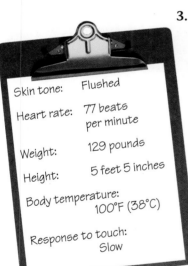

Skin tone: Flushed

Heart rate: 77 beats
              per minute

Weight: 129 pounds

Height: 5 feet 5 inches

Body temperature:
              100°F (38°C)

Response to touch:
              Slow

   a. List at least three kinds of qualitative data you will collect.
      Hint: Think about what information you would collect from the volunteers and what information you would collect about the medicine in order to determine the safety and effectiveness of the medicine.

   b. List at least three kinds of quantitative data you will collect.
      Hint: Think about what information you would collect from the volunteers and what information you would collect about the medicine in order to determine the safety and effectiveness of the medicine.

4. Fill in the "After" column for statements 13–16 on Student Sheet 1.1, "Anticipation Guide: Ideas about Experimental Design." Did your thinking change?

5. Think about the activities you have done so far in this unit. What are the common elements of a well-designed experiment?

6. **Reflection:** Both qualitative and quantitative data provide evidence for making decisions. How have you used each of these types of data to make decisions? Describe your experiences.

LABORATORY

Because of differences among individuals, a **range**, or set of values, is often used to used to describe the variation in normal results found in a larger group of people. For example, you may have had nurses take your pulse. What can your pulse tell them? Through scientific study, a normal pulse range for people at rest has been established. The normal range for adults is 60–80 beats per minute. The use of a range (60–80) instead of a specific number helps take into account the differences among people.

To establish a range, data are collected from many trials. Increasing the number of people tested increases the chance that the conclusions are true for most people.

If you play baseball, softball, or other games that involve throwing and catching, your teacher or coach may tell you to catch the ball with two hands. Does catching with two hands (as compared to one) really increase your ability to catch a ball?

CHALLENGE ➡ **How can you study people scientifically? Find out by collecting data on people and then designing your own experiment.**

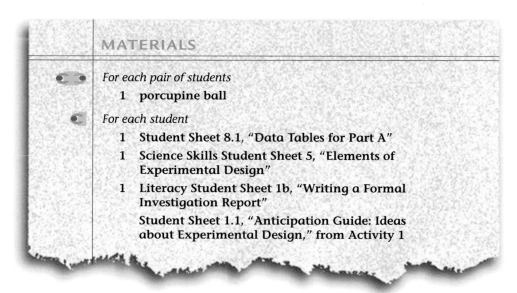

MATERIALS

For each pair of students
   1 **porcupine ball**

For each student
   1 **Student Sheet 8.1, "Data Tables for Part A"**
   1 **Science Skills Student Sheet 5, "Elements of Experimental Design"**
   1 **Literacy Student Sheet 1b, "Writing a Formal Investigation Report"**
      Student Sheet 1.1, "Anticipation Guide: Ideas about Experimental Design," from Activity 1

PROCEDURE

Part A: One Hand Compared to Two

1. Based on what you know about catching balls, record a hypothesis about whether the ability to catch a ball increases when using two hands (as compared to one).

2. With your partner, brainstorm all of the variables that you will try to keep the same while conducting the experiment.

3. As a class, discuss the variables you will keep the same. Draw a larger version of the chart below in your science notebook. Record the variables your class has decided on and how your class has decided to control them.

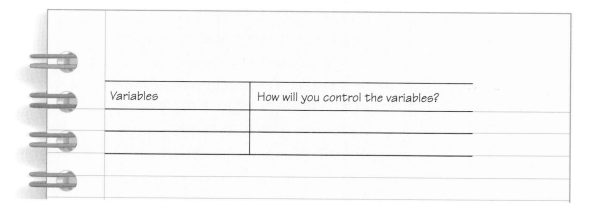

Variables	How will you control the variables?

4. Stand 2–3 meters away from your partner, as directed by your teacher.

5. Have your partner toss you the ball while you catch it using only one hand. Remember to keep all variables, except for the one being tested, the same.

6. *Did you find catching the ball with one hand easy, difficult, or somewhere in between?* Record your response in Table 1, "My Data," of Student Sheet 8.1, "Data Tables for Part A."

7. Have your partner toss you the ball 20 times while you continue to catch it using only *one hand*. Record the results of each catch in Table 2, "My Data: Number of Completed Catches." Place an "X" in the box when you catch the ball using one hand, and an "O" when you do not. When you are done, count and record the total number of completed catches.

8. Repeat Steps 4–7, but use *two hands* to catch the ball.

9. Now repeat Steps 4–8 for your partner to collect his or her own data.

10. Share your results with the class. Use the class data to complete Tables 3 and 4 on Student Sheet 8.1.

11. Complete Analysis Questions 1–4.

Part B: Designing Your Own Experiment

12. Design an experiment to investigate the effect of one variable on your ability to catch a ball. For example, you may want to investigate your ability to catch with one eye closed, to compare your ability to catch with your right or your left hand, or to vary the size of the ball. When designing your experiment, think about the following questions:

    • What is the purpose of your experiment?

    • What variable are you testing?

    • What is your hypothesis?

    • What variables will you keep the same?

    • How many trials will you conduct?

    • Will you collect qualitative and/or quantitative data? How will these data help you to reach a conclusion?

    • How will you record these data?

    Look at the list of variables you identified in Part A for additional ideas.

13. Record your hypothesis and your planned experimental procedure in your science notebook.

14. Make a data table that has space for all the data you need to record. You will fill it in during your experiment.

15. Obtain your teacher's approval of your experiment.

16. Conduct your experiment and record your results.

17. If you have time, switch procedures with another pair of students. Conduct their experiment and record the results while they do the same with yours. Then exchange results so that each pair has two sets of results for the experiment they designed.

EXTENSION

Conduct your experiment with different age groups, such as children compared with adults. Compare your data with the data collected in class. Are your conclusions the same?

ANALYSIS

Part A: One Hand Compared to Two

1. Explain whether your own data supported or disproved your hypothesis about the ability to catch a ball with two hands (as compared to one).

2. Look at the class data on Student Sheet 8.1.

   a. In Table 4, what was the range of students' ability to catch a ball with one hand?

   b. In Table 4, what was the range of students' ability to catch a ball with two hands?

   c. Use the class data to explain whether the ability to catch a ball increases when using two hands (as compared to one).

3. a. What qualitative data did you collect in Part A of this activity?

   b. What quantitative data did you collect in Part A of this activity?

   c. Which type of data was more useful for comparing results among the class members?

4. Fill in the "After" column for statements 17–19 on Student Sheet 1.1, "Anticipation Guide: Ideas about Experimental Design." Did your thinking change?

5. Your coach asks you whether she should continue to recommend that players on the team catch with two hands. Explain your recommendation and whether it is based on your own data or that of the class.

Part B: Designing Your Own Experiment

6. Prepare a full report for the investigation according to the guidelines on Literacy Student Sheet 1b, "Writing a Formal Investigation Report." Write your report on a clean sheet of paper.

   The analysis section of your report should include the following:

   a. a graph of your results

   b. a discussion of the variables you were able to keep the same

   c. a discussion of the variables (except the one being tested) that you could not keep the same

7. Was it possible for another pair to repeat your experiment? Were the results similar to your original results? Explain.

8. How do scientists use good experimental design to collect reproducible data about people?

ROLE PLAY

You may feel healthy most of the time. But when you feel sick, you may turn to medicines for relief. How do you decide whether to take a medicine, and what kind of medicine to take? Can you use some of the methods scientists use to solve problems to decide which medicine to take?

CHALLENGE ➡ **What are the trade-offs of taking a medicine when you feel sick?**

MATERIALS

For each student
- 1 Student Sheet 9.1, "Notes on Medicines"
- 1 Student Sheet 9.2, "Intra-act Discussion: Taking Medicines"

PROCEDURE

Part A

1. Assign a role for each person in your group.

2. Read the role-play aloud as a group.

3. Imagine you have the same symptoms as Sam has. Discuss what you think Sam should do and record your ideas in your science notebook.

4. In your science notebook, create a larger version of the chart shown below. In the chart, record the qualitative and quantitative facts about Sam's illness. The first one is done for you.

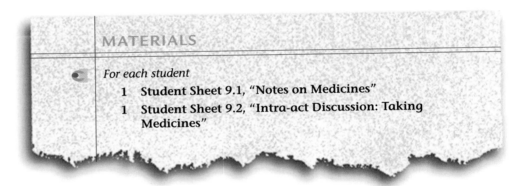

Facts about Sam's illness	Qualitative	Quantitative
Sam feels awful	X	

FEELING SICK

Sam and his older brother and sisters are talking one Saturday morning.

Sam: I feel so sick. It's just not fair! Yesterday I felt fine, but today I feel awful. I don't want to miss the birthday party at the twins' house tonight.

Andrea: You must feel pretty bad to talk about missing a party. What's wrong?

Sam: You don't really want to know. My stomach hurts so much it feels like an elephant sat on it. I had to get up and run to the bathroom four times last night and now I feel dizzy and weak.

Marta: Sounds pretty bad. Let me feel your forehead . . . Oh yeah, you are hot. You probably have a fever.

Andrea: Here's the thermometer. Let's take your temperature.

Robert: Don't we have something Sam can take to feel better?

Marta: Hmm, you have a fever of 101.2ºF (38.4ºC). Let me check the medicine cabinet.

Andrea: I say aspirin is the best answer. It always works for me when I get a headache.

Sam: It doesn't always work for me when I have a headache.

Robert: Uncle Richard takes an herbal remedy. I forget what he calls it. He says it works for him and it's safer than medicines.

Andrea: Yeah, but Aunt Jan says herbal remedies aren't tested the way medicines are. She says you can't be sure they work and if they're safe.

Marta: We have fever medicines, herbal tea, and some stomach medicine. I could also give you some ginger ale or soup. That's what Mom always has when she is sick.

Robert: Why don't we get them and look at the labels?

Marta: Good idea. And I'll call the doctor and describe your symptoms. Dad left the number by the phone.

Part B

5. Read the doctor's response to Marta to learn more about Sam's choices:

    "It sounds like Sam has a common stomach virus. He should feel better in a day or two as long as he drinks plenty of liquids. It's important that he doesn't get dehydrated. If his fever doesn't get any worse, Sam can decide for himself whether he would like to take any medicine.

    "Fever and diarrhea are sometimes ways that the body fights off bad germs. They're the body's way of trying to make you better. But a fever reducer or diarrhea medicine may help Sam feel better now. It's up to him. I'm leaving town for a couple of days, so call the hospital if his fever goes up or if he doesn't feel better in two days."

6. Shown below and on the next page are the labels from the medicines that Robert found in the medicine cabinet. Use Student Sheet 9.1, "Notes on Medicines," to help you analyze the labels. Read them carefully as you decide what Sam should do.

7. Discuss what you think Sam should do. Record your ideas in your science notebook.

8. Mark whether you agree or disagree with the statements on Student Sheet 9.2, "Intra-act Discussion: Taking Medicines." Then predict what you think other members of your group will say. Discuss the statements with your group. Have each person explain his or her opinion about each statement.

Medicine A: Pain Reliever/Fever Reducer Tablet

Warning: If you consume three or more alcoholic drinks every day, ask your doctor whether you should take this product or other pain relievers/fever reducers. This product may cause liver damage. **Do not use** with other pain killers/fever reducers unless directed by a doctor. Keep this and all drugs out of the reach of children.

Stop using and consult a doctor if: · symptoms do not improve · new symptoms occur · pain or fever persists or gets worse · redness or swelling is present.

Medicine B: Pain Reliever/Fever Reducer Tablet

Warning: Children and teenagers should not use this medicine for chicken pox or flu symptoms before a doctor is consulted about Reye's Syndrome, a rare but serious illness associated with this medicine. Do not take this product if you are allergic to aspirin or if you have asthma, unless directed by a doctor.

Drug Interaction Precaution: Do not take this product if you are taking a prescription drug for anticoagulation (thinning the blood), diabetes, gout, or arthritis, unless directed by a doctor.

Medicine C: Diarrhea Tablet

Warning: Keep this and all drugs out of the reach of children. Do not use for more than two days unless directed by a physician. Do not use if diarrhea is accompanied by high fever (greater than 101°F), or if blood or mucus is present in the stool, or if you have had a rash or other allergic reaction to this medication. If you are taking antibiotics or have a history of liver disease, consult a physician before using this product.

Medicine D: Herbal Tea

This plant grows wild in the United States, and Native Americans have used it for centuries for a variety of purposes. This tea contains a blend of leaves, flowers, and stems of an organically grown plant. In modern studies, leaves, flowers, and roots of this plant have shown measured effects in supporting the immune system.*

*The Food and Drug Administration has not evaluated these statements. This product is not intended to diagnose, treat, cure, or prevent any disease.

ANALYSIS

1. What kinds of information are provided on the labels?

2. What questions do you have about the medicines?

3. Sam decided to make a decision based on the information he has. Think about all of the options available to Sam. He could

   a. drink liquids and wait until he feels better,

   b. drink liquids and take one of the medicines, or

   c. drink liquids and take a combination of the medicines.

   If you were Sam, what would you do? Assume that Sam's medical history is the same as your own. Support your answer with evidence and identify the trade-offs of your decision.

   Hint: To write a complete answer, first state your opinion. Provide two or more pieces of evidence that support your opinion. Then consider all sides of the issue and identify the trade-offs of your decision.

4. Explain whether you used more qualitative or quantitative evidence to make your decision. Support your answer with examples.

5. What are the trade-offs of taking a medicine when you feel sick?

10 Evaluating Clinical Trials

Conducting studies on people is time-consuming and expensive. Researchers need funding. The U.S. National Institutes of Health (NIH) is one organization that provides money for such studies. What does NIH look for when researchers request money to study people scientifically?

CHALLENGE ➔ **Which proposals have an experimental design worth funding?**

The NIH Committee

Listed on the following pages are proposals for four studies requesting money to conduct clinical trials. Most of the studies are based on actual research projects. As a member of the NIH review committee, your job is to evaluate the experimental design of each proposed study. Based on your review, make a recommendation as to whether NIH should fund each study.

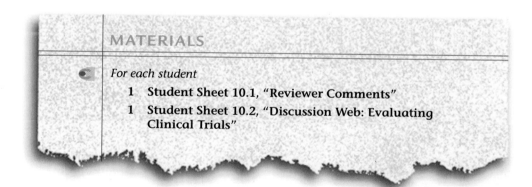

MATERIALS

For each student

1 **Student Sheet 10.1, "Reviewer Comments"**
1 **Student Sheet 10.2, "Discussion Web: Evaluating Clinical Trials"**

PROCEDURE

1. With your group, brainstorm all of the factors that are important in designing a scientific experiment involving people. Work together to agree on a complete list.

   • Listen to and consider the explanations and ideas of other members of your group.

   • If you disagree about a factor with others in your group, explain to the rest of the group why you disagree.

2. Read Study 1, "Clinical Trial of 'Summer Fever' Vaccine." (The studies begin below.)

3. Use your list of experimental design factors from Step 1 and Student Sheet 10.1, "Reviewer Comments," to evaluate the study. Record the name of the study, the factors of its experimental design, and any other comments you have.

4. Based on your comments, decide whether you would recommend funding for this study.

5. Repeat Steps 2–4 for the remaining studies.

Study 1:
Clinical Trial of "Summer Fever" Vaccine

We are working to prevent "summer fever," a contagious disease that kills or paralyzes many children each summer. The disease attacks the motor neurons of the body, which control the muscles, causing paralysis. Sometimes the disease attacks the nerves in the base of the brain and then swallowing and breathing are affected. This disease is spreading quickly across the United States. We have developed a vaccine that we believe will prevent children from catching this disease. We would like to conduct a clinical trial to find out if our vaccine is effective in children. Our plan is to give the vaccine to 12,000 children in the state's capital city. We will count how many of these children catch summer fever. We are sure that all of these children will be completely protected as a result of taking this vaccine.

To prove that the vaccine is safe for humans, my assistant, my 14-year-old child, and I have all taken it. We have not suffered any bad effects from the vaccine.

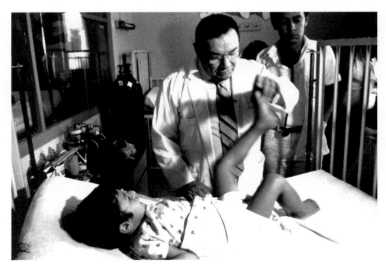

This child's legs are paralyzed as a result of a disease similar to "summer fever."

Study 2:
Clinical Trial of Burn Cream

We have developed a new, medicated cream that helps heal burns on animals. Faster healing reduces pain and reduces the chance that the burns will become infected. We would like to test this cream on humans to see if it helps heal their burns faster. We plan to conduct clinical trials on 200 people ages 20–40. Half of the people will be men and half will be women. Each person must have third-degree burns that are no larger than 3 centimeters by 3 centimeters. They must also be healthy except for their burns.

Fifty of the men and fifty of the women will be treated with our new medicated cream. The other half will receive a placebo cream that does not contain the medication. We will not let either group know which cream they are receiving. Each person will apply 2 grams of cream to the burn every morning for 20 days.

Three studies done by the local veterinary school have shown that the medicated cream is effective in healing burns on rabbits, cats, and dogs. Each study involved 100 animals. Half of the animals received medicated cream and half received cream without medication. The burns on animals treated with medicated cream healed faster.

Study 3:
Clinical Trial of Weight Loss Method

More than half of the adults in the United States are overweight. Many of them try risky fad diets to lose weight. One way to help people lose weight is to find effective ways in which they can reduce the number of calories they eat. For this reason, we would like to conduct a clinical trial of one method of reducing calorie intake. We would like to find out whether drinking water and eating an appetizer before a meal will help people reduce the number of calories they eat.

We will begin with 24 volunteers who will be told about all aspects of the trial. We will select volunteers who are men between the ages of 35–55 and who are at least 20% overweight. In our control, each volunteer will eat a chicken-rice appetizer that contains exactly 200 calories. We will then count how many calories the volunteer eats for lunch after eating this appetizer. To measure the effect of drinking water with the appetizer, the same volunteer will eat the same appetizer on a different day, but this time with a 12-ounce glass of water. We will again count the number of calories the volunteer eats for lunch afterward.

Each volunteer will repeat the control and the experiment three times. We will then average the results to determine any change in the number of calories eaten in each part of the trial.

Study 4:
Clinical Trial of Relaxin

We have developed a new drug called Relaxin. We believe Relaxin can be used to calm and relax people as well as prevent nausea. For these reasons, we think this drug would be useful to pregnant women. We would like to conduct a clinical trial to find out if this drug is effective for pregnant women. We will provide Relaxin to some doctors. These doctors will be asked to prescribe Relaxin to pregnant women who ask for a drug to prevent nausea. Of course, we will tell the women that they are getting Relaxin, because people testing new drugs should give their permission. We will then record the effects on these women by asking them if they feel calmer and less nauseated.

Relaxin has been tested for its effectiveness and safety. Our scientists conducted an experiment on mice. Half of these mice were given Relaxin, while the other half were given a placebo. We observed and recorded how much the mice moved. The mice that were given Relaxin moved less than the mice that were given the placebo. This showed that the drug is effective. None of the mice had any side effects from this drug. To further test the safety of Relaxin, we gave large doses to some mice. None of these mice showed any permanent side effects from the large doses.

ANALYSIS

1. Which study—1 through 4—had the best experimental design? Explain.

2. Discuss your funding recommendations with your group. Do you agree on which studies, if any, should be funded? What other concerns do you have?

3. You find out that NIH has only enough money to fund one study and plans to fund the best one. Explain which study you would fund. Support your answer with evidence and identify the trade-offs of your decision.

   Hint: To write a complete answer, first state your opinion. Provide two or more pieces of evidence that support your opinion. Then consider all sides of the issue and identify the trade-offs of your decision.

4. Choose one of the studies. Review your comments about its experimental design and think about how the study could be improved. Rewrite the study to include your recommendations for improving the quality of the experiment.

5. **Reflection:** Based on what you have learned in this unit, how do you solve problems? How do scientists solve problems? Compare your methods to scientists' methods and describe the similarities and differences between them.

EXTENSION

Bring in news articles that describe scientific studies involving people. Analyze the studies according to the procedures you used in this activity. What issues do scientists face when studying people scientifically?

Index

A **bold** page number identifies the page on which the term is defined.

motor neurons, **A26**
movement, brain function, A27
muscle control
    involuntary, A27
    voluntary, A26

N

National Institute of Health (NIH),
   A43
nerve cells. *See* neurons.
nerve impulse path, diagram, A26
nervous system
    automatic, A27
    brain
        brain stem, A27–28
        cerebellum, A27–28
        cerebrum, A27–28
        composition of, A27
        folds, A27
        weight, A27
        wrinkles, A27
    brain functions
        balance, A27
        basic life functions, A28
        blood pressure, A28
        breathing, A28
        hearing, A27
        heartbeat, A28
        motor control, A27
        movement, A27
        posture, A27
        pressure, A27
        smell, A27
        speech, A27
        taste, A27
        thinking and reasoning, A27
        thought processes and
           actions, A27
        touch, A27
        vision, A27
    definition, **A25**
    involuntary, A27

nerve cells. *See* neurons.
nerve impulse path, diagram, A26
neurons
    definition, **A25**
    information gathering.
        See sensory neurons.
    interneurons, **A26**
    motor neurons, **A26**
    muscle control, involuntary,
       A27
    muscle control, voluntary, A26
    pressure detection. *See* touch
       receptors.
    spinal cord and brain. *See*
       interneurons.
    touch receptors, **A28**
    sensory neurons, **A25**
    voluntary. *See* motor neurons.
neurons
    definition, **A25**
    information gathering. *See*
       sensory neurons.
    interneurons, **A26**
    motor neurons, **A26**
    muscle control, involuntary, A27
    muscle control, voluntary. *See*
       motor neurons.
    pressure detection. *See* touch
       receptors.
    spinal cord and brain. *See*
       interneurons.
    touch receptors, **A28**
NIH (National Institute of Health),
   A43

O

objective data. *See* quantitative data.

P

pellagra, cause of, A8–10, A20, A31
placebo effect, **A16–17**
placebos, **A16**

Credits

Abbreviations: t (top), m (middle), b (bottom), l (left), r (right), c (center)

All illustrations by Seventeenth Street Studios.

"Talking It Over" icon photo: ©Michael Keller/The Stock Market

Unit A

Unit opener (A-2, A-3): bl: ©S. Fraser/Photo Researchers, Inc.; bc: ©2001 Richard Price/FPG; br: Donna Markey; tl: ©2001 Charles Thatcher/Stone; tc: ©2001 B. Busco/The Image Bank.

A-8 ©2001/The Image Bank; A-9 ©Bettmann/CORBIS; A-25 ©Digital Art/CORBIS; A-32 Heart Pacemaker ©Department of Clinical Radiology, Salisbury District Hospital/SPL/Photo Researchers, Inc.; A-44 photo courtesy of the World Health Organization; A-46 ©Laura Dwight/ DoctorStock.com.

Front cover photo (DNA analysis): © 2008 Kevin Curtis/Photo Researchers, Inc.

SEPUP Issues & Life Science

ECOLOGY

SCIENCE
EDUCATION FOR
PUBLIC
UNDERSTANDING
PROGRAM

S E P U P

UNIVERSITY OF CALIFORNIA AT BERKELEY

LAWRENCE HALL OF SCIENCE **LHS**⋆

INCORPORATED

RONKONKOMA, NEW YORK

This book is part of SEPUP's middle school science course sequence:

Issues and Earth Science

Studying Soils Scientifically
Rocks and Minerals
Erosion and Deposition
Plate Tectonics
Weather and Atmosphere
The Earth in Space
Exploring the Solar System

Issues and Life Science

Experimental Design: Studying People Scientifically
Body Works
Cell Biology and Disease
Genetics
Ecology
Evolution
Bioengineering

Issues and Physical Science

Studying Materials Scientifically
The Chemistry of Materials
Water
Energy
Force and Motion

Additional SEPUP instructional materials include:
CHEM-2 (Chemicals, Health, Environment and Me): Grades 4–6
SEPUP Modules: Grades 7–12
Science and Sustainability: Course for Grades 9–12
Science and Global Issues Biology: Course for Grades 9–12

 This material is based upon work supported by the National Science Foundation under Grant No. 9554163. Any opinions, findings, and conclusions or recommendations expressed in this material are those of the authors and do not necessarily reflect the views of the National Science Foundation.

For photo and illustration credits, see page E-91, which constitutes an extension of this copyright page.

The preferred citation format for this book is
SEPUP. (2009). Issues and Life Science. Lawrence Hall of Science, University of California at Berkeley. Published by Lab-Aids®, Inc., Ronkonkoma, NY

SEPUP
Lawrence Hall of Science
University of California at Berkeley
Berkeley CA 94720-5200

e-mail: sepup@berkeley.edu
Website: www.sepuplhs.org

Published by:

17 Colt Court
Ronkonkoma NY 11779
Website: www.lab-aids.com

A Letter to *Issues and Life Science* Students

As you examine the activities in this book, you may wonder, "Why does this book look so different from other science books I've seen?" The reason is simple: it is a different kind of science program, and only some of what you will learn can be seen by leafing through this book!

Issues and Life Science, or *IALS,* uses several kinds of activities to teach science. For example, you will design and conduct an experiment to investigate human responses. You will explore a model of how species compete for food. And you will play the roles of scientists learning about the causes of infectious disease. A combination of experiments, readings, models, debates, role plays, and projects will help you uncover the nature of science and the relevance of science to your interests.

You will find that important scientific ideas come up again and again in different activities. You will be expected to do more than just memorize these concepts: you will be asked to explain and apply them. In particular, you will improve your decision-making skills, using evidence and weighing outcomes to decide what you think should be done about scientific issues facing society.

How do we know that this is a good way for you to learn? In general, research on science education supports it. In particular, the activities in this book were tested by hundreds of students and their teachers, and they were modified on the basis of their feedback. In a sense, this entire book is the result of an investigation: we had people test our ideas, we interpreted the results, and we revised our ideas! We believe the result will show you that learning more about science is important, enjoyable, and relevant to your life.

IALS Staff

ISSUES & LIFE SCIENCE PROJECT
  Director (2003–2008): Barbara Nagle
  Director (1995–2002): Herbert D. Thier

AUTHORS
  Barbara Nagle
  Manisha Hariani
  Donna Markey
  Herbert D. Thier
  Asher Davison
  Susan K. Boudreau
  Daniel Seaver
  Laura Baumgartner

OTHER CONTRIBUTORS
  Kathaleen Burke
  Richard Duquin

CONTENT AND SCIENTIFIC REVIEW
  Peter J. Kelly, Emeritus Professor of Education and Senior Visiting Fellow, School of
    Education, University of Southampton, Southampton, England
  Deborah Penry, Assistant Professor, Department of Integrative Biology, University
    of California at Berkeley, Berkeley, California

RESEARCH ASSISTANCE
  Marcelle Siegel, Leif Asper

PRODUCTION
  Design and composition: Seventeenth Street Studios
  Administrative assistance: Roberta Smith and Anna Vorster

We would also like to thank Miriam Shein and Sylvia Parisotto for their contributions
to this publication.

FIELD TEST CENTERS

This course is a revision of *Science and Life Issues*. The following centers participated in field testing the original course or the revised materials. We are extremely grateful to the center directors and teachers who taught the program. These teachers and their students contributed significantly to improving the course.

REGIONAL CENTER, SOUTHERN CALIFORNIA

Donna Markey, *Center Director*
Kim Blumeyer, Helen Copeland, Pat McLoughlin, Donna Markey, Philip Poniktera, Samantha Swann, Miles Vandegrift

REGIONAL CENTER, IOWA

Dr. Robert Yager and Jeanne Bancroft, *Center Directors*
Rebecca Andresen, Lore Baur, Dan Dvorak, Dan Hill, Mark Kluber, Amy Lauer, Lisa Martin, Stephanie Phillips

REGIONAL CENTER, WESTERN NEW YORK

Dr. Robert Horvat, *Center Director*
Kathaleen Burke, Dick Duquin, Eleanor Falsone, Lillian Gondree, Jason Mayle, James Morgan, Valerie Tundo

JEFFERSON COUNTY, KENTUCKY

Pamela Boykin, *Center Director*
Charlotte Brown, Tara Endris, Sharon Kremer, Karen Niemann, Susan Stinebruner, Joan Thieman

LIVERMORE, CALIFORNIA

Scott Vernoy, *Center Director*
Rick Boster, Ann Ewing, Kathy Gabel, Sharon Schmidt, Denia Segrest, Bruce Wolfe

QUEENS, NEW YORK

Pam Wasserman, *Center Director*
Gina Clemente, Cheryl Dodes, Karen Horowitz, Tricia Hutter, Jean Rogers, Mark Schmucker, Christine Wilk

TUCSON, ARIZONA

Jonathan Becker, *Center Director*
Peggy Herron, Debbie Hobbs, Carol Newhouse, Nancy Webster

INDEPENDENT

Berkeley, California: Robyn McArdle
Fresno, California: Al Brofman
Orinda, California: Sue Boudreau, Janine Orr, Karen Snelson
Tucson, Arizona: Patricia Cadigan, Kevin Finegan

Contents

Ecology

E

TALKING IT OVER

CHALLENGE ➤ **What are the trade-offs of introducing a species into a new environment?**

Have you ever thought that it would be cool to have parrots flying around in your backyard? Or wished that there were hippos in your local lake? What happens when you introduce an organism into a new environment?

Fishing on Lake Victoria

James Abila is a Kenyan boy of 17. His family has a small fishing boat on Lake Victoria. He sat outside his hut to talk to us. Inside, his mother was preparing lunch, while his sister and younger brother were laying out a few fish to dry in the afternoon sun.

James started his story. "My father made our boat. He was always one of the best fishermen in the village. He still catches all kinds of fish, though he says it's not as easy as it used to be. Most of the fish in the lake used to be very small, just 2–4 inches long. So it was easy to use our net to catch hundreds of small fish. But about the time I was born, the number of fish seemed to go down. Luckily, the government introduced new fish into the lake. Now, the most common fish in the lake is Nile perch. It's a much bigger fish and can be too heavy to catch with a net. That's why I work for one of the fishing companies. They have the large boats needed to catch Nile perch. And I can earn money to help feed my family."

Uganda
Kenya
Lake Victoria
Tanzania

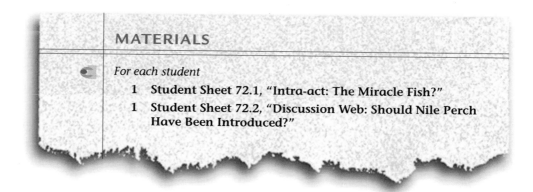

MATERIALS

For each student

1   Student Sheet 72.1, "Intra-act: The Miracle Fish?"
1   Student Sheet 72.2, "Discussion Web: Should Nile Perch Have Been Introduced?"

PROCEDURE

1. Work with your group to read the story of Nile perch in Lake Victoria.

2. Discuss whether you think Nile perch should have been introduced into Lake Victoria.

3. Use Student Sheet 72.1, "Intra-act: The Miracle Fish?" and have each member of your group take a different perspective from the list below:

   • James

   • James's father

   • An owner of a fishing company

   • An environmentalist

4. From the perspective of your character, mark whether you agree or disagree with the statements on Student Sheet 72.1, "Intra-act Discussion: The Miracle Fish?" Predict what you think other members of your group will say.

5. Discuss the statements with your group.

This man is holding a large Nile perch.

NILE PERCH

Lake Victoria is the second largest lake in the world and it contains some extremely large fish. One type of fish found there, known as Nile perch *(Lates niloticus),* can grow to 240 kilograms (530 pounds), though its average size is 3–6 kilograms (7–13 pounds). But Nile perch weren't always found in Lake Victoria. Until the 1980s, the most common fish in Lake Victoria were cichlids (SICK-lids), small freshwater fish about 2–4 inches long. (If you've ever seen aquarium fish such as oscars, Jack Dempseys, or freshwater angelfish, you've seen a cichlid.)

Lake Victoria cichlids interest **ecologists**—scientists who study relationships between organisms and environments—because there are so many species of these fish. Although they all belong to the same family (see Table 1), at one time there were over 300 different species of cichlids in Lake Victoria. Almost 99% of these species could not be found anywhere else in the world!

Table 1: Classification of Cichlids	
Kingdom	**Animalia**
Phylum	Chordata
Class	Osteichthyes (bony fish)
Family	Cichlidae

There used to be many other kinds of fish in the lake, including catfish, carp, and lungfish. The 30 million people who lived around Lake Victoria relied on the lake for food. Because most of the fish were small, they could be caught by using simple fishing nets and a canoe. The fish were then dried in the sun and sold locally.

By the late 1950s, however, it appeared the lake was being overfished. So many fish were caught that the populations remaining did not have enough members left to reproduce and grow. If the lake continued to be overfished, there might not be enough fish left for people to eat. As a result, the British government (which ruled this part of Africa at that time) decided to introduce new fish species, such as Nile perch, into the lake. They wanted to increase the amount of fish that was available to eat; they

Cichlids are one of the many small fish commonly found in Lake Victoria.

hoped to provide more high-protein fish for local people and to be able to sell extra fish to other countries. Ecologists were opposed to this idea. They were worried that the introduction of Nile perch, which had no natural enemies within the lake, would negatively affect the lake's ecosystem. Before a final decision could be made, Nile perch were secretly added into the lake. Eventually, more Nile perch were deliberately added by the government in the early 1960s.

During the 1960s and 1970s, before there were a lot of Nile perch in the lake, about 100,000 metric tons of fish (including cichlids) were caught each year. By 1989, the total catch of fish from Lake Victoria had increased to 500,000 metric tons. Today, each of the three countries surrounding the lake (Uganda, Kenya, and Tanzania) sells extra fish to other countries. In the graph below, you can see how the amount of fish caught by Kenyan fisheries has changed over a 15-year period.

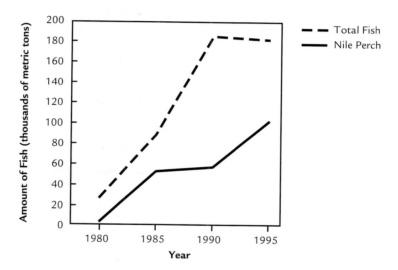

AMOUNT OF FISH CAUGHT IN LAKE VICTORIA BY KENYA

Besides increasing the amount of fish, there have been other consequences of introducing Nile perch into the lake. Because Nile perch are large and eat other fish, they are believed to have caused the extinction of as many as 200 species of cichlids. The populations of other types of fish, including catfish and lungfish, have also declined. Many ecologists are upset that their predictions have come true.

Some of the cichlids that have become extinct ate algae. With their extinction, the amount of algae in the lake has increased 5-fold. Algae use up a lot of oxygen, making it difficult for other tiny plants and animals to survive in the lake. Today, many of the deeper parts of the lake are considered "dead" because they don't contain much living matter.

However, many of the original goals have been met. In 1979, there were 16,000 fishermen along the Kenyan shores of the lake. In 1993, there were 82,300. Many people are now employed by companies that process and sell Nile perch overseas. Over time, these fish have brought more money into the African countries surrounding the lake. Local people, who now eat Nile perch as part of their diet, consider Nile perch a "savior."

Some ecologists wonder how long the current situation can last. Nile perch are predators. As populations of other fish decline, the Nile perch's food sources are declining. The stomachs of some large Nile perch have been found to contain smaller, juvenile Nile perch. What will happen to the population of Nile perch if their food supply dwindles even further? Will the Nile perch population be overfished like the fish populations before it? Only time will tell.

ANALYSIS

1. Based on the reading, how did the amount of fish caught in Lake Victoria change from the 1960s to 1989?

2. Based on the graph showing amounts of fish caught in Lake Victoria, describe how the amount of Nile perch caught by Kenya changed from 1980 to 1995.

3. Look again at the graph. How do you think the number of metric tons of fish caught relates to the size of the total fish population from year to year? Explain your reasoning.

4. How did the introduction of Nile perch affect the food supply of the people who lived near Lake Victoria?

5. What effect did the introduction of Nile perch have on the organisms that lived in the lake?

6. Should Nile perch have been introduced into Lake Victoria? Support your answer with evidence and discuss the trade-offs of your decision.

   Hint: To write a complete answer, first state your opinion. Provide two or more pieces of evidence that support your opinion. Then consider all sides of the issue and identify the trade-offs of your decision.

7. What do you predict will happen to Lake Victoria over the next 20–30 years? Why?

EXTENSION

Find current information about the ecology and distribution of the Nile perch and about efforts to manage the perch on the *Issues and Life Science* page of the SEPUP website.

PROJECT

ntroduced, non-native, exotic, and non-indigenous are all words used to describe species that humans have introduced outside of the species' normal range. The Nile perch is an **introduced species** that was placed deliberately into Lake Victoria. In other cases, the introduction of a new species into a new environment is accidental. Consider the case of the zebra mussel, which is named for the black and white stripes found on its shell. It was accidentally introduced into the United States in the 1980s and it is now estimated to cause up to $5 billion dollars of damage each year!

CHALLENGE ➡ **What effect can an introduced species have on an environment? What, if anything, should be done to control introduced species?**

MATERIALS

For the class
    books, magazines, CD-ROMs, Internet access, etc.

For each student
  1 Student Sheet 73.1, "Introduced Species Research"

PROCEDURE

1. Read about the introduced species described on the following pages. As directed by your teacher, decide which one species your group will research.

2. Over the next few days or weeks, find information on this species from books, magazines, CD-ROMs, the Internet, and/or interviews. You can also go to the *Issues and Life Science* page of the SEPUP website to link to sites with more information on species mentioned in this activity.

3. Use this information to complete Student Sheet 73.1, "Introduced Species Research." You should provide the following:

    - common and scientific name of your species

    - its native and current range; its relationship to and effect on people

    - its effect on new ecosystem(s)

    - its place in a foodweb

    - the reasons for its success

    - issues related to its future growth or spread.

    Later in this unit, you will use your research to create a class presentation.

EXTENSION

Visit a local greenhouse or botanical garden. Look at the labels of ornamental plants used in landscaping. Where did these plants originally come from? Is the introduction of these species considered to be good or bad?

Kudzu Brings Down Power Lines!

Kudzu (KUD-zoo), sometimes referred to as "the vine that ate the South," has finally pushed local patience to the limit. Properly called *Pueraria lobata*, it was first introduced in the 1920s to the southern United States as food for farm animals and to reduce soil erosion. Today, this fast-growing vine from Japan has overgrown entire forests and choked local ecosystems. Last week, the weight of kudzu vines pulled down power lines, causing a two-day power outage. Mayor Lam has called for control measures. All community members are invited to a town council meeting to consider what should be done to control this destructive vine.

Response to Tiger Mosquitoes Raises Questions

The public outcry over the worsening problem with the tiger mosquito (*Aedes albopictus*) continues. In response, the city

has begun nighttime spraying of insecticide. Jesse Butler, principal of the Little Town Pre-school, said, "How can the city be allowed to spray poison on the backyards where children play?" City spokesperson Kate O'Neil told reporters that the insecticide is harmless to people. "Tiger mosquitoes are very aggressive. They are much worse than the native mosquitoes. Apart from the nuisance, tiger mosquitoes can spread diseases such as yellow fever. We have to take action!" O'Neil invites interested residents to attend the Camford Mosquito Abatement Board presentation on the tiger mosquito problem and possible solutions.

Nutria Hunting on State Marshes?

Ecologists from City University are considering teaming with local hunters in a surprise move to reduce the population of nutria (NEW-tree-uh) in state marshes. Nutria (*Myocastor coypus*) are large, beaver-like rodents whose burrows and voracious grazing are causing serious damage to marshes.

Ecologist Charlie Desmond told reporters that nutria are native to South America. They were brought to North America for their fur. When they escaped into the wild, their population exploded. "If we don't act soon, we could lose our marshlands in just a few years," he cautioned. Duck hunters, bird watchers, sport fishers, and hikers are pressuring the state legislature to come up with a solution. Nutria hunting is one option being seriously explored.

Aquarium Plant Turns Out to Be Worst Weed

You may have seen this aquatic plant sold in small bunches at aquarium stores. It's a popular plant because goldfish like swimming between its stems. But when aquariums are dumped out into lakes, ponds, or rivers, hydrilla (hie-DRILL-uh) can quickly grow into a dense mat that chokes out other vegetation. This change of the environment is dramatic for native animals and plants. *Hydrilla verticillata*, as it is known scientifically, can clog up city water intake valves and get tangled in boat propellers. "We used to have the best swimming hole down by the bridge," said Rita Aziz, a 7th grader at Junior Middle School. "Now it's filled with this gross weed. The last time I swam there, I got tangled in it. It was scary. I would really like to find a way to do something about it."

Cut Down Trees to Protect Them?
Agency Advises on Longhorn Beetle Threat

When Keesha Murray, age 3, was injured by a falling branch in Tot Play Park, local neighborhoods woke up to the threat of the Asian longhorn beetle. Her father, Toby Murray, said that Keesha had played under the big maple tree many times. Under the attack of the Asian longhorn beetle, the tree had recently died, which led to the loss of the tree limb. "Keesha was scratched up and scared. We were lucky it wasn't worse," he said.

Shade trees all over the city have been dying due to the recent invasion of this wood-boring beetle from Japan, known scientifically as *Anoplophora glabripennis*. The beetle larvae are very hard to kill. One suggestion is to cut down all trees within city parks to prevent the beetle from spreading.

A Landscape Beauty Is Taking Over

What is the link between landscaping your yard and the recent reports that local marsh species are declining? Purple

loosestrife (*Lythrum salicaria*), whose magenta flowers are admired by gardeners, is the weed to blame. It was introduced from Europe as a medicinal herb in the early 1800s and is still sold today as a landscaping plant. According to the Fish and Wildlife Service ecologist Johanna Brown, "It totally takes over an area, crowding out native species. It's really devastating for fragile marsh ecosystems." Brian Van Horn, a teacher at Middleton Junior High, is also concerned. "It's a tough plant to get rid of and killing it can damage the marshes even more." A meeting at Middleton Junior High will be held to discuss this issue.

Farmers Rally to Scare Off Starlings

The recent outbreak of hog cholera may be related to starling *(Sturnus vulgaris)* droppings getting into pig food. Carol Polsky, a pig farmer in Poseyville, encouraged local farmers to work together to help get rid of the birds. "In addition to spreading disease, those birds eat crops, seeds, and animal feed. A flock of starlings will eat just about anything and they poop everywhere. That spreads disease to other animals, not just pigs," Polsky told reporters.

Many control options are available, according to Dr. Tony Caro of the Agricultural Sciences Board. Dr. Caro commented, "In 1891, 60 starlings were released in New York and now they are the most common bird in America!" But a representative of the local nature society told reporters that the latest annual survey showed that starling populations had dropped since the previous year. Dr. Caro will be speaking at the next meeting of the County Farm Association, where control measures for starlings will be discussed.

Brown Snake Problem Bites Guam

Guam, a tiny, tropical island, is a U.S. territory with a problem. People have been bitten. Bird, bat, and lizard populations have declined. The culprit? The brown tree snake *(Boiga irregularis)* from New Guinea.

After baby Oscar Gonzalez was bitten by a brown tree snake, local people were spurred to action. "Most of us know about them. Those snakes climb the power poles and short out electricity on the island several times a week," Nicki DeLeon, a long-time resident of Guam, told reporters. "Back in the 1960s and even the 1970s, the jungle was full of birds singing. We used to see bats and little lizards running around. They're not so easy to find now."

Scientists are working to find ways to control the snake before the last of the unique island species disappear forever. Dr. Sheila Dutt, a researcher with EcoSave International, said, "As well as helping with snake control on Guam, we are desperate to prevent this snake from hitching a ride in air cargo. I don't even want to think of the effect this snake could have in other parts of the United States."

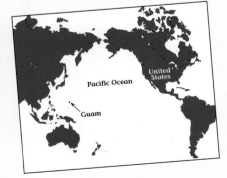

How do scientists know how introduced species affect ecosystems? Natural environments are constantly changing. How do you figure out what changes are due to the introduced organism and what changes are due to other factors? **Ecology** is the study of relationships between living organisms and the physical environment. Ecologists begin by studying organisms in the natural environment. They often supplement this information with laboratory investigations.

CHALLENGE   **What can you discover about an organism in a laboratory investigation?**

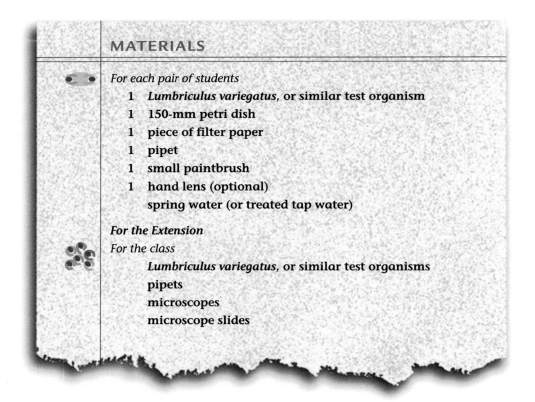

MATERIALS

For each pair of students

1   *Lumbriculus variegatus*, or similar test organism
1   150-mm petri dish
1   piece of filter paper
1   pipet
1   small paintbrush
1   hand lens (optional)
    spring water (or treated tap water)

For the Extension
For the class

   Lumbriculus variegatus, or similar test organisms
   pipets
   microscopes
   microscope slides

PROCEDURE

1. Discuss with your group some guidelines for studying animals in the classroom. Record your ideas in your science notebook. Be prepared to share these ideas with the class.

2. Draw a table in your science notebook like the one below, and record your observations and inferences about the blackworm. Not every observation will result in an inference.

Blackworm

Observations	Inferences

3. Pour 1–2 cm of water into the bottom of the petri dish.

4. Use the pipet to add a single blackworm from the culture to your petri dish. (Do not pick a blackworm that is dark and has a lighter section at one or both ends; this worm has recently been broken and is regenerating itself.)

5. Carefully observe the blackworm. Then use the brush to gently investigate this organism.

6. Record your observations. How much can you find out about a blackworm? Without injuring the worm, explore its behavior. For example, watch to see:

   • How does it move?

   • Does it respond differently to different actions on various parts of its body, such as touching?

   • Can you identify which end is the head?

   • What else do you observe?

7. Place the filter paper in the lid of the petri dish. Use the pipet and a few drops of water to completely moisten the filter paper.

8. Use the pipet to move the blackworm onto the filter paper.

9. Observe the blackworm's movement on this surface. How does its movement here compare with its movement in water? Record your observations.

10. Return your blackworm to the class culture before cleaning up.

EXTENSION

Place a blackworm on a microscope slide. Add one drop of water. (If there is too much water on the slide, use a pipet to suction off the excess water.) Observe the worm under low and medium power. What internal structures can you see?

ANALYSIS

1. Review your notes on how the blackworm responded to touch. How could these reactions help it to survive in the wild?

2. Based on what you now know about blackworms, in what type of environment do you think blackworms live? Explain your reasoning.

3. As an ecologist, you are asked to write an entry in an encyclopedia on the blackworm, *Lumbriculus variegatus*. Use your laboratory notes to write a paragraph describing the blackworm.

4. a. A student reading your encyclopedia entry thinks that you should include more information about blackworms. What questions do you think he or she might have after reading your entry?

   b. How might you get the information necessary to answer his or her questions?

There are many types of introduced species—just think about the differences between starlings and purple loosestrife! Most of the well-known cases belong to the plant or animal kingdom. While you may recognize kudzu, loosestrife, and hydrilla as plants, you may not have realized that all of the other introduced species discussed so far, including zebra mussels and tiger mosquitoes, are part of the animal kingdom. In fact, there are over one million known animal species in the world today, with many more being discovered every year. With such a large diversity of species, how do you know if the animal you are studying is similar to one another scientist is studying?

Scientists use classification systems to help them describe similar organisms. Several systems classify organisms in various ways. The five-kingdom classification scheme was based on observations of the physical structures and other characteristics of species. Then new evidence that bacteria can be divided into two groups—bacteria and archaea (are–KAY–uh)—led to a six-kingdom system. Although archaea are made up of a single cell and look like bacteria, they are genetically distinct from bacteria.

To better classify living organisms according to their genetic makeup, in 1990, scientists proposed the three-domain system. The three-domain system divides all living things into three groups—archaea, bacteria, and eukaryote (you–CARE–ee–ott) domains. The Eukaryote Domain is made up of all living things that have cells with a nucleus. It includes animals, plants, fungi, and protists. Because archaea and bacteria do not have a nucleus they are considered to be prokaryotes (pro–CARE–ee–otts).

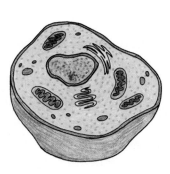

ANIMAL CELL　　　　AMOEBA CELL

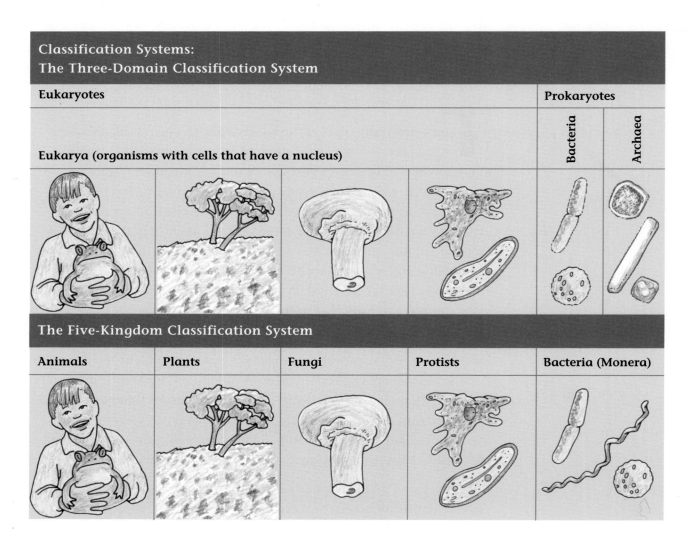

Classification Systems:
The Three-Domain Classification System

Eukaryotes | Prokaryotes

Eukarya (organisms with cells that have a nucleus) | Bacteria | Archaea

The Five-Kingdom Classification System

Animals | Plants | Fungi | Protists | Bacteria (Monera)

Both the five- and six-kingdom classification systems grouped organisms by their physical characteristics, while the three-domain system groups organisms by their genetic similarity. These systems help scientists make sense of the diversity of life. They allow scientists to compare an organism, such as a zebra mussel, to other organisms with similar characteristics. In this activity you will focus on organisms found in the animal kingdom.

CHALLENGE   **What are some similarities and differences among animals?**

MATERIALS

For each group of four students
   1   Set of 18 Animal Cards

PROCEDURE

Part A: Exploring the Animal Kingdom

1. Spread your Animal Cards out on a table.

2. Look at each of the Animal Cards, noting similarities and differences among the animals.

3. Read the information on each card. This information represents what you might discover if you observed the animals more closely and were able to dissect a specimen.

4. With your group of four, classify the Animal Cards into four to eight groups. Work together to agree on a classification system.

   - Listen to and consider explanations and ideas of other members of your group.

   - If you disagree with your group members about how to classify an animal, explain why you disagree.

5. In your science notebook write down the groups that you created.

6. Share your categories with another group of students. Explain why you classified the animals the way you did. Discuss how your group's categories were similar to or different from those of the other student group.

Part B: A Biologist's Perspective

7. Get a set of Phylum (FIE–lum) Cards from your teacher. (The plural of phylum is phyla.) Rearrange your classification of animals if necessary, and record your changes in your science notebook.

8. Biologists use information such as that found on the Phylum Cards to classify animals. Each phylum contains similar species. There are about 35 animal phyla. Your teacher will share with you how biologists group the animals on your cards into six of these phlya. Humans are grouped in the phylum Chordata, as shown below.

Humans are members of one of many phyla of animals.

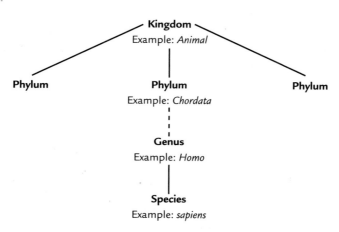

9. Adjust your animal groups so they look like the phyla used by biologists today. Then complete Analysis Questions 1–3.

ANALYSIS

1. How did your categories change when you followed the biologists' system of phyla? Did your number of categories increase, decrease, or stay the same?

2. Look carefully at how biologists group these animals into phyla. What types of characteristics are used to group animals into phyla?

3. Animals without backbones are called invertebrates. How many invertebrate phyla do the animals on your Animal Cards represent? List these phyla.

4. **Reflection:** What characteristics were most important to you when you grouped the Animal Cards? How are these characteristics different from the ones that biologists use to classify? What do you now think is the best way to group animals? Explain.

INVESTIGATION

One of the 35 animal phyla—phylum Chordata—includes all species with backbones. Most of the chordates have a jointed backbone and are classified in the sub-phylum Vertebrata, or vertebrates. Although only about 50,000 vertebrate species have been identified (compared to about 1 million invertebrate species), the most familiar animals are vertebrates, such as humans, elephants, eagles, and frogs. How are vertebrates classified into smaller groups?

CHALLENGE ⟹ **What kinds of evidence can you use to classify vertebrates?**

PROCEDURE

1. Carefully read the Classification Chart on the last two pages of this activity to compare characteristics of the five classes of vertebrates. "Cold-blooded" animals are animals that adjust their body temperature by moving to warmer or cooler locations. Their temperatures sometimes vary with the environment's temperature, but they aren't always cold. "Warm-blooded" animals regulate their body temperature to a fairly constant level by generating heat within their bodies, but they aren't always warm. Because of this, scientists now use different terms to describe these animals.

2. Pretend you work at a zoo. Some people have discovered some strange vertebrates and ask you for help in identifying them. They have sent you letters containing pictures and descriptions of these creatures. You can find the letters on the following pages.

   For each mystery vertebrate:

   a. Read the letter and look at the picture.

   b. Discuss with your group members which vertebrate class might include this species.

   c. In your science notebook, record which class you believe it belongs to and your reasons. You do not need to agree with your group members.

ANALYSIS

1. What characteristics do you think best distinguish each vertebrate class?

2. Why do some vertebrates appear to fit into two or more different classes?

EXTENSION

Find out how technological advances are being used to study the various classes of animals on the *Issues and Life Science* page of the SEPUP website.

My husband and I were having lunch outside at our hotel in Mexico when I saw a small creature flash across the wall. I later saw a similar animal sunning itself outdoors. I'm enclosing a picture. The next day, I managed to catch one. It was sunning itself on a rock and its skin felt hot and dry, not moist. I could feel a line of bones along its back. As I held it, it seemed to get a little stressed; I noticed that it started to breathe faster. So I set it down and it ran off. We really liked these creatures and would like one as a pet. What kinds of animals are these?

J. Stirbridge

One of my kindergarten students brought in a picture of this animal. Hariette told the class that she saw one of these animals when she lived in New Zealand. She said that it looked hairy and that it was very rare. Harriette and her dad saw the animal poke around for worms with its sharp beak. Her dad is out of the country and Harriette wants to do a project on this animal. What is it? Thank you.

Mr. Kalmus and Class K-1

May 23, 1860

My collecting party was recently in the new territory of Australia, where we were astounded to find a most amazing variety of strange and unknown animals. The animal I have sketched below appears to be truly new to the world of science. We have also made observations of these creatures in their natural habitat. They live in ponds and streams and are covered by dark fur. The animal has a bill like a duck, which it uses to find snails and food in the mud of the stream. We then observed something most extraordinary. The female lays an egg which she keeps in her pouch until it hatches. The tiny baby licks milk from the skin of the mother's belly.

What is your opinion of these mysterious new creatures?

Sincerely,

Murray Jones

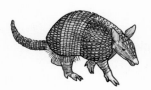

MY girlfriend and I accidentally ran over this thing on our last road trip! Melia ran over to pick up the animal as soon as I stopped. The animal looked scaly, but had some hairs poking out between the "scales." Although it was a cold night, Melia said its body was still warm. Melia wants to put up signs warning people to look out for these animals so that no one else accidentally runs one over, but we don't know what they are. She's an artist, so she drew a picture of it for you. Can you help us identify this animal?

Tim

Nina and I are in 5th grade. We love to go snorkeling near the reefs by my house in Guam. We saw some very strange-looking animals underwater. I tried to draw one for you. They have a head like a horse but they have a fin on their back. One day, we saw one of them moving around and then some babies came out near its stomach! The babies swam straight to the surface but then came back down. We watched and watched but never saw them go back up to the surface. How can they breathe? What are they?

Thanks, Thomaso

I was scuba diving in Thailand when I saw this long, striped creature, maybe as thick as my thumb, working its way along the bottom and sticking its head into holes. Its head was smaller than an eel's and I know that eels stay in their holes during the day. (This was a day dive.) Also, the animal was smooth and round, with no fins. I also noticed that it regularly went to the surface for air. Any ideas about what it is?

Phil

I am writing to ask you about some flying animals that nearly flew right into us when Pearl and I went caving last summer. We were near the entrance to a cave when I heard this twittering sound and saw some shadows fly past

me. Pearl panicked and ran. She wouldn't go back to the cave. Later that night, I went exploring myself. When I shone my flashlight on the ceiling, I saw hundreds of really tiny animals hanging there. They seemed to be grouped together to keep warm because the cave was so cold. I think they were babies, because they looked much smaller than the creatures I had seen before. I saw one of the larger creatures fly into the cave and go to one of the babies. The baby seemed to be getting milk from the adult. I was wondering if you could help me figure out what these things are.

Sincerely yours,

Thelma

From: Ruby Riter

Subject: strange animal

I'm a travel writer with the Leisure Time Gazette. I was on assignment in Malaysia and saw these strange animals on the mud near mangrove swamps. I want to write about them for next week's travel section, but I need more information. I saw some of these animals swimming underwater, but I didn't see any of them come up for air. However, they seemed to do okay on land too. When I checked them out through a telephoto lens, I noticed that they had some kind of fin going down their back as well as scales on their bodies. Can you get back to me ASAP? My deadline is in three days. Thanks a lot.

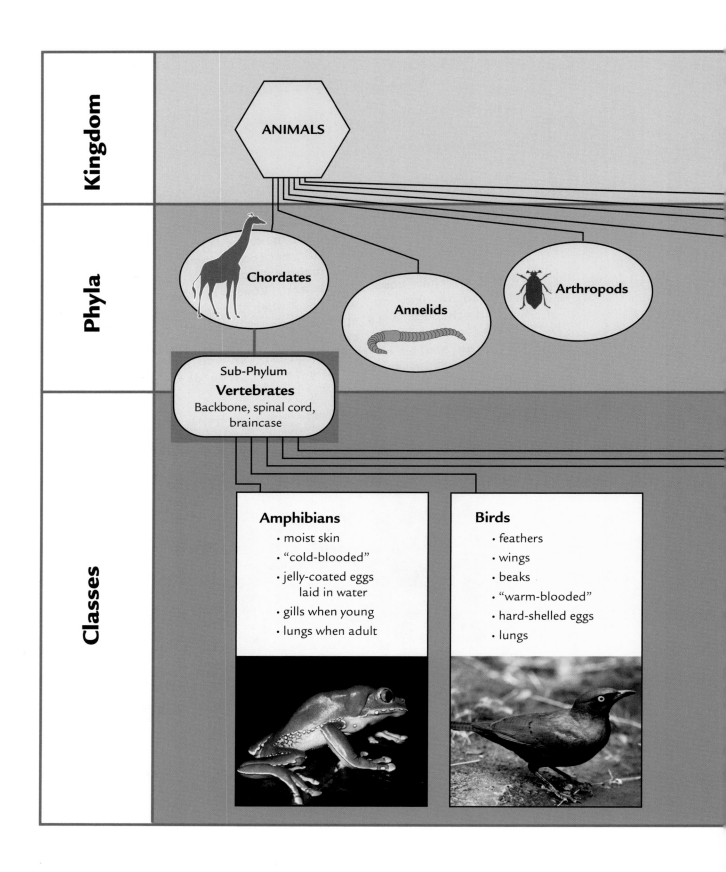

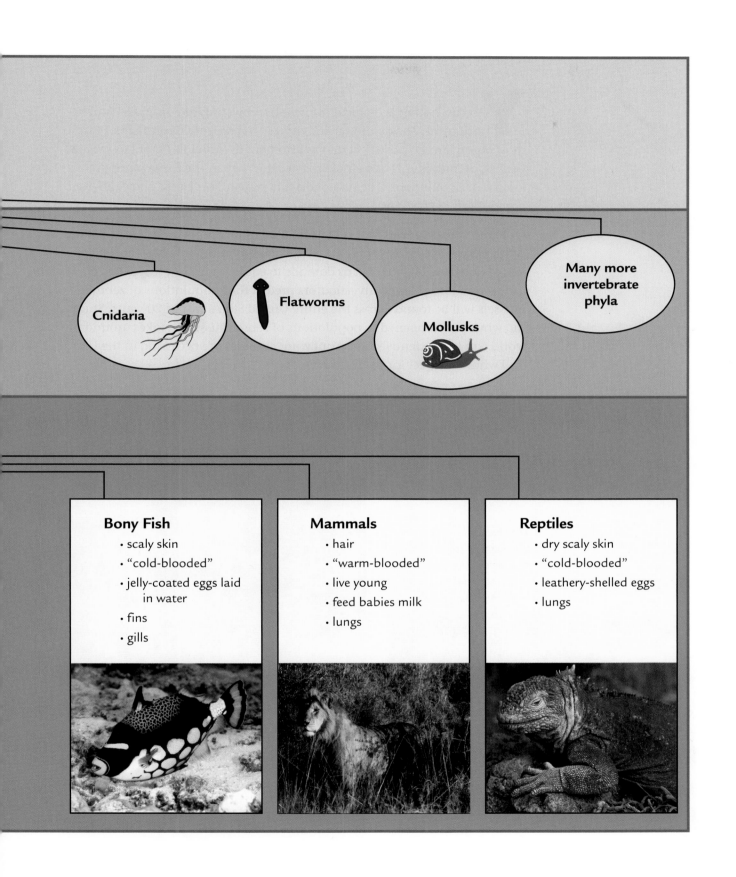

Cnidaria

Flatworms

Mollusks

Many more invertebrate phyla

Bony Fish
- scaly skin
- "cold-blooded"
- jelly-coated eggs laid in water
- fins
- gills

Mammals
- hair
- "warm-blooded"
- live young
- feed babies milk
- lungs

Reptiles
- dry scaly skin
- "cold-blooded"
- leathery-shelled eggs
- lungs

You can gather ecological information by studying an individual organism, as you did in Activity 74, "Observing Organisms." But most organisms do not affect an environment as individuals, but as groups. Groups of individuals of a single species that live in the same place are known as populations. The photos on this page and the next show different populations of sea lions.

One introduced species that is causing a lot of problems in the United States is the zebra mussel. Its success in freshwater environments has caused the loss of native wildlife as well as damage to equipment. How fast is this population spreading? Some investigators predict that populations of zebra mussels will be found across the entire United States within 20 years. Studying what has happened to populations of zebra mussels in lakes around the world can help scientists figure out what changes are occurring in the U.S. and what to expect for the future.

CHALLENGE ➤ **How do scientists study the size of a population and predict future population changes?**

The photo below shows a population of sea lions living on a beach. The photo at right shows a population of sea lions living on piers in a harbor.

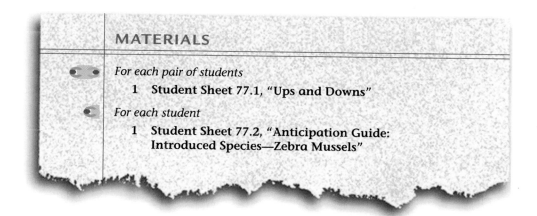

MATERIALS

For each pair of students
   1 Student Sheet 77.1, "Ups and Downs"
For each student
   1 Student Sheet 77.2, "Anticipation Guide:
       Introduced Species—Zebra Mussels"

PROCEDURE

*Complete the "Before" column of Student Sheet 77.2, "Anticipation Guide: Intro-
duced Species—Zebra Mussels."*

Part A: Initial Observations

1. In your group of four, review the two tables below. Imagine that two different groups of ecologists collected data on the size of the zebra mussel
population in Lake Miko for two different time periods.

Table 1: Zebra Mussel Population in Lake Miko, Period 1 (1959 to 1968)				
Year	1959	1960	1962	1968
Number of Zebra Mussels (per square meter)	2,211	95	93	97

Table 2: Zebra Mussel Population in Lake Miko, Period 2 (1971 to 1976)				
Year	1971	1972	1974	1976
Number of Zebra Mussels (per square meter)	393	802	1,086	2,179

2. Divide your group in half. Assign one of the two data tables to each pair within your group.

3. With your partner, create a line graph of the data in your table using Student Sheet 77.1, "Ups and Downs." Remember, independent variables, such as time, are always graphed on the x-axis. Since you will compare graphs within your group, make sure that the x-axes of both graphs use the same scale.

4. After completing your graph, respond to the two questions on Student Sheet 77.1 as directed.

Part B: A More Complete Analysis

5. Show your graph to the other students in your group. Point out the over-all population trend—is the population increasing, decreasing, or staying the same?

6. Compare the two graphs. Discuss what conclusions you can make about the population trend in Lake Miko during Period 1 vs. Period 2.

7. Place the two graphs together, with the graph for Table 1 first and the graph for Table 2 second. If necessary, fold the edges of your sheets to fit the graphs together.

8. As a group, discuss what happens to the population trends when the two graphs are connected. Discuss how what you see with the two graphs together is different from what you see with each of the individual graphs. Be sure to:

   • Describe what happens to the population size of zebra mussels in Lake Miko from 1959–1976.

   • Discuss whether you can make any definite conclusions about whether the population is increasing, decreasing, or staying the same.

ANALYSIS

1. **a.** Sketch a line on your graph predicting what you think will happen to the size of this population of zebra mussels during the ten years after 1976.

   b. Explain your prediction. Why do you think the graph will look that way?

   c. What additional information would make you more confident of your prediction? Explain.

2. a. What factors do you think affect the size of a population?

   b. Explain how each factor might affect population size: Would it cause the population to increase, decrease, or stay the same? Why?

3. As you know from your own graph, data were not collected every year. Explain whether you would expect a well-designed experiment to collect data every year. What might prevent the collection of such data?

4. Shown below are graphs of zebra mussel populations in three lakes near Lake Mikolajskie. Describe the population trend in each graph. How does each population change over time?

ZEBRA MUSSEL POPULATIONS IN THREE LAKES

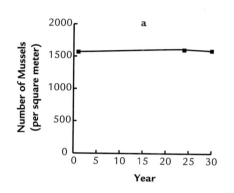
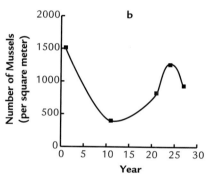
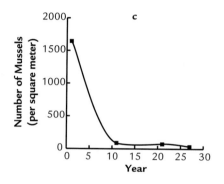

5. The data presented in this activity are similar to actual data collected in Lake Mikolajskie, Poland, between 1959 and 1987. Zebra mussels have been found in lakes in that area for over 150 years. Shown below are the data collected from 1977–87. How does this additional information compare to your answer to Question 1?

Table 3: Zebra Mussel Population in Lake Miko, Period 3 (1977 to 1987)					
Year	1977	1979	1982	1983	1987
Number of Zebra Mussels (per square meter)	77	104	81	55	85

6. Zebra mussels were introduced in the United States in the late 1980s. They first appeared in Lake Erie, one of the Great Lakes. Today, the population of zebra mussels has reached as high as 70,000 mussels per square meter in some parts of Lake Erie.

   a. How does this compare to the populations of zebra mussels found in the lakes in Poland?

   b. Before 1988, the population of zebra mussels in Lake Erie was zero. Draw a graph showing what you think the data might look like for the population of zebra mussels in Lake Erie from 1985 to the present.

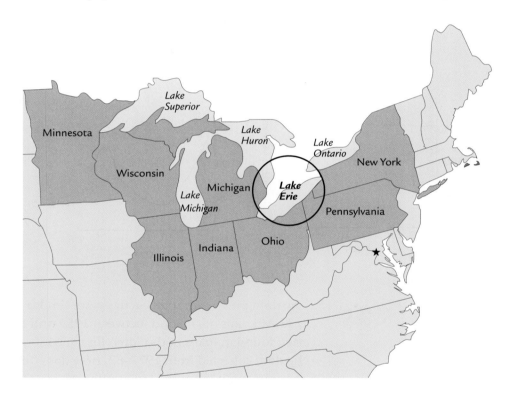

7. Consider the zebra mussel population in Lake Mikolajskie from 1959 to 1987. Describe what you think happened to the zebra mussel population from 1987 to 1997. Explain your reasons for your prediction.

8. Fill in the "After" column for Statements 1 and 2 only on Sheet 77.2, "Anticipation Guide: Introduced Species—Zebra Mussels." Did your thinking change?

How do introduced species affect other organisms within a habitat? What happens to the populations of native species when a new organism is introduced? Scientists often draw diagrams, called **food webs**, to model the feeding relationships within an ecosystem. By showing what each organism eats, food webs model the energy relationships among species.

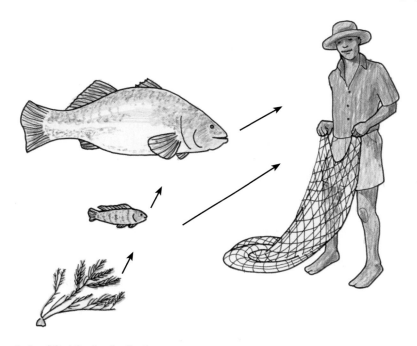

A simplified food web of Lake Victoria

How can you find out what an organism eats? One way is to examine its stomach contents. But in the case of owls, you can also examine an owl pellet. An owl pellet is a combination of bones and fur that an owl coughs up, just as a cat coughs up a hairball. Owl pellets are formed when owls swallow their prey whole and their digestive system cannot break down fur and bones. Within 12–24 hours after eating, an owl throws up a pellet. Piles of pellets are often found at the base of the tree on which an owl is perched. These pellets help ecologists learn what and how much owls eat.

CHALLENGE ⟹ **What can an owl pellet tell you about an owl's diet? How can you use this information to develop part of a food web?**

MATERIALS

For each group of four students
1   owl pellet
1   small petri dish or other small container (optional)
    glue (optional)
    cardboard or paper (optional)

For each student
2   pointed wooden sticks

PROCEDURE

1. Use the wooden sticks to carefully pull the owl pellet into four equal-sized pieces. Provide each member of your group with one of the four pieces.

2. Use your pair of sticks to gently separate all of the bones from the fur of your piece of owl pellet.

3. Work with your group to divide all of the bones into groups based on their shapes. Use Table 1, "Guide to Owl Pellet Bones," to help you.

4. Count and record the number of bones in each of your categories.

5. Try to arrange the bones to make a skeleton of one (or more) animal. Sketch your final arrangement(s).

ANALYSIS

1. What did you learn about the diet of owls from investigating an owl pellet? Include information about the type and number of organisms in an owl's diet. (Remember that an owl ejects a pellet within 12 to 24 hours after eating.)

2. **a.** The organisms that you uncovered in your owl pellet are likely to be voles, small rodents similar to mice. Owls also eat other small mammals, such as shrews, and insects. Use this information on owl diet to develop a food web.

    b. Voles eat mostly plant material such as grass, seeds, roots, and bark. Shrews eat insects. Add these relationships to your food web.

    c. The great horned owl sometimes eats other owls. It also eats small mammals like voles. Add the great horned owl to your food web.

Table 1: Guide to Owl Pellet Bones

Skulls	
Jaws	
Shoulder blades	
Front legs	
Hips	
Hind legs	
Assorted ribs	
Assorted vertebrae	

3. Copy the graph shown below, which is similar to graphs you made in Activity 77, "Ups and Downs." It predicts the change in the population of owls as they first move into a new habitat.

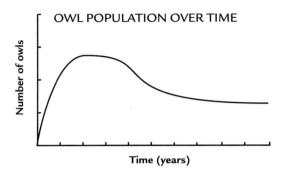

OWL POPULATION OVER TIME

Number of owls

Time (years)

a. Draw a line showing what you think will happen over the same time period to the population of one of the species that owls eat.

b. Draw a line, using a different color or symbol, showing what you think might happen over the same time period to the population of one of the species that eats owls. Be sure to include a key identifying what species each line represents.

4. **Reflection:** All living things have a place in a food web. What would your personal food web look like?

EXTENSION 1

To identify the skulls you found in your owl pellet and learn more about owl pellets, go to the *Issues and Life Science* page of the SEPUP website.

EXTENSION 2

Research the food web of the introduced species you are studying. What effects, if any, has your species had on native species? What effects do you predict it will have in the future?

READING

One important part of every organism's habitat is a source of food. The introduction of new species into an ecosystem often changes the availability of food.

CHALLENGE How are the energy relationships among organisms in an ecosystem affected by the introduction of a new species?

MATERIALS

For each student

Student Sheet 77.2, "Anticipation Guide: Introduced Species—Zebra Mussels," from Activity 77

1 Student Sheet 79.1, "Talking Drawing: Eating for Energy"

READING

Use Student Sheet 79.1, "Talking Drawing: Eating for Energy," to prepare you for the following reading.

Is it possible that a scenario like the one in Lake Victoria could happen in the United States? Scientists are waiting to see. But in the United States, the main concern isn't a large predator like the Nile perch, but a seem-

Zebra Mussels feeding.

ingly unimportant mussel less than two inches long. The tiny zebra mussel *(Dreissena polymorpha)* (shown at left) doesn't seem large enough to cause serious problems. But its ability to reproduce and spread quickly is making it into a big issue.

Zebra mussels reproduce by releasing eggs and sperm into the water. The fertilized eggs grow into tiny larvae. Because of their small size, they are very hard to see at this stage.

STOPPING TO THINK 1

Brainstorm ways in which zebra mussels might accidentally be spread from one lake to another.

Zebra mussels feed on some of the smallest members of the aquatic food chain: microscopic animals and plants known as **plankton** (PLANK-tun) (shown below). (When discussing them in more detail, biologists usually use the words *zooplankton* [zoe-uh-PLANK-tun] for microscopic animals and *phytoplankton* [fie-toe-PLANK-tun] for microscopic plants.) Plankton are found throughout the water, from the very deepest part of a lake to the surface. They are the food for a variety of other organisms, including many kinds of fish. In addition, zooplankton eat phytoplankton. Thus, phytoplankton are at the base of many aquatic food chains.

Phytoplankton include microscopic plants and algae. These tiny organisms are especially important in aquatic ecosystems because they produce food for all the other living things in that ecosystem. You may know that plants and algae require sunlight in order to grow. They use sunlight as energy to convert carbon dioxide and water into food—a process known as **photosynthesis** (foe-toe-SIN-thuh-sis). (You will learn more about photosynthesis in Activity 81, "A Producer's Source of Energy.") The food that the plant produces is stored within the plant as starch or sugar. The plant can then use its food for activities within its own cells—until the plant is eaten by another organism! Since most plants and algae do not eat other organisms for food but are able to produce their own food, they are called **producers**. Producers such as phytoplankton form the base of the food chain because they have the ability to use the sun's energy to make their own food.

All other organisms rely on this ability of producers to convert the energy from the sun into food energy. Organisms that get their energy by eating food are known as **consumers**. Some consumers eat plants for energy, while other consumers eat the animals that eat plants. Some consumers, such as zebra mussels and humans, eat both plants and animals.

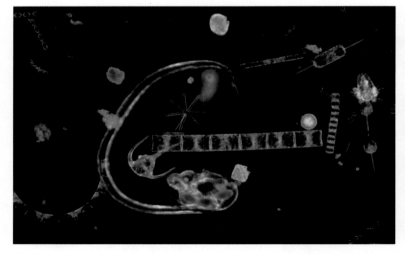

Plankton

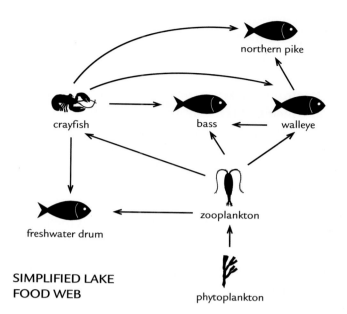

SIMPLIFIED LAKE FOOD WEB

STOPPING TO THINK 2

Why are producers, such as plants, an essential part of any ecosystem?

The figure at left shows a simplified lake food web with both producers and consumers. The transfer of energy that takes place when one organism eats another is shown by arrows. Each arrow shows where the energy from the food is going within the ecosystem. The arrows show who is eaten by whom, not who eats whom. Many other species eat phytoplankton; food webs become more complicated when additional relationships are added.

STOPPING TO THINK 3

a. Copy the diagram above into your science notebook. Identify each organism as either a producer or a consumer.

b. Think about the kinds of food that people eat. Use this knowledge to add humans into this lake food web.

c. In the lake food web, humans are consumers. Are humans always consumers? Explain.

After zebra mussels appeared in the Great Lakes ecosystem, they changed the food web. Zebra mussels filter water and catch the microscopic plankton that live in the water. They rely on phytoplankton and zooplankton for food. Because zebra mussels are often more common than other sources of food, crayfish and freshwater drum are starting to eat zebra mussels as part of their diet.

STOPPING TO THINK 4

Using the diagram above as a guide, create a lake food web that includes zebra mussels. Be sure to show how zebra mussels get their energy *and* how other organisms get energy from them.

At first, these changes don't seem too important. After all, couldn't the lake ecosystem support one more consumer? Adult zebra mussels filter about one liter of water per day. This means that a two-inch mussel can filter enough water to fill half of a large soft drink bottle every day. In some parts of the Great Lakes, the concentration of zebra mussels has reached as high as 70,000 mussels in a square meter. This means that just a small area of mussels would be able to filter 70,000 liters of lake water each day! As a result of zebra mussels, the clearness of the water has changed: it is now 600% clearer than it was before the introduction of the zebra mussels. Clear water sounds like a good thing, but biologically speaking, extremely clear water can mean that there is not much alive in the water. In fact, the zebra mussel population has been so effective at filtering plankton that the populations of some types of phytoplankton have decreased by 80%.

Remember, phytoplankton are the base of this aquatic food chain. By removing large amounts of phytoplankton from the water, zebra mussels remove the food for microscopic zooplankton. Many types of fish depend on zooplankton for food. In some cases, these fish are the food for other fish and for humans and other mammals. Some ecologists predict that zebra mussels will change the entire food web of the lake ecosystem. However, there is no evidence yet that zebra mussels have affected fish populations in the lake.

There is evidence, though, that the types of plants in the lake are changing. Because of the increased clearness, sunlight is now able to penetrate deeper into the lake. Plants such as algae are now growing along the lake bottom. This provides habitat and food for other organisms, such as sunfish, that are currently not common in the lake. Some scientists predict that the fish populations will change: populations of some fish, like walleye, will decrease, while populations of other fish, like sunfish, will increase.

What will happen to the lake ecosystem? At this point, no one is sure. The one thing that everyone is sure of is that zebra mussels will spread. The dots on the map below mark areas where the zebra mussel is now found.

SPREAD OF ZEBRA MUSSELS ACROSS THE UNITED STATES JUNE 2008

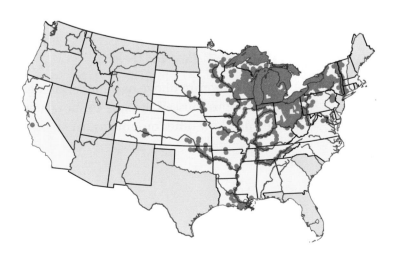

....

STOPPING TO THINK 5

Look at the Zebra Mussel map, the lines across the U.S. represent large rivers. Where do you predict zebra mussels will be found in the next 10 years? The next 20 years? The next 50 years? Explain your predictions.

....

ANALYSIS

1. Fill in the "After" column for Statements 3–5 only on Sheet 77.2, "Anticipation Guide: Introduced Species—Zebra Mussels." Did your thinking change?

2. Complete steps 2 and 3 on Student Sheet 79.1, "Talking Drawing: Eating for Energy." Has your thinking changed? Explain.

3. A volcano erupts 40 miles from the lake ecosystem whose food web you drew in Stopping to Think 4. Ash from the eruption blocks sunlight over your ecosystem for several months. Explain what happens to each population within the lake food web in the weeks that follow the eruption.

4. The ash clears and several more months go by. Think about what is now happening to your lake ecosystem. Identify what factors will affect how quickly it recovers.

5. **Reflection:** Think about what you have learned about introduced species as well as ecosystems. What effect(s) can an introduced species have on an ecosystem?

EXTENSION

Go the *Issues and Life Science* page of the SEPUP website to link to the website of the United States Geological Survey. What is the current status of zebra mussel spread across the U.S.?

LABORATORY

You have learned about the roles of producers and consumers in a food web. But what about worms, bacteria, and fungi? What role do they play within an ecosystem? Organisms that eat dead organisms and wastes from living organisms are known as **decomposers.** Worms, bacteria, and fungi are decomposers. You can think of decomposers as a special type of consumer: they consume dead organisms and waste material.

Fungi such as these decompose wood and other dead plant material.

Decomposers like worms and bacteria can seem unimportant. The decay they cause can look (and smell) horrible. But decomposers are essential to the ability of ecosystems to recycle important nutrients like carbon and nitrogen. Decomposers like bacteria and fungi break down dead matter into chemicals that can be absorbed by plants. Without decomposers, dead organisms would pile up and the nutrients they contain could not be re-used by plants. Eventually, the fertility of soil and aquatic ecosystems would be reduced to nothing. Imagine what the bottom of a lake would look like without any decomposers!

CHALLENGE

Where can you find some decomposers? What do these decomposers look like?

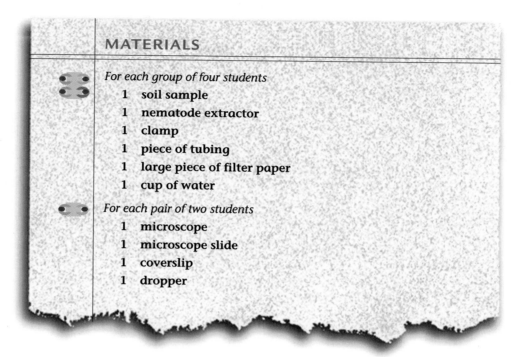

MATERIALS

For each group of four students

  1   **soil sample**
  1   **nematode extractor**
  1   **clamp**
  1   **piece of tubing**
  1   **large piece of filter paper**
  1   **cup of water**

For each pair of two students

  1   **microscope**
  1   **microscope slide**
  1   **coverslip**
  1   **dropper**

PROCEDURE

Part A: Investigating Soil

NEMATODE EXTRACTOR

1. Gather ½ cup of soil from outdoors by scraping or shaking moist soil from around the roots of a clump of grass or other plant or from an area of decomposing leaf litter.

2. Place the tubing on the spout of the funnel. Then attach the clamp onto the middle of the tubing, as shown at left. Make sure that the tubing is pushed as far as it can go into the clamp; otherwise the water can drip out.

3. Place the funnel in the stand and the perforated disc into the funnel.

4. Add water to the funnel to the level of the perforated disc.

5. Put a single layer of filter paper in the funnel. You may need to separate the layers. Add a layer of your soil sample, no more than 1 cm deep, onto the filter paper.

6. Fold the filter paper over the soil. Add just enough water to cover the soil and filter paper. Set aside for one day.

Part B: Searching for Nematodes

7. Carefully remove the clamp to release a small amount (less than 5 mL) of water into the cup. Share this sample in your group of four.

8. You might be able to see some small, white thread-like objects in the water. Try to suck up one of the thread-like objects into the dropper. Then squeeze a couple of drops from the dropper onto a microscope slide.

9. Carefully touch one edge of the coverslip, at an angle, to the mixture. Slowly allow the coverslip to drop into place.

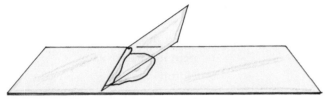

10. Begin by observing the slide on low power (usually the 4x objective). Be sure that the sample is in the center of the field of view (you may need to move the slide slightly) and completely in focus before going on to the next step.

    Hint: To check that you are focused on the sample, move the slide slightly while you look through the eyepiece—the sample that you are focused on should move as you move the slide.

11. Without moving the slide, switch to medium power (usually the 10x objective). Adjust the microscope settings as necessary.

    Hint: If material on the slide is too dark to see, increase the amount of light on the slide: do this by slightly opening the diaphragm under the stage.

12. While looking through the eyepiece, move the slide around slowly so that you see all parts of your sample. As you scan the slide, look for movement, especially of thin, colorless organisms like the ones shown in the photo below. These organisms look like small earthworms, but are actually members of a different phylum. These tiny worms are called nematodes (NEM-uh-toads). (If you do not find any nematodes on your slide, make another slide from your sample.)

13. Try to count the number of nematodes on your slide. Compare the number of nematodes you and your partner find with the rest of your group.

14. When you have completed your observations, turn off the microscope light and set the microscope back to low power.

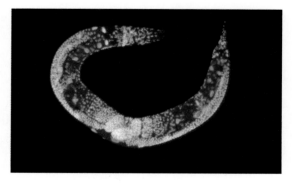

A Nematode

ANALYSIS

1. Think about where some nematodes are found. What do you think they eat? Describe the role of nematodes in the ecosystem.

2. **a.** A simplified food web is shown below. Which of the organisms in this ecosystem are producers? Which are consumers? Which are decomposers?

   b. Use the food web to explain why decomposers could be considered a special type of consumer.

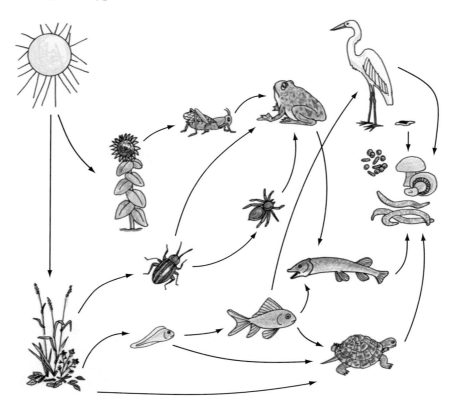

3. Like all organisms, birds like the egret need energy to live. Explain how the original source of energy for egrets, and all other consumers, is the sun.

4. Imagine that something kills most of the bacteria and other decomposers in a lake. What are some possible effects of killing these decomposers?

EXTENSION

To learn more about food webs and explore different food webs, go to the *Issues and Life Science* page of the SEPUP website.

Organisms that use energy from the sun to make food are known as producers. These include plants that you are familiar with, such as trees and grass, as well as organisms that live in the ocean, such as phytoplankton. Most phytoplankton are microscopic but they have a very big role in earth's ecosystems. They produce oxygen and provide energy for all living creatures—for the consumers that eat plants, the consumers that eat animals that eat plants, and the decomposers that live off dead plants and animals. They do this by means of photosynthesis, a process by which plants use the energy from sunlight to convert carbon dioxide and water into food for themselves (and indirectly, for consumers). During this process, plants release oxygen gas into the atmosphere. Photosynthesis can be described by the following word equation:

$$\text{carbon dioxide } + \text{ water } \xrightarrow{\textit{sunlight}} \text{ food } + \text{ oxygen}$$

Is light necessary for photosynthesis? How important is sunlight to an ecosystem? In this activity, you will use the indicator bromthymol blue (BTB) to collect evidence for the role of light in photosynthesis.

CHALLENGE ⟹ **How do scientists study the role of light in photosynthesis?**

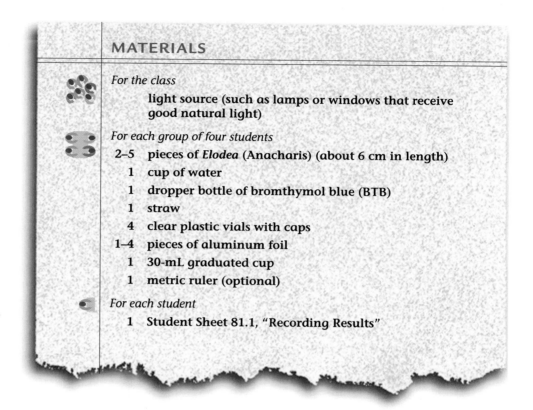

MATERIALS

For the class
   light source (such as lamps or windows that receive good natural light)

For each group of four students
2–5 pieces of *Elodea* (Anacharis) (about 6 cm in length)
   1 cup of water
   1 dropper bottle of bromthymol blue (BTB)
   1 straw
   4 clear plastic vials with caps
1–4 pieces of aluminum foil
   1 30-mL graduated cup
   1 metric ruler (optional)

For each student
   1 Student Sheet 81.1, "Recording Results"

PROCEDURE

Part A: Collecting Evidence

1. If you have completed previous units of *Issues and Life Science,* review your notes from Activity 17, "Gas Exchange," and Activity 39, "Cells Alive!" Use your notes to complete Tables 1 and 2 on Student Sheet 81.1, "Recording Results." If you haven't completed these activities, your teacher will help you fill in the tables.

2. Fill a plastic cup half-full of water. (Your teacher may have already done this.) Add 15 drops of BTB.

3. Have one person in your group use a straw to blow into the BTB solution until it stops changing color. Record this as the initial BTB color in Table 3 of Student Sheet 81.1.

4. Place a piece of *Elodea* into one of the vials. Carefully fill the rest of this vial with your BTB solution. Cap the vial tightly and place it in the light. **Caution:** Do not put your vial in a place that is extremely warm.

5. Fill a second vial with the same BTB solution only. Cap this vial tightly and place alongside the first vial.

6. With your group, discuss what you think might happen. Record your prediction in your science notebook.

7. After at least 45 minutes (or during your next class period), observe your vials. Use your observations to complete Table 3 of Student Sheet 81.1, as well as Analysis Questions 1 and 2.

Part B: The Role of Light

8. Design an experiment to investigate the role of light in plant photosynthesis.

   Hint: Use the introduction to the activity and your results from Part A to help you.

   When designing your experiment, think about the following questions:

   - What is the purpose of your experiment?
   - What variable are you testing?
   - What variables will you keep the same?
   - What is your hypothesis?
   - How many trials will you conduct?
   - Will you collect qualitative and/or quantitative data? How will these data help you to make a conclusion?
   - How will you record these data?

9. Record your hypothesis and your planned experimental procedure in your science notebook.

10. Make a data table that has space for all the data you need to record. You will fill it in during your experiment.

11. Obtain your teacher's approval of your experiment.

12. Conduct your experiment and record your results.

EXTENSION 1

Observe a capped vial containing a plant in BTB solution at different times of the day. What color is the solution first thing in the morning? At lunchtime? Explain your observations. What process may be taking place in plants at night?

ANALYSIS

Part A: Collecting Evidence

1. What was the purpose of the vial containing only BTB solution?

2. In the introduction to this activity, you were told that plants need carbon dioxide during photosynthesis. What evidence do you have from Part A of your investigation to support this claim?

Part B: The Role of Light

3. Describe your experimental results. Use the word equation at the beginning of this activity to help explain your results.

4. Explain the role that light plays in photosynthesis. How do your results provide evidence for your explanation?

5. A second-grader comes up to you and says, "We just learned that the sun made all the stuff in my lunch. But my lunch was a tuna sandwich." Using language a second-grader would understand, explain how the sun was the original source of the energy in the tuna sandwich. Then try out your explanation on a child you know!

6. Think back to how the lake ecosystem described in Activity 79, "Eating for Energy," was affected by zebra mussels. Using your understanding of photosynthesis and ecosystems, explain why a decrease in phytoplankton allows more aquatic plants to grow on the lake bottom.

EXTENSION 2

Your experiment looked at the *inputs* needed by a plant for photosynthesis. Design another experiment to collect evidence for the *outputs* of photosynthesis. Describe what materials you would need to perform this experiment, and what data you would collect.

LABORATORY

As you have been learning, producers such as plants play a unique role within an ecosystem. By transferring the sun's energy into chemical energy stored in food, plants provide energy in a form that can be used by consumers and decomposers. What is different about plants that allows them to do this? Find out by investigating the cells of plants and then comparing them to animal cells.

A botanist (a person who studies plants) gathers plants for his research.

CHALLENGE

How are the cells of producers such as plants different from the cells of consumers such as animals? How do plant cell structures relate to their function as producers?

MATERIALS

For each group of four students

- 1 celery stalk
- 1 ½-in. slice of onion
- 1–2 leaves of *Elodea* (Anacharis)
- 1 fresh spinach leaf or similar plant leaf
- 1 pair of scissors
- 1 pair of forceps
- 1 bottle of Lugol's solution (optional)
- 4 droppers
- 1 cup of water
- 4 microscope slides
- 4 coverslips
- 2 microscopes
- 1–2 paper towels
- 1 toothpick
- 1 compass

For each student

- 1 Student Sheet 82.1, "Cell Drawings"

PROCEDURE

1. Have each person in your group complete one of the following four steps. You will share all four slides within your group.

   a. Pull a string of celery off the stalk. At the edge of the string, you will see a thin film. This is the outer layer of the celery stalk and the part where you will see plant cells most clearly. Use scissors to cut a short length of this outer film. Place this piece of celery on a microscope slide. Add a drop of water and slowly drop the coverslip, at an angle, into place (as shown in the figure below).

   b. Get a small square of onion. Use your forceps to peel off a thin film of tissue from the inside layer of the onion square. Place this thin film on a microscope slide. Add a drop of water and slowly drop the coverslip, at an angle, into place (as shown in the figure below).

   c. Get a piece of *Elodea* and break off a leaf. Place a piece of this leaf on a microscope slide. Add a drop of water and slowly drop the coverslip, at an angle, into place (as shown in the figure below).

   d. Get a fresh spinach leaf or similar plant leaf. Use the toothpick to gently scrape some plant cells from the underside of the leaf. Place some of the scrapings on the slide. Add a drop of water and slowly drop the coverslip, at an angle, into place (as shown in the figure below).

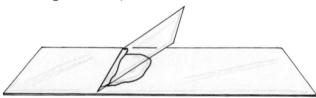

PLACING THE COVERSLIP

2. With your partner, observe the cells of each plant. Begin by observing the slide on low power (usually the 4x objective). Be sure that the plant material is in the center of the field of view (you may need to move the slide slightly) and completely in focus before going on to Step 3.

   Hint: When viewing celery, focus on the thinnest parts of the sample.

3. Without moving the slide (which can be secured with stage clips), switch to medium power (usually the 10x objective). Adjust the microscope settings as necessary.

   Hint: If material on the slide is too dark to see, increase the amount of light on the slide: do this by slightly opening the diaphragm under the stage.

4. Turn the fine focus knob up and down just a little to reveal details of the plant cells at different levels of the slide.

5. Draw your observations of a cell from each plant. Be sure to record the type of plant and the level of magnification. Include details inside the cell and along the edge of the cell membrane on your drawing.

6. When you have completed your observations, turn off the microscope light and set the microscope back to low power.

EXTENSION

Place a drop of salt water at the edge of the coverslip while looking at either the piece of *Elodea* or the piece of red onion. Place the corner of a paper towel at the opposite edge of the coverslip. What happens? What does this tell you about the importance of fresh water to plants?

ANALYSIS

1. Using various microscope techniques, scientists have identified the structures most commonly found in plant cells. Some of these structures are shown in the diagram of the plant cell at right. Not all plant cells contain every structure, though most plant cells do contain the majority of them. However, some of these structures are very difficult to observe if you only use a light microscope.

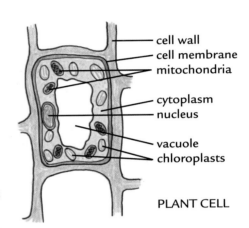

PLANT CELL

a. Which cell structures appear to be ones that you observed? List them.

b. Which cell structures were not visible to you? List them.

2. Compare the various plant cells you observed. Which cell structures did all of the plant cells appear to have in common?

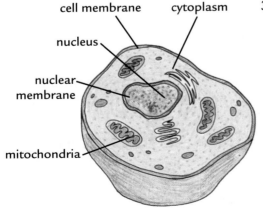

ANIMAL CELL

3. Look at the simplified diagram of an animal cell shown at left. Animal cells, as well as plant cells, contain many structures; this diagram shows only some of these structures.

a. Which cell—plant or animal—is the cell of a consumer?

b. Compare the plant cell diagram with the animal cell diagram. Based on these diagrams, what structures would you expect to find in both plant and animal cells?

c. Based on your comparisons, which structure(s) within a plant cell do you think is most important in food production?

4. Copy a larger version of the Venn diagram shown here. Complete it by writing in the characteristics of animal cells, plant cells, and bacterial cells (which you may have first studied in Activity 44, "Who's Who?"). Record unique features of each type of cell in the individual spaces. Record common features among groups in the spaces that overlap.

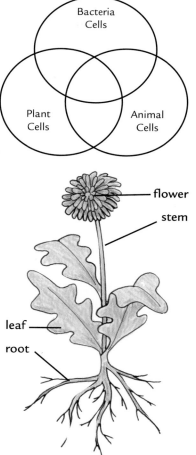

5. a. Many plants have leaves, stems, roots, and—during the blooming season—flowers. Which of these parts are likely to absorb sunlight and carry out photosynthesis?

   b. Of the cells you observed—celery stem, onion, *Elodea* leaf, and the other plant leaf—which would you expect to carry out photosynthesis?

   c. What cell structures are seen only in cells that absorb sunlight and carry out photosynthesis?

6. Three of the introduced species described in Activity 73, "Introduced Species," are plants: kudzu, purple loosestrife, and hydrilla. Each of these plants is growing successfully in different parts of the United States, partly because they are very well adapted to absorb sunlight and carry out photosynthesis.

   a. What effect do you think the growth and spread of these introduced plants will have on native plants? Explain.

   b. What effect do you think the growth and spread of these introduced plants will have on animals in the native ecosystems? Explain.

LABORATORY

Introduced species do not always survive in new environments. This is because all species have requirements for the place in which they can live. These requirements define the species' **habitat** (HAB-ih-tat). What makes up a habitat? Think about different aquatic ecosystems, such as a small pond or a coral reef. While both of these environments contain water, they have very different characteristics. Coral reefs are found in the ocean, which contains salt water, while most ponds are freshwater. An organism that lives in freshwater, like a zebra mussel, cannot survive in the coral reef environment. The photos below show several different habitats.

Producers, consumers, and decomposers are the living components of an ecosystem. Every ecosystem also has many non-living elements, such as rainfall, light, and temperature. The interaction of all these determines whether a habitat is suitable for a specific organism.

CHALLENGE ➤ **What are some of the important non-living characteristics of a habitat?**

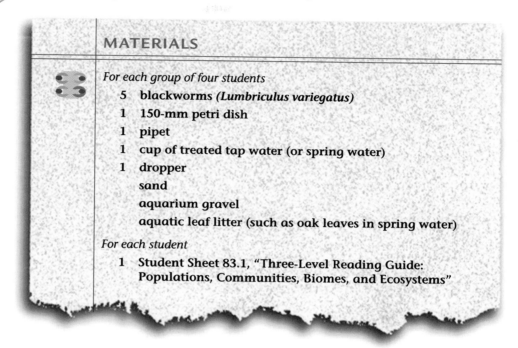

MATERIALS

For each group of four students

5 **blackworms** (*Lumbriculus variegatus*)
1 **150-mm petri dish**
1 **pipet**
1 **cup of treated tap water (or spring water)**
1 **dropper**
sand
aquarium gravel
aquatic leaf litter (such as oak leaves in spring water)

For each student

1 **Student Sheet 83.1, "Three-Level Reading Guide: Populations, Communities, Biomes, and Ecosystems"**

PROCEDURE

Part A

1. Fill the base of a petri dish with treated tap water (or spring water) and place 5 blackworms in it.

2. Observe how the blackworms respond over the next few minutes. Discuss with your group any behaviors that seem to be true of all or most of the blackworms.

3. As a class, discuss what type of data you could collect on the blackworms in order to determine which type(s) of material provides a good habitat for them.

4. Compare the different materials you can use to create a blackworm habitat. Record any similarities and differences in the physical characteristics of the different habitat materials.

Numerous habitats make up a pond ecosystem.

5. With your group, design an experiment to investigate which type(s) of material provides a good blackworm habitat.

When designing your experiment, think about the following questions:

- What is the purpose of your experiment?
- What variable are you testing?
- What variables will you keep the same?
- What is your hypothesis?
- How many trials will you conduct?
- Will you collect qualitative and/or quantitative data? How will these data help you to make a conclusion?
- How will you record these data?

6. Record your hypothesis and your planned experimental procedure in your science notebook.

7. Make a data table that has space for all the data you need to record. You will fill it in during your experiment.

8. Obtain your teacher's approval of your experiment.

9. Conduct your experiment and record your results.

Part B

Use Student Sheet 83.1, "Three-Level Reading Guide: Populations, Communities, Biomes, and Ecosystems," to guide you as you complete the following reading.

READING

You have been investigating the habitat of the blackworm. Using sand, gravel, and leaf litter, you created a habitat. Then, you observed blackworms interacting with that habitat. A group of blackworms living in the same habitat is known as a **population**. In one habitat there may be numerous populations of various species. For example, in a freshwater pond, there might be populations of blackworms, snails, water plants, and fish. Populations of diverse organisms that live in one area are known as a community.

The food webs that you looked at in Activity 79, "Eating for Energy," and in Activity 80, "Nature's Recyclers," were examples of communities. Scientists think that communities with many populations are more stable than those with only a few populations. If a change occurs in a community with many populations, the chance that some of those populations will survive is good.

This pond is filling with sediment and will eventually disappear. What will happen to the aquatic organisms that depend on the pond?

The interaction between communities of living things and the nonliving environment is known as an **ecosystem.** An ecosystem can be as small as a puddle or as large as the earth. Ecosystems are constantly changing. Take, for example, the effects on the ecosystem if a pond fills with sediment from erosion. Aquatic animals and water plants would die. Even birds and insects that depend on the pond for food would disappear. Eventually, a new ecosystem would develop based on the grasses that would sprout from the new sediments.

Organisms have adaptive characteristics that allow them to survive in a particular ecosystem. For instance, in the desert water is scarce. Cacti and other desert plants have thick, waxy surfaces that hold water inside the plant. Animals have adaptive characteristics and behaviors as well. To avoid the heat, many desert animals only hunt at night.

Environments have varying temperatures, amounts of moisture, and amounts of light. These contribute to the climate of an area. In a particular area, the interaction of climate, geography, and plant and animal life is called a **biome** (BY-oam). While biomes that are similar to each other exist throughout the world, the ecosystems that exist in each biome are not the same. Think about the rain forest biomes of the Amazon in South America and those of Australia. Although the physical characteristics are similar, the plant and animal life and the ecosystems they are part of make the biomes very different.

On the next page are the major types of biomes of the world. Think about the unique features of each one.

FRESHWATER

- Includes lakes, rivers, and wetlands
- Many types of animals
- Primary source of water for drinking and irrigation

MARINE (SALTWATER)

- Includes oceans, coral reefs, and estuaries
- Supports many forms of life
- Plays a role in regulating the earth's temperature

DESERT

- Dry, may be hot or cold
- Sandy soil
- Few plants and animals, mostly reptiles and small mammals

TUNDRA

- Dry and cold
- Permafrost (frozen soil)
- Few plants and animals, mostly migrating mammals

CONIFEROUS FOREST (TAIGA)

- Adequate water, cool year-round
- Poor and rocky soil
- Many mammals, birds, insects, and conifers (cone-bearing plants)

DECIDUOUS FOREST

- Adequate water, cool and warm season
- Fertile soil
- Many animals and deciduous plants (plants that lose their leaves yearly)

GRASSLAND

- Both dry and wet season, warm to hot
- Fertile soil
- Many animals and grasses, with very few or no trees

TROPICAL RAIN FOREST

- Very wet and very warm
- Acidic soil with few nutrients
- Many animals and plants, with great diversity

All of these biomes make up the earth's ecosystem. Human activities pose threats to each of these biomes. Some of these threats are shown in the table below.

Examples of Threats to Biomes	
Biome	**Ecological Threat**
Freshwater	Farmland runoff and industrial pollution
Marine	Overfishing and pollution
Desert	Recreation and development
Tundra	Hunting and pollution
Taiga (coniferous forest)	Logging, commercial and private development
Deciduous forest	Logging, commercial and private development
Grassland	Development
Tropical rain forest	Logging, slash-and-burn farm development

Another potential threat to earth's biomes is global climate change. Consider the marine biome. Microscopic phytoplankton produce more than half of the oxygen in the atmosphere. Scientists have collected data that suggest that warmer oceans might reduce phytoplankton populations. This in turn could reduce the amount of oxygen and food available for other organisms.

ANALYSIS

Part A

1. Based on your experiment, which type(s) of material provides a good habitat for blackworms? Explain how your experimental results support your conclusions.

2. Describe the non-living characteristics of a habitat.

    Hint: What non-living factors could affect whether organisms will survive and reproduce?

3. What could you do with your blackworms to investigate if a warm or cold habitat is better for them? Write a procedure that anyone in your class could follow to investigate this question.

Part B

4. What are two common biomes in the United States? Where are they located?

5. Draw a diagram that shows the relationship among ecosystems, habitats, biomes, populations, and communities.

6. Choose one of the biomes, and explain how serious damage to this biome would affect ecosystems on earth.

7. **Reflection:** Do you think that introduced species are always successful in new environments? Explain.

EXTENSION

Go to the *Issues and Life Science* page of the SEPUP website to find out more about relationships within an ecosystem and ecological threats to the world's biomes.

MODELING

Populations usually vary from season to season and year to year, often depending on non-living factors such as rainfall or temperature variations. Populations of a species can also be affected by living factors, such as other species that may provide food, compete for food, or provide shade or shelter.

When a new species is introduced into an area, it can compete with native species for food and other resources. Clams and zebra mussels are both mollusks that feed by filtering plankton from the water. What happens when zebra mussels are introduced into a habitat containing a clam population?

CHALLENGE

How might the introduction of a competing species, such as zebra mussels, affect a population of native clams?

Zebra mussels growing on a native clam

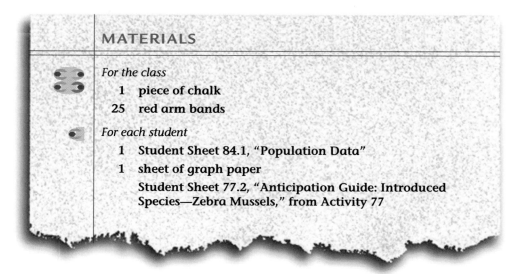

MATERIALS

For the class
  1   piece of chalk
 25   red arm bands

For each student
  1   Student Sheet 84.1, "Population Data"
  1   sheet of graph paper
      Student Sheet 77.2, "Anticipation Guide: Introduced Species—Zebra Mussels," from Activity 77

PROCEDURE

Part A: Clam Population Size

1. As directed by your teacher, determine which students will initially represent clams and which students will initially represent plankton.

2. If you represent a clam, stand inside a chalk circle. There should be only one clam per circle. The space between the clams represents the amount of space a clam needs to survive. As long as you represent a clam, you must stay inside the circle.

3. If you represent plankton, stand behind the safety line on one side of the clam bed.

4. Your teacher will instruct the plankton to run through the clam bed, from one safety zone to the other (see map below). A clam can use only one hand to tag its food. Each clam will try to "catch" (tag) plankton to survive; any plankton that is caught becomes a clam and has to find a home circle. Any clam that does not catch any plankton dies from lack of food; the student becomes plankton and must go to the safety zone.

5. Count and record the total population of clams.

6. Repeat Steps 4 and 5 at least ten times.

CLAM CATCH GAME MAP

Part B: Competition

7. Zebra mussels have invaded the clam bed! As directed by your teacher, determine which students will initially represent clams, which students will initially represent plankton, and which students will initially represent zebra mussels.

8. If you represent a zebra mussel, wear an arm band to identify yourself and then stand inside a chalk circle. Since zebra mussels grow very close together, a zebra mussel can grow in (i.e. share) the same circle as a clam. If no clams are present, two zebra mussels can occupy the same circle. As long as you represent a zebra mussel, you must stay inside a circle.

9. If you represent a clam, stand inside a chalk circle. There can still be only one clam per circle (although one zebra mussel can occupy the same circle). As long as you represent a clam, you must stay inside the circle.

10. If you represent plankton, stand behind the safety line on one side of the clam bed.

11. Your teacher will instruct the plankton to run through the clam bed, from one safety zone to the other (see the Clam Catch Game map). A clam can use only one hand to tag its food, while a zebra mussel can use both hands. Each clam and zebra mussel will try to catch plankton to survive; any plankton that is caught becomes a clam or a zebra mussel (depending on who catches it). If you become a zebra mussel, collect an arm band to wear.

    Any clam or zebra mussel that does not catch any plankton dies from lack of food and becomes plankton. When a zebra mussel dies, the arm band should be removed.

12. Record and count the total population of clams and zebra mussels.

13. Repeat Steps 11 and 12 at least ten times.

14. Record the class data on Student Sheet 88.1, "Population Data."

EXTENSION

Are Introduced Species Always Successful?

Introduce a mobile predator that eats only clams. Figure out how to modify the game to include this predator. Predict what you think will happen to the predator population and the clam population over time. Then test your ideas by playing the game for at least ten rounds.

ANALYSIS

Part A: Clam Population

1. **a.** Graph the population of clams over time from Part A of the Procedure. Decide which type of graph (bar or line) would best represent the data. Remember to label your axes and to title your graph.

   b. Look at your graph and describe how this population of clams changed over time.

2. What factor limited the size of the clam population?

Part B: Competition

3. **a.** Graph the population of clams and zebra mussels over time from Part B of the Procedure. Use the same type of graph you used in Part A. Remember to label your axes and to title your graph. Use a key to show what represents the clam population and what represents the zebra mussel population.

   b. Look at your graph and describe how the population of clams changed over time.

   c. Look at your graph and describe how the population of zebra mussels changed over time.

4. **a.** What happened to the clam population after zebra mussels were introduced?

   b. Why did zebra mussels have this effect on the clam population? Explain.

5. **a.** In a real lake, what non-living factors might affect the size of clam and zebra mussel populations? List them.

   Hint: Go outside and look at an ecosystem around you. Observing an actual ecosystem may help you think of more factors.

   b. In a real lake, what living factors might affect the size of clam and zebra mussel populations? List them.

6. Fill in the "After" column for Statements 6–8 only on Sheet 77.2, "Anticipation Guide: Introduced Species—Zebra Mussels." Did your thinking change?

READING

In this unit, you've learned to interpret population graphs and to analyze effects of factors such as competition, predators, and various environmental conditions on population size. Can a population graph tell you how much room there is for a particular species in a habitat? What does it mean for a population to run out of space?

CHALLENGE What is carrying capacity?

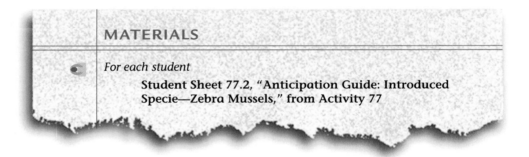

MATERIALS

For each student
Student Sheet 77.2, "Anticipation Guide: Introduced Specie—Zebra Mussels," from Activity 77

READING

Imagine that you are a field ecologist. You've been studying a small lake called Lake Ness for the past ten years. You first began work at the lake when you heard that zebra mussels had invaded a nearby river, one that connects to Lake Ness. After ten years of study, you feel satisfied that you have a good idea of how quickly the zebra mussel can populate a lake of this size. You've been keeping an ongoing count of the zebra mussels in the lake (in mussels per square meter). At this point, your graph of population size looks like Graph 1.

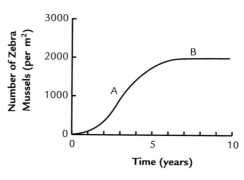

GRAPH 1: ZEBRA MUSSEL POPULATION OF LAKE NESS OVER 10 YEARS

STOPPING TO THINK 1

Recall that zebra mussels get their food by filtering plankton out of the water. Look at Graph 1. What do you think is happening to the quantity of plankton at:

a. Point A? Explain your reasoning. *increasing*

b. Point B? Explain your reasoning.

As a result of your analysis, you think you have identified the maximum number of zebra mussels that could live successfully in Lake Ness. You think this might be the **carrying capacity** of the lake for zebra mussels. This term suggests the amount a container can hold, or carry. But unlike the capacity of a container, the number of zebra mussels that the lake can successfully hold may change over time, based on both living and non-living factors.

A few days later, your friend Nadia comes to visit you from the city. She drove up to the lake in her new car. "It has a carrying capacity of five passengers," she brags. Since you've never seen her drive anyone but her best friend and her dog, you simply shrug.

STOPPING TO THINK 2

a. Look again at Graph 1. What is the carrying capacity of zebra mussels in Lake Ness? How did you determine this? *2000*

b. List some of the factors that might affect this carrying capacity.

After Nadia leaves, you spend a week organizing your data. You decide to stop studying Lake Ness so closely for a while. Instead, you'll return to the lake once a year. During each visit, you'll check on the zebra mussel population. Fifteen years pass. A graph of your data now looks like Graph 2.

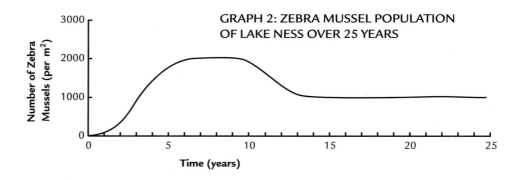

GRAPH 2: ZEBRA MUSSEL POPULATION OF LAKE NESS OVER 25 YEARS

STOPPING TO THINK 3

a. What is the carrying capacity for zebra mussels in Lake Ness between Years 13 and 25? 1006

b. Identify at least three non-living factors that may have caused the carrying capacity to change. Explain how each factor could cause this change in carrying capacity.

c. Identify at least three living factors that may have caused the carrying capacity to change. Explain how each factor could cause this change in carrying capacity.

d. Do you think that the zebra mussel population will return to the level it had reached between Years 5 and 10? Why or why not?

For twelve years now, you've been puzzled by the change in the zebra mussel population. For example, in all your years of study, you've found no evidence of a new predator of zebra mussels appearing in the lake. You remain convinced that something about the zebra mussel's habitat must have changed to cause this shift in the population level. Consulting public records, you discover that a new factory was built just three miles from the lake about fifteen years ago!

Energized, you decide to test your hypothesis. You set up two identical tanks. One tank contains water from Lake Ness. The other tank contains water from a similar lake that is higher up in the mountains and farther from the factory. You add exactly ten adult zebra mussels to each tank. Every day, you supply the two tanks with fresh plankton, which you culture in a separate tank. Several months later, you are puzzled to find no difference at all in the zebra mussel populations of the two tanks.

STOPPING TO THINK 4

Is this a good experiment to test the hypothesis that the factory was affecting the zebra mussel population? Explain.

ANALYSIS

1. Shown below is the population graph from the Analysis section of Activity 78, "Coughing Up Clues."

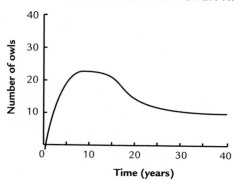

OWL POPULATION OVER TIME

a. What is the carrying capacity for owls in this habitat?

b. How did the carrying capacity change during this 40-year period? Explain.

c. What living and non-living factors might explain this change in carrying capacity?

2. Fill in the "After" column for Statements 9 and 10 only on Sheet 77.2, "Anticipation Guide: Introduced Species—Zebra Mussels." Did your thinking change?

3. Turn back to Activity 72, "The Miracle Fish?" and look at the graph showing the amount of fish caught in Lake Victoria. Can you determine the carrying capacity of Nile perch in Lake Victoria based on this graph? Explain.

4. **Reflection:** Consider the introduced species you have been researching. Identify one ecosystem into which it has been introduced. Do you think this species has reached its carrying capacity in this ecosystem? Explain.

FIELD STUDY

Until now, you have focused on studying ecology in the laboratory. But ecology is the study of living organisms in the physical environment. This means that a majority of ecological study is done in the natural habitat of organisms, which is usually outdoors. This type of outdoor investigation is known as **field study.** The scientist you read about in Activity 85, "Is There Room for One More?" performed a long-term field study of Lake Ness.

The "field" in field study can refer to any kind of ecosystem.

CHALLENGE ➡ **What do you observe when you conduct a field study?**

MATERIALS

For each pair of students
1   metric ruler (optional)
1   magnifier (optional)
1   thermometer (optional)

PROCEDURE

1. Select an ecosystem on your school grounds or near your school. Think about locations where you are most likely to observe interactions between living and non-living factors. Be sure to consider all of the possible habitats that are available in the area. For example, an over-hanging roof may be home to a population of birds. Long grasses may contain many small animals, such as insects. Streams or ponds are also excellent places for field study.

2. Spend some time carefully observing your ecosystem. Start by simply sitting quietly and watching. Then record all the different types of habitat found within your ecosystem. For example, if you chose a small pond, you might identify the pond edge, the shallow water, and the deep water as three different types of habitat.

3. Record the characteristics of each habitat found within your ecosystem. For example, how much light and oxygen are available? How much rainfall is your habitat likely to receive? What is the temperature within the habitat? Will the temperature change a lot over a 24-hour period? Over the entire year?

4. Look for the presence of living organisms within your ecosystem. You may observe living creatures by gently looking among the different habitats, such as under leaves and rocks, or you may observe signs, such as animal tracks or other disturbances, that show that living creatures have been through the habitat.

5. Study your habitat for the next few days:

   a. Every day, observe your ecosystem for at least five minutes. Note any changes that occur. You may want to consider making your observations as an answer to a question, such as "Do I observe more species in the shady part of this ecosystem compared to the sunlit areas?"

   b. Quantitatively investigate one physical factor, such as temperature. Do this by taking measurements of this factor each time you observe your ecosystem.

6. If possible, create a food web for the organisms within your ecosystem. Identify the role (producer, consumer, or decomposer) that each organism plays within the ecosystem.

ANALYSIS

1. Summarize the results of your field study. What did you learn about this ecosystem? How did the physical factor you measured change over time? Was there any relationship between your observations and the physical factor you measured?

2. Compare the advantages of field study to laboratory work in studying ecology. Explain your ideas.

3. You may have seen documentaries or read books on ecosystems around the world. How do you think the information presented in these sources is gathered?

4. Many ecologists spend their entire lives studying a single ecosystem or population of organisms. For example, Dian Fossey spent almost 19 years studying the mountain gorillas of central Africa. Jane Goodall spent many years studying chimpanzees in their natural environment. Today, ecologists study ecosystems and organisms in all different parts of the world. Why do you think people spend their lives studying such systems? What can such studies tell us about the natural environment?

5. **Reflection:** How did field study differ from your laboratory work on ecology?

TALKING IT OVER

Having completed his research project, Ondar has a dilemma. He wants to do something about the problem of introduced species. He's particularly concerned about zebra mussels, which have been found in rivers and lakes around his state. What, if anything, should he do?

CHALLENGE ➡ **What are the trade-offs of trying to control an introduced species?**

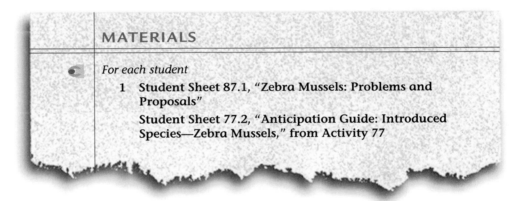

MATERIALS

For each student

1 Student Sheet 87.1, "Zebra Mussels: Problems and Proposals"

Student Sheet 77.2, "Anticipation Guide: Introduced Species—Zebra Mussels," from Activity 77

In this photo, you can see zebra mussel shells piled along the beach in a stack more than a foot high.

PROCEDURE

1. Read the statements that follow.

2. Complete Student Sheet 87.1, "Zebra Mussels: Problems and Proposals."

3. Decide what you would do if you were Ondar.

Johnson Poole, Engineer, Mantee Water Treatment Plant

A worker uses a hose to suction zebra mussels from inside a pipe at a power plant.

"Zebra mussels cause a lot of problems for us. We supply water to the city of Mantee. It's our job to provide clean water for homes and businesses. To do that, large pipes bring water into the plant from Bear Lake. Here at the plant, we filter and treat the water before sending it on to the city.

"But we've had a hard time lately getting the water into the plant. Those zebra mussels grow on everything, including the insides of the pipes. We have seen up to 750,000 zebra mussels in a square meter of pipe! As you might imagine, all of these zebra mussels begin to block the flow of water.

"Right now, we shut down the plant every few months. Then we send someone into the pipes to physically remove all the mussels. This costs tons of money—the U.S. Fish and Wildlife Service reports that dealing with this problem in the Great Lakes area alone has cost billions of dollars!

"In the meantime, we're looking at other solutions. For instance, we're exploring ways to prevent zebra mussels from settling and growing on the pipes in the first place. Zebra mussels grow best on hard surfaces, such as rocks. That's also why they sometimes grow on other animals with hard shells like clams. We're trying to find out if we can coat the pipes with some type of paint or something else that would prevent the mussels from growing on them. You could say we're trying to make the pipes a less suitable habitat for the mussels!"

Adrienne Vogel, Chemist, Bear Industrial Company

"Our company uses water from Bear Lake. Chemicals have been shown to kill both larval and adult zebra mussels. That's one way we prevent zebra mussels from growing in our water supply. We can't afford for zebra mussels to grow inside our water containment ponds. So, after the water comes into our plant, we treat it with a variety of chemicals. While this is very effective in dealing with the zebra mussels, the treated water does contain a lot of chemicals. This means that we can't release the water back into the lake as is. Luckily for us, we are able to recycle and re-use the water within the company for several months. Before we release the water, we treat it to isolate the chemicals and dispose of them according to state regulations. But this all costs money."

Talia Mercata, Biologist, State Fish and Wildlife Service

"I sympathize with the people at both plants. Humans are not the only ones that are affected by zebra mussels. Zebra mussels may be changing the native ecology of lakes and rivers. We know that Bear Lake is clearer as a result of zebra mussels. zebra mussels. Pollution from a nearby industry had caused the algae to grow out of control, making visibility very poor. Fish were dying because of the lack of oxygen. One thing is certain—zebra mussels have filtered out most of that algae. Some people think that is a good thing. Now that the fish have come back, however, we are worried that the zebra mussels will change the food webs in the lake.

"Some scientists are investigating how predators may help control zebra mussel populations. In Europe, where zebra mussels first came from, there are a lot more native predators, such as fish that have teeth. Here in the U.S., the populations of fish that might be good predators aren't that high.

"Ducks are one possible predator here in the U.S. But using predators to control zebra mussels is complicated. How do you control where ducks and fish decide to search for food? How can you guarantee that they'll eat zebra mussels and not some other food? How will they reduce populations in hard-to-reach areas, such as inside pipes? What happens if the introduction of the predator causes other imbalances in the ecosystem?

"Because of these difficulties, my research focuses on the use of parasites to control zebra mussels. If my research is successful, I may identify a parasite that could infect and kill zebra mussels. I'm not sure how quickly this would affect their populations, though."

Henry Wai, Activist, People for Responsible Action

"It's a shame that zebra mussels were ever introduced into the United States. We can only predict how they'll affect the ecology of our lakes and rivers. We don't know for sure.

"People caused this problem in the first place and I think every person should take responsibility for trying to prevent further damage. It's easy to forget that things we do every day might contribute to the problem of introduced species, but it's true.

"For example, just carrying equipment like inner tubes and diving gear from one lake to another can introduce a species like the zebra mussel. After all, its larval stage is very small. That's why it's important for people to rinse and dry their equipment before going from one body of water to another. Think about it—if every boater, fisher, swimmer, and diver took care to clean off his or her equipment, we might prevent zebra mussels and other organisms from spreading across the U.S. so quickly!"

ANALYSIS

1. What, if anything, do you think should be done about the growing population of zebra mussels in the United States? Support your answer with evidence and discuss the trade-offs of your decision.

   Hint: To write a complete answer, first state your opinion. Provide two or more pieces of evidence that support your opinion. Then discuss the trade-offs of your decision.

EXTENSION

Go to the *Issues and Life Science* page of the SEPUP website for links to sites with information about zebra mussels and management options.

Introduced species can have an enormous impact on the economy as well as on native ecosystems. Your research project and your study of ecology have helped you to become an expert on one introduced species. Why are some introduced species more likely to be successful than others?

CHALLENGE

What, if anything, should be done about the introduction of a new species into an ecosystem?

These workers are removing hydrilla and other aquatic plants from a lake.

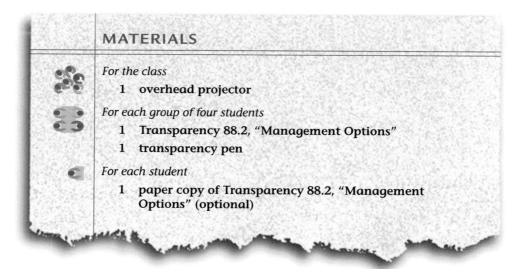

MATERIALS

For the class
1   overhead projector

For each group of four students
1   Transparency 88.2, "Management Options"
1   transparency pen

For each student
1   paper copy of Transparency 88.2, "Management Options" (optional)

PROCEDURE

1. In Activity 73, "Introduced Species," you began a research project on an introduced species. You will now present your research to the class. Use Student Sheet 73.1, "Introduced Species Research," as you plan your presentation. Your presentation should help your audience make an informed decision about what, if anything, to do about this introduced species.

   When planning your presentation, remember:

   - All the members of your group must participate.

   - Since any group member may be asked to answer questions from the class, all group members should fully understand the report.

   - Your presentation time is limited.

   - Many people learn best from a mix of visual, written, and spoken information. Include graphs and maps when possible.

   - While you have your own opinions on this issue, it is important that you present unbiased and complete information. The members of your audience can then make their own decisions.

   - You may want to role-play different experts when presenting your information, such as the people who might present information at a city council meeting. The class would represent the community members who would be voting on a decision.

2. List all of the options that are available for dealing with your introduced species on Transparency 88.2, "Management Options."

3. Begin by presenting general information about your introduced species to the class. Respond to any questions that other students may have.

4. Ask the class what they think are the pros and cons of each of the options you presented. Record their responses on Transparency 88.2.

5. If you are aware of issues that were not brought up by the class, add them onto the transparency.

6. Have the class vote on what, if anything, should be done about the introduction of this species into new ecosystems.

7. Listen to and participate in other groups' presentations.

ANALYSIS

1. Many species are accidentally introduced into North American ecosystems from other countries each year. The opposite is also true: North American species are also introduced into other countries.

   a. What other countries or other areas of the United States are most likely to exchange species with the area where you live?

   b. Only a small fraction of species that are introduced are successful enough to create problems in their new environment. What features of a species do you think make it likely to be successful in a new environment? Use specific examples from the project presentations in your answer.

2. How do you think the number of introduced species in the United States will change over the next 50 years? Explain your reasoning.

3. Write a letter to the editor of a local newspaper describing the situation of an introduced species. Explain what, if anything, you think should be done about the species. Support your answer with evidence and discuss the trade-offs of your decision.

   Hint: To write a complete answer, first state your opinion. Provide two or more pieces of evidence that support your opinion. Then discuss the trade-offs of your decision.

Index

A **bold** page number identifies the page on which the term is defined.

definition, **E61**

food chain. *See* food webs.

interaction of climate, geography, plants, and animals. *See* biomes.

inter-species energy relationships. *See* food webs.

introduced species, effect on the food web, E41. *See also* Nile perch; zebra mussels.

size, E61

energy relationships between species. *See* food webs.

environmental requirements. *See* habitats.

eukaryotes, E19–20

exotic species. *See* introduced species.

F

field studies. *See also* population studies.

definition, **E74**

food chain. *See* food webs.

observations, E74–76

population changes, E32–36, E66–69

fish

bony, classifying, E31

cichlids, E6–7

Great Lakes, E44

introducing new species, E6–8

Lake Victoria, E6–7

miracle fish. *See* Nile perch.

five-kingdom classification system, E19–20

flatworms, E31

food chain. *See* food webs.

food webs

animals, microscopic. *See* zooplankton.

consumers, **E42**

dead organisms, consumers of, E46

decomposers, **E46**

definition, **E37**

effects of introduced species, E41–45

examples, E37, E43, E49

food-consuming organisms. *See* consumers.

food-producing organisms. *See* producers.

nematodes, E47–48

organic waste, consumers of, E46

owl pellets, bone analysis, E39

owls, E37–40

photosynthesis, **E42**, E50–53

phytoplankton, E42

plankton, **E42**

plants, microscopic. *See* phytoplankton.

producers

cell structure, E54–57

definition, **E42**

energy source, E50

photosynthesis, E50–53

sunlight as energy source. *See* photosynthesis.

zebra mussels, effects of, E41–45

zooplankton, E42

food-consuming organisms. *See* consumers.

food-producing organisms. *See* producers.

freshwater biome, E62

G

genetic makeup, classifying organisms by. *See* three-domain system.

global climate change, effect on biomes, E64

T

taiga (coniferous forest) biome, E63
three-domain system, E19–20
tiger mosquito *(Aedes albopictus)*, E11
tropical rain forest biome, E63
tundra biome, E62

V

Vertebrata sub-phylum, E23
vertebrates, E23

W

warm blooded animals, E24

Z

zebra mussels *(Dreissena polymorpha)*
  chemical control, E78–79
  controlling, trade-offs, E77–80
  damage caused by
    annual costs, E9
    Bear Lake, E78–80
    effects on native clams,
      E66–69
    Great Lakes ecosystem, E43–
      44
    water treatment plants, E78
  geographic distribution, U.S.A.,
    E44
  Great Lakes, E36, E43–44
  Lake Erie, E36
  Lake Mikolajskie, E35
  photographs, E9, E41, E77
  physical control, E78
  population studies, E32–36,
    E66–69
  predator control, E79
zooplankton, E42

Credits

ISSUES
& Earth Science

THE EARTH IN SPACE

SCIENCE
EDUCATION FOR
PUBLIC
UNDERSTANDING
SEPUP PROGRAM

UNIVERSITY OF CALIFORNIA AT BERKELEY
LAWRENCE HALL OF SCIENCE LHS

LAB-AIDS®
INCORPORATED
RONKONKOMA, NEW YORK

This book is part of SEPUP's middle school science course sequence:

Issues and Earth Science

Studying Soils Scientifically
Rocks and Minerals
Erosion and Deposition
Plate Tectonics
Weather and Atmosphere
The Earth in Space
Exploring the Solar System

Issues and Life Science

Experimental Design: Studying People Scientifically
Body Works
Cell Biology and Disease
Genetics
Ecology
Evolution
Bioengineering

Issues and Physical Science

Studying Materials Scientifically
The Chemistry of Materials
Water
Energy
Force and Motion

Additional SEPUP instructional materials include:
CHEM-2 (Chemicals, Health, Environment and Me): Grades 4–6
SEPUP Modules: Grades 7–12
Science and Sustainability: Course for Grades 9–12
Science and Global Issues Biology: Course for Grades 9–12

 This material is based upon work supported by the National Science Foundation under Grant No. 0099265. Any opinions, findings, and conclusions or recommendations expressed in this material are those of the authors and do not necessarily reflect the views of the National Science Foundation.

For photo and illustration credits, see page F-70, which constitutes an extension of this copyright page.

The preferred citation format for this book is SEPUP. (2006). *Issues and Earth Science*. Lawrence Hall of Science, University of California at Berkeley. Published by Lab Aids®, Inc., Ronkonkoma, NY

1 2 3 4 5 6 7 8 9   12 11 10 09 08 07
©2007 The Regents of the University of California
ISBN: 978-1-60301-060-3

SEPUP
Lawrence Hall of Science
University of California at Berkeley
Berkeley CA 94720-5200

e-mail: sepup@berkeley.edu
Website: www.sepuplhs.org

Published by:

17 Colt Court
Ronkonkoma NY 11779
Website: www.lab-aids.com

A Letter to *Issues and Earth Science* Students

As you examine the activities in this book, you may wonder, "Why does this book look so different from other science books I've seen?" The reason is simple: it is a different kind of science program, and only some of what you will learn can be seen by leafing through this book!

Issues and Earth Science uses several kinds of activities to teach science. For example, you will observe and test the properties of soil, rocks, and minerals. You will examine a model of the way water moves earth materials to change the surface of the land. You will conduct a computer simulation to investigate the causes of earthquakes and volcanoes. A combination of experiments, readings, models, debates, role plays, and projects will help you uncover the nature of science and the relevance of science to your interests.

You will find that important scientific ideas come up again and again in different activities throughout the book. You will be expected to do more than just memorize these concepts: you will be asked to explain and apply them. In particular, you will improve your decision-making skills by using evidence to weigh outcomes and to decide what you think should be done about the scientific issues facing our society.

How do we know that this is a good way for you to learn? In general, research on science education supports it. In particular, the activities in this book were tested by hundreds of students and their teachers, and then modified on the basis of their feedback. In a sense, this entire book is the result of an investigation: we had people test our ideas, we interpreted the results, and we then revised our ideas! We believe the result will show you that learning more about science is important, enjoyable, and relevant to your life.

SEPUP Staff

ISSUES & EARTH SCIENCE PROJECT

Director (2003–2006): Barbara Nagle
Director (2001–2002): Herbert D. Thier
Coordinator: Janet Bellantoni

UNIT F AUTHORS

Barbara Nagle
Janet Bellantoni
Daniel Seaver

OTHER CONTRIBUTORS

Lee Amosslee, Kathaleen Burke, Ryan Chinn, Kevin Cuff, Asher Davison,
Sara Dombkowski, Gayle Gutierrez, Kate Haber, Laura Kretschmar,
Donna Markey, Linda Mead, Mike Reeske, Suzanne Scott

CONTENT AND SCIENTIFIC REVIEW

Isabel Hawkins, Research Astronomer, Space Sciences Laboratory, University
of California at Berkeley, Berkeley, California *(Space Exploration)*

William Prothero, Professor of Geological Science, University of California at
Santa Barbara, Santa Barbara, California *(Complete course)*

Greg Schultz, Education/Outreach Scientist, Space Sciences Laboratory, University of California at Berkeley, Berkeley, California *(The Earth in Space, Space Exploration)*

PRODUCTION

Production Coordinator: Ayse Frosina
SEPUP Publications Coordinator: Miriam Shein
Design and Composition: Seventeenth Street Studios
Photo Research: Seventeenth Street Studios
Editor: Trish Beall
Administrative Assistance: Roberta Smith, Ezequiel Gonzalez

Field Test Centers

The classroom is SEPUP's laboratory for development. We are extremely appreciative of the following center directors and teachers who taught the program during the 2003–04 and 2004–05 school years. These teachers and their students contributed significantly to improving the course.

ATLANTA, GEORGIA
Geeta Verma, *Center Director*

Felecia Bell, Wanda Ellis, Lillian Harris, Patricia Lewis, Millicent McCaskill, Demetra McCoy, Melanie Robinson, Nicole Satchell

BUFFALO, NEW YORK
Kathaleen Burke, *Center Director*

Delores Anderson, Dianne Johnson, Deborah Kimble, Steven Koch, Corean Lofton

DALY CITY, CALIFORNIA
Andrew Coblentz, *Center Director*

Andrew Coblentz, Ken Klein, Catherine Macay, Benjamin Moser, Lucy Schoening

GREELEY-EVANS, COLORADO
Ray Tschillard, *Center Director*

Joann Angus, Djems Domerson, Nick Durham, Christina Kauffman, Jason McLaughlin, Gemarie Romero, Ruby Sabzevari, Mark Wiegers

LEMON GROVE, CALIFORNIA
Samantha Swann, *Center Director*

Jennifer Bates, Jim Haynes, Linda Schultz, Patti Sherillo, John Tessier

PINELLAS COUNTY, FLORIDA
Dr. Chin-Tang Liu and Nancy Stitt, *Center Directors*

Shirley Green, Lisa Mackey, Jennifer Sinphay, Nancy Stitt

WAKE COUNTY, NORTH CAROLINA
Michael Tally, Kim Gervase, and Catherine Norris, *Center Directors*

James Akins, Jon Corcoran, Karen Farnham, Jennifer Koch, Carla Steger

WINSTON-SALEM/FORSYTH COUNTY, NORTH CAROLINA
Jim Bott, *Center Director*

Amelie Bartolino, Ed Beiles, Mary Kay Bell, John Cardarelli, Megan Clayton, Jennifer Sasser, Barbara Strange, Jane Trace

VISTA, CALIFORNIA
Donna Markey, *Center Director*

Amy Alexander, Melissa Boeche, Nicole Buchanan, Dorothy Jones, Stacy Robe, Zamaria Rocio

Contents

The Earth
in Space

F

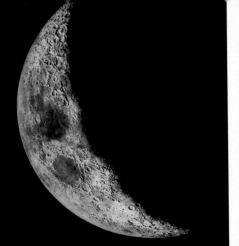

The Earth in Space

Mia woke up suddenly one Monday morning in early March. "Oh no!" she thought. "It's already light out. I must have forgotten to set my alarm clock."

"Wake up, Sleepy," Mia said to her sister. "And hurry up! We're late!" She jumped out of bed and began searching in her closet for something to wear to school.

Just then the alarm clock went off. "You see? We're not late," said her sister. "It's 7:00—the same time the alarm was set for last week."

When Mia went down to breakfast, she told her mother how confused she was when she woke up and saw it was already light.

"I know," said her mother, "It's March now and I'm beginning to notice that the days are getting longer. Last Friday was the first day that it was still light when I got home from work."

That reminded Mia of how gloomy it had felt when the days became shorter in the fall. When she had left school after practicing for the school play, it was already dark out.

"I'm glad there's more daylight now. It's so much easier to get up in the morning when it's light out."

• • •

Why do the daylight hours get shorter in the fall and then longer again in the spring? Does the amount of daylight explain why it is warmer in summer than in winter?

In this unit, you will investigate the cause of the day–night cycle, the year, and the seasons. You will also investigate changes in the phases of the Moon. You will relate these changes to the motions of Earth and the Moon in space and to the way people measure time.

TALKING IT OVER

An important part of scientists' work is discussing and presenting their results and ideas to other scientists. It begins with informal discussions and eventually leads to formal presentations and written papers in scientific journals. When scientists present their work, other scientists review their ideas and comment on them. With this exchange, human knowledge moves forward—from discovering planets to curing diseases, and from exploring the past to thinking about the future.

In this activity, you will review the work of another scientist—a middle school student named Tyler. His class is studying the Earth, Sun, and Moon. Everyone in the class has to do a project, and Tyler's is on sunlight and shadows.

CHALLENGE

How can Tyler improve his investigation?

MATERIALS

For each student

1 Student Sheet 71.1a, "My Ideas About the Day, Year, Seasons, and Moon Phases: Before"

1 Student Sheet 79.1, "My Moon Observations"

READING

Read Tyler's science notebook. When you come to the "Talking It Over" questions, stop and think about them. Then discuss them with your group.

Tyler's Science Notebook

MARCH 15

Yesterday was the first hot day this year. It gets hot much earlier here than it did when we lived in Chicago.

We had an early dismissal day, and Emily came home from school with me. She wanted to sit outside in the shade of the little tree in our backyard. We just planted the tree last year, so I didn't think there would be enough shade. But she was right; there was just enough room for both of us in the shade.

It was kind of annoying though. We had to keep moving to stay in the shady spot. I asked my science teacher why the shadow moved. She explained that it was a phenomenon—a simple or amazing event related to how the world and universe work. She suggested I investigate this question for my science project. I plan to start making observations this weekend.

TALKING IT OVER 1

a. Why do you think Tyler's shady spot keeps moving?

b. During a single day have you ever noticed a change in position of:

- your shadow?

- the shade from a tree or other object?

MARCH 18

PROCEDURE: Today I began collecting data about the shadow from the tree. I decided to check which way the tree's shadow was moving twice in the morning and three times in the afternoon.

RESULTS: Here are pictures of my results.

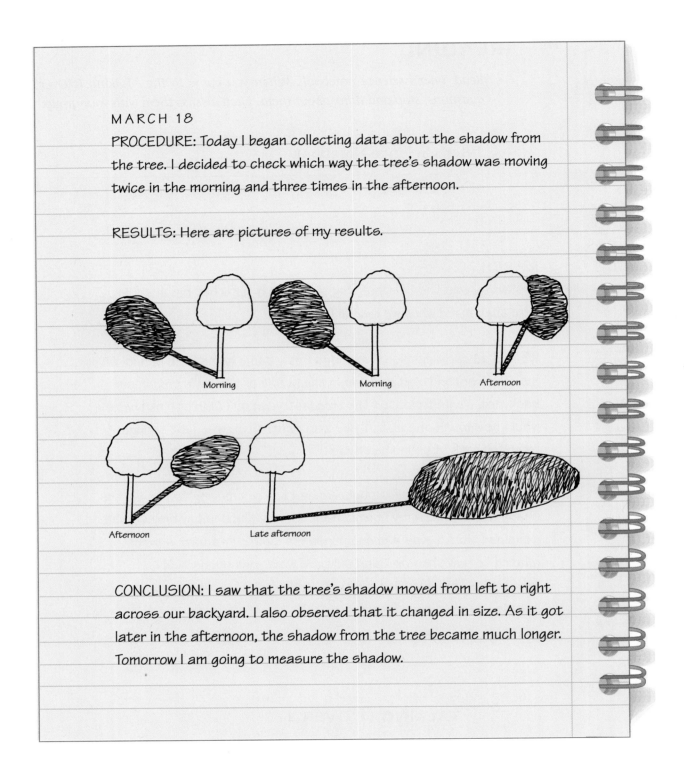

Morning

Morning

Afternoon

Afternoon

Late afternoon

CONCLUSION: I saw that the tree's shadow moved from left to right across our backyard. I also observed that it changed in size. As it got later in the afternoon, the shadow from the tree became much longer. Tomorrow I am going to measure the shadow.

MARCH 19

PROCEDURE: Today I will measure the length of the tree's shadow and note its direction in the morning, at noon, and in the afternoon.

First Observation:

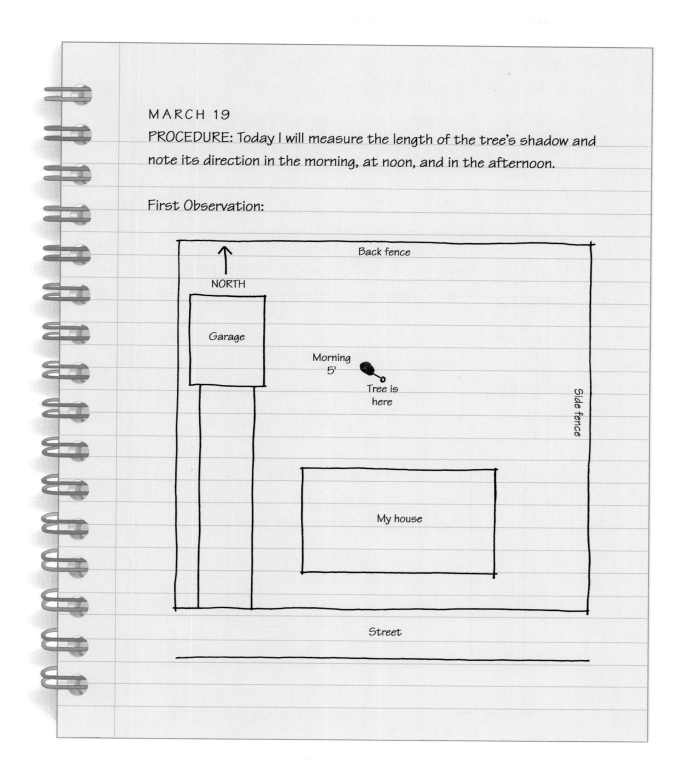

MARCH 19, CONTINUED

At first I just drew a picture and measured the shadow length in feet. Later I remembered that scientists use meters. To make it easier to see, I used an arrow to show the tree's length and direction. I also added my observations of the weather, because the wind and clouds made it hard to measure the shadow at noon. I decided to put all these observations in a table so I could compare the data.

RESULTS: My results are shown below and on the next page.

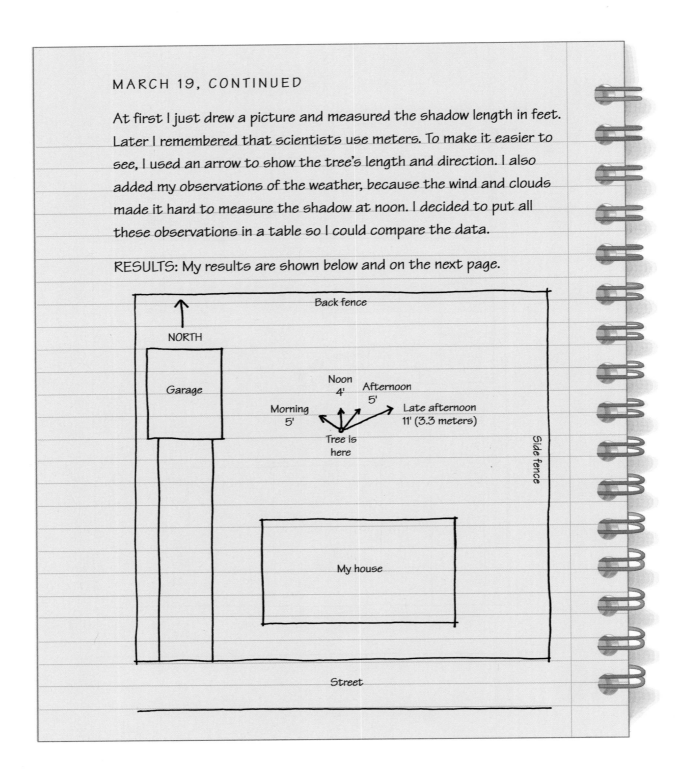

SHADOW OBSERVATIONS

Time	Shadow Direction	Shadow Length (feet)	Shadow Length (meters)	Observations
Mid-morning		5 feet		
Noon		4 feet		A little windy and cloudy, so shadow came and went.
Early afternoon	I noticed the shadow was moving. This morning it pointed toward the garage on the left side of our backyard, but now it's pointing toward the back fence and a little to the right.	5 feet		No clouds, no wind, very hot
Late afternoon	The shadow has moved again and points toward the fence to the right of our backyard.	11 feet	3.3 m	No clouds. No wind. Sun is almost behind the tall trees
6:00 p.m.				No shadow. It was getting dark and chilly because the Sun just set.

SUMMARY: The length of the shadow really does change during the day. It gets especially long in the afternoon.

TALKING IT OVER 2

a. Based on the data he collected, how could Tyler improve his summary of his results?

b. How could Tyler improve his data collection?

ANALYSIS

1. **a.** What do you think is causing the changes in the *direction* of the shadow from Tyler's tree from early to late in the day?

   b. What do you think is causing the changes in the *length* of the shadow from Tyler's tree from early to late in the day?

2. What data would you collect to test your ideas?

3. Do you think Tyler's measurements would be the same if he made them at the same times of day the next month? Explain why or why not.

4. **Reflection:** In hot weather Tyler likes to sit in his favorite shady spot under his tree. How does the Sun affect you each day?

INVESTIGATION

In the last activity, you read Tyler's science notebook and suggested how he could improve his investigation. In this activity, you will have a chance to plan and conduct your own investigation of the shadows cast by the Sun.

Instead of investigating the shadow a tree casts, you will investigate the shadow of a stick. Your investigation should be reproducible (ree-pro-DEW-si-bul). That means that another scientist could follow your procedure to do the same investigation and obtain similar results. This is common in science. Scientists read each other's work and attempt to repeat and extend their findings and conclusions.

Your investigation should also provide enough observations and measurements, or data, to be convincing.

CHALLENGE

How can you improve Tyler's investigation?

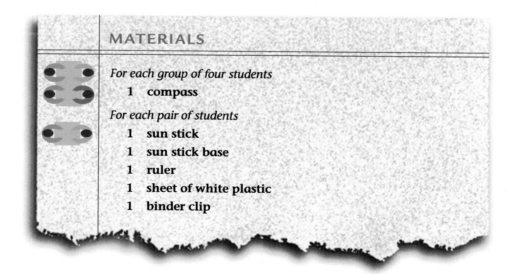

MATERIALS

For each group of four students
   1   compass

For each pair of students
   1   sun stick
   1   sun stick base
   1   ruler
   1   sheet of white plastic
   1   binder clip

PROCEDURE

1. Insert the sun stick into the base.

2. Using Tyler's approach, design a better investigation to answer the questions: How do the position and length of a shadow change during the day? What causes these changes?

   When designing your investigation, think about these questions:

   - What is the purpose of your investigation?
   - How will you describe and conduct your investigation so that it will be reproducible—so that someone else can repeat it and get the same results?
   - What materials will you need to conduct your investigation?
   - Where is the best place to put your sun stick?
   - What observations and measurements will you make?
   - How will you record your data?
   - How will you use your data to make a conclusion?

3. Discuss your investigation design with your group to come up with the best possible combined approach. Record your group's plan in your science notebook.

4. Get your teacher's approval of your investigation.

5. Conduct your investigation, and record your results.

ANALYSIS

1. What changes did you observe in the shadow at several different times on the same day?

2. Why do you think the shadow moved during the day?

3. What observations did you make that support your answer to Question 2?

4. Why do you think the length of the shadow changed during the day?

5. What observations did you make that support your answer to Question 4?

6. How did your observations compare to Tyler's observations?

7. Explain how you could use your sun stick to tell time.

EXTENSION

Conduct an investigation of the shadows from the Sun over a period of a month. Repeat your shadow measurements at the same time of day and in the same location at least once a week for three or four weeks. Record your data and conclusions in your science notebook.

MODELING

The Sun shines on every planet, but the time from one sunrise to the next—one full day–night cycle—is different for each planet. On Earth, one full day–night cycle lasts 24 hours, one complete day. On average, each day on Earth has about 12 hours in light and 12 hours in darkness. On Mercury, a day–night cycle lasts about 4,223 hours, or nearly 176 Earth days! On Jupiter, one full day–night cycle takes less than 10 Earth hours.

Have you ever wondered why night and day happen here on Earth, or anywhere else?

As Tyler took his last measurement, he began to wonder what caused the day–night cycle. When he asked a friend, she said that the Sun just turns dark at night. This didn't seem right to Tyler, but he wasn't sure.

CHALLENGE

What causes the day–night cycle?

MATERIALS

For each pair of students

1 Student Sheet 73.3, "Possible Explanations: A Day On Earth"

For each student

1 Student Sheet 73.1, "Talking Drawing 1: A Day On Earth"

1 Student Sheet 73.2, "Talking Drawing 2: A Day On Earth"

This ancient Greek bowl shows Helios, the Greek god of the Sun, travelling across the sky in his chariot. This is how the Greeks explained the day–night cycle.

PROCEDURE

1. What do you think causes the day–night cycle on Earth? Take a moment to think about this.

2. Create a drawing and add words to describe your ideas on Student Sheet 73.1, "Talking Drawing 1: A Day On Earth." Save your drawing for later in the activity.

3. Read the explanations of the causes for day and night on Student Sheet 73.3, "Possible Explanations: A Day On Earth."

4. Choose the explanation(s) that are closest to your ideas about how night and day happen. You may select more than one explanation. Place a check mark next to the one(s) that you think are closest to your ideas. Explain to your partner why you chose that explanation(s).

5. With your partner, re-read the explanations carefully. Next to each explanation in the table, record any observation that supports or contradicts the explanation.

6. Watch your teacher's demonstration of how the Earth and Sun look from outer space during a 24-hour day–night cycle on Earth.

7. Circle the explanation from the table that is the same as the model you watched.

ANALYSIS

1. What causes daylight and night on Earth? Create another drawing and description of your ideas on Student Sheet 73.2, "Talking Drawing 2: A Day On Earth."

2. Compare and contrast your work on Student Sheets 73.1 and 73.2.

    a. What is the same? What is different?

    b. What did you learn?

    c. What are you unsure about?

    d. What else would you like to know?

3. Think about what you observed and learned from this activity and Activity 72, "Measuring Shadows, Measuring Time."

    a. How does the Sun's position in the sky change from early morning to late afternoon?

    b. What is the reason for these changes?

4. Jupiter's day–night cycle is 10 hours long. What does this tell you about Jupiter's rotation around its axis?

5. **Reflection:** If you were to try to live on another planet, do you think it would be important to go to a planet with a similar length of day as Earth's? Why or why not?

Although the changing position of the Sun throughout the day makes it look like the Sun is moving, you now know that it is really Earth that moves. The rotation of Earth around its axis causes the 24-hour cycle of day and night.

CHALLENGE

What effect does the rotation of Earth have on the way people measure time?

This photograph taken from space shows the light and dark sides of Earth and the Moon.

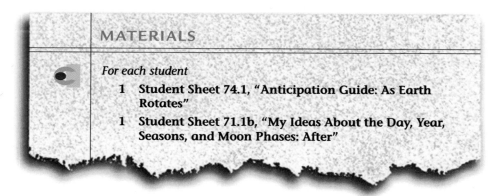

MATERIALS

For each student

1 Student Sheet 74.1, "Anticipation Guide: As Earth Rotates"

1 Student Sheet 71.1b, "My Ideas About the Day, Year, Seasons, and Moon Phases: After"

READING

Use Student Sheet 74.1, "Anticipation Guide: As Earth Rotates," to help prepare you for this reading.

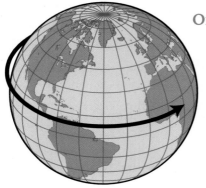

Figure 1: Earth's Rotation
The globe rotates counterclockwise when viewed from above the Northern Hemisphere.

One Day–Night Cycle is One Complete Rotation of Earth

Every 24 hours, Earth **rotates**, or turns around its axis. The **axis** is an imaginary line through the center of Earth, from the North Pole to the South Pole. One complete turn of Earth is called a **rotation** (row-TAY-shun). You can simulate this movement by slowly spinning a globe on its stand. If you look down onto the North Pole at the top of the globe, you should spin the Earth counterclockwise, as shown in Figure 1 at left.

At sunrise where you live, you see the Sun coming up on the eastern horizon as your region of Earth rotates into the light from the Sun. Then the Sun appears to move across the sky from east to west, until it sets. Figure 2 below shows approximately where the Sun appears in the sky during a typical day in most of the United States in early spring and early fall. In spring and fall, day and night are about equal in length, at 12 hours each.

Figure 2: The Sun's Position in the Sky
If you face south on a spring day, you will see the Sun in different positions at different times of the day.

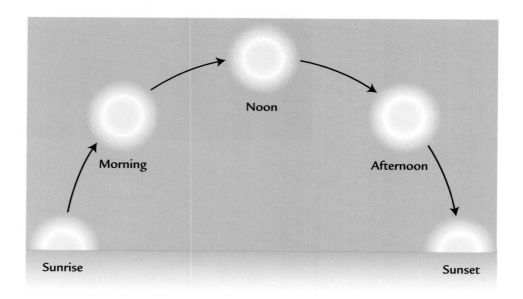

Noon

Morning

Afternoon

Sunrise

Sunset

Using the Sun to Make a Clock

You observed that the shadow from your sun stick moved in the same direction as the hands on a clock, or "clockwise." You may not have realized it, but your sun stick observations are a lot like methods people used to measure time long ago.

Researchers think that ancient peoples in Africa and the Middle East put sticks into the ground and scratched marks in the ground to track the movement of the shadow cast by the stick. This would have shown the passage of time during the day—that's just what a clock does.

Eventually, people began to build structures for keeping time. As early as 5,000 years ago, the Egyptians built tall stone towers called obelisks. Some people think they used the obelisks' shadows to show the time of day. Sometime after that, sundials were invented, probably in many places by different cultures. Although we can't say for sure who first invented sundials, the earliest known sundial was found in Egypt and was made about 3,500 years ago.

Like sun sticks, sundials use shadows to indicate the time, as shown in Figure 3. Each sundial has an upright piece that casts a shadow on a disc marked with the hours of the day. The shadow from a stick or on

Figure 3: Examples of Sundials

The shadow cast onto each of these sundials indicates the time.

a sundial is shortest at noon, when the Sun is at its highest point in the sky. The direction of the sundial shadow changes just as your sun stick shadow does. In the Northern Hemisphere, the shadow moves across a sundial from morning to night. The clockwise movement of the shadow is no coincidence: inventors arranged the hands and hours on clocks to imitate the movement of the shadow and the hour marks on a sundial. Sundials are no longer used to keep time, but you might see them in special places in gardens and parks.

Earth's Rotation and Time Zones

Every day in the United States, the Sun shines first on East Coast cities such as New York and Miami. It takes about three more hours for Earth to rotate enough to move West Coast cities like Seattle and Los Angeles into the sunlight. That's why sunrise on the East Coast is about three hours earlier than sunrise on the West Coast.

Until the mid-1800s, cities and towns kept their own time. For each of them noon was the exact time when the Sun reached its highest point in the sky. This meant that when the clocks in one town read exactly 12:00, the clocks in a town 50 miles to the east might have read 12:03. As train travel became common, these time differences began to confuse everyone. With each town using its own local time, scheduling arrival and departure times was very complicated. And the train engineers and conductors had to keep resetting their watches to the correct local time. Something had to be done to standardize the time of day.

First, each railroad company used its own standard time for its train schedules. That meant its time didn't match local times or times for other railroads' trains. Passengers kept missing their trains, and trains crashed into each other, too. The answer to this problem was time zones. A **time zone** is an area of the world where all clocks are set to the same time. The maps in Figure 4 on the next page show the time zones for the whole world and a close-up view of the U.S. time zones. Earth is divided into 24 major time zones, because it takes 24 hours for Earth to make a complete rotation around its axis. In 1883, all the railroads divided the United States into four time zones to make a single system of standard time that was known for many years as "railroad time." When it is noon everywhere in the Eastern Time Zone, it is only 9 a.m. everywhere in the Pacific Time Zone. It's even earlier in most of Alaska and Hawaii and midnight in some parts of Asia.

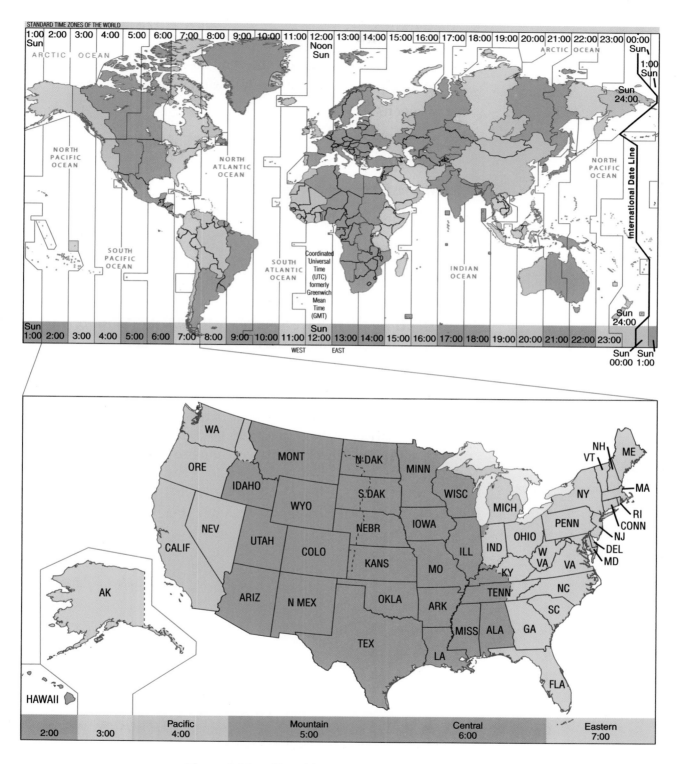

Figure 4: Time Zone Maps

The map at the top shows time zones of the world. The map below it shows those of the United States.

ANALYSIS

1. In the United States, in what direction does the shadow from a stick or sundial point at each of the following times:

   a. at noon?

   b. in the morning?

   c. in the afternoon?

2. How does a sundial show the time?

3. Why is the world divided into time zones?

4. Why weren't time zones created until the late 1800s?

5. When it is 5 p.m. in the Eastern Time Zone, what time is it in the Mountain Time Zone?

6. **Reflection:** How have your ideas about the cause of Earth's day–night cycle changed since you began this unit?

EXTENSION

Go to the *Issues and Earth Science* page of the SEPUP website for links to information about ancient structures used to mark the movement of the Sun during the day and for instructions on how to make your own sundial.

June 15 was the last day of school. Tyler invited Emily to his house to listen to music. Since the temperature was almost 90°F, they got cold drinks and went outside to sit in the shade and listen there. But Tyler was surprised to find that the shady spot was much smaller than he expected it to be at that time of day.

You have investigated changes in the position of the Sun from early in the day to later in the day. Now you will investigate changes in the Sun's position in the sky over a year. This will help you explain why the shady spot from Tyler's tree is smaller in June than it was earlier in the year.

CHALLENGE

What do you observe about the length of daylight and the position of the Sun in the sky during the course of a year?

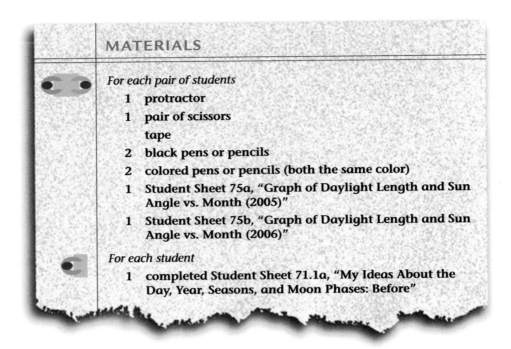

MATERIALS

For each pair of students
  1 protractor
  1 pair of scissors
     tape
  2 black pens or pencils
  2 colored pens or pencils (both the same color)
  1 Student Sheet 75a, "Graph of Daylight Length and Sun Angle vs. Month (2005)"
  1 Student Sheet 75b, "Graph of Daylight Length and Sun Angle vs. Month (2006)"

For each student
  1 completed Student Sheet 71.1a, "My Ideas About the Day, Year, Seasons, and Moon Phases: Before"

PROCEDURE

1. Review the data in Tables 1 and 2 on the next page. It is typical of data that would be collected in the United States.

2. Record in your science notebook the pattern you observe for each of the following (be sure to include a detailed description of your observations):

   a. time of sunrise

   b. time of sunset

   c. length of daylight

   d. the highest angle of the Sun in the sky

3. Record in your science notebook any relationships you see among the patterns you described for Step 2.

4. Working as partners, one person should use Student Sheet 75a to prepare a scatterplot of daylight length and the Sun's highest angle vs. month for 2005 based on the data in Table 1. The other should use Student Sheet 75b to prepare a similar scatterplot for 2006, based on the data in Table 2. Agree on which color to use to plot daylight length and which to use to plot the Sun's highest angle.

5. When you complete your graph, cut it at the line indicated on your Student Sheet and tape it to your partner's graph.

6. Draw a curve to smoothly connect the points on your graph.

Table 1: Daylight Hours and Sun Angle (2005)

Month*	Time of Sunrise (a.m.)	Time of Sunset (p.m.)	Daylight (hours)	Sun's Highest Angle
January	7:20	5:19	10.0	32°
February	6:50	5:54	11.1	41°
March	6:09	6:21	12.2	52°
April	5:24	6:50	13.4	64°
May	4:53	7:17	14.4	72°
June	4:46	7:34	14.8	75°
July	5:02	7:26	14.4	73°
August	5:28	6:53	13.4	64°
September	5:55	6:06	12.2	53°
October	6:23	5:22	11.0	42°
November	6:56	4:52	10.0	32°
December	7:21	4:52	9.5	29°

*21st day of month

Table 2: Daylight Hours and Sun Angle (2006)

Month*	Time of Sunrise (a.m.)	Time of Sunset (p.m.)	Daylight (hours)	Sun's Highest Angle
January	7:19	5:19	10.0	32°
February	6:50	5:54	11.1	41°
March	6:09	6:21	12.2	52°
April	5:24	6:51	13.4	64°
May	4:53	7:17	14.4	72°
June	4:46	7:34	14.8	75°
July	5:03	7:26	14.4	73°
August	5:28	6:53	13.4	64°
September	5:55	6:06	12.2	53°
October	6:23	5:22	11.0	42°
November	6:56	4:49	10.0	32°
December	7:21	4:52	9.5	29°

*21st day of month

7. Label each curve.

8. Record in your science notebook the pattern you see now that you have graphed the data.

9. Discuss with your partner what you think will happen over the next year.

ANALYSIS

1. Based on your graph, what do think was the length of daylight for each of the following days?

   a. March 6

   b. July 6

   c. November 6

2. When are the daylight hours:

   a. shortest?

   b. longest?

   c. about equal to the length of the night (12 hours)?

3. When is the Sun:

   a. lowest in the sky?

   b. highest in the sky?

4. **What** is the relationship between the length of daylight and the Sun's angle?

5. How do the Sun's position in the sky and the length of daylight relate to the seasons of the year?

6. In June, why was the shadow of Tyler's tree shorter than he expected?

7. What do you think will happen to the shadow from Tyler's tree in the fall?

EXTENSION

1. Explain how you could use a sun stick to tell the month of the year.

2. Go to the *Issues and Earth Science* page of the SEPUP website to investigate ways ancient civilizations used shadows from the Sun to indicate the passage of the seasons.

You have learned that Earth's 24-hour day–night cycle is caused by Earth's rotation around its axis. The year is another cycle caused by Earth's motion. A year is the amount of time it takes a planet to make one complete trip around the Sun. Scientists use the term **revolve** to describe the movement of a planet around the Sun. The path a planet follows around the Sun is called its **orbit**. One complete orbit around the Sun is called a **revolution** (rev-ah-LOO-shun). Earth's year is about 365¼ days long because Earth rotates a little more than 365 times in the same amount of time it takes for Earth to make one complete revolution around the Sun.

After school let out in June, it got hotter and hotter, and Tyler wondered why the seasons change each year. He thought it might have something to do with what he was noticing about the Sun's position and the length of daylight.

CHALLENGE

What causes the yearly cycle of the seasons on Earth?

Diagrams like this one of Earth in its orbit around the Sun are much too small to show sizes and distances to scale, but they can help show how Earth revolves in its orbit around the Sun.

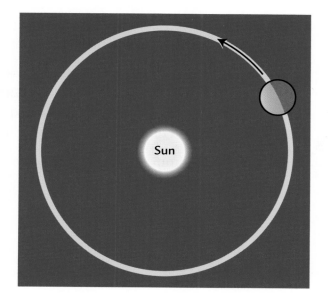

Sun

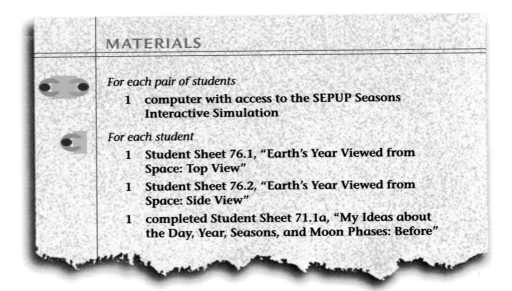

MATERIALS

For each pair of students

1 computer with access to the SEPUP Seasons Interactive Simulation

For each student

1 Student Sheet 76.1, "Earth's Year Viewed from Space: Top View"

1 Student Sheet 76.2, "Earth's Year Viewed from Space: Side View"

1 completed Student Sheet 71.1a, "My Ideas about the Day, Year, Seasons, and Moon Phases: Before"

PROCEDURE

Part A: Analyzing Data on the Distance from Earth to the Sun

1. Open the Seasons Interactive Simulation and review the introduction. Find each of the following on the screen:

   - North America and the United States
   - the Northern Hemisphere
   - the equator
   - the Southern Hemisphere

2. Begin the simulation by clicking in the box on the upper right of the screen that says, CONTINUE TO INTERACTIVE. Find Earth and the Sun. Remember, the size of Earth and the Sun, and the distance between Earth and the Sun, are *not to scale*.

3. Use the diagram on the next page to find and set the following things on the screen:

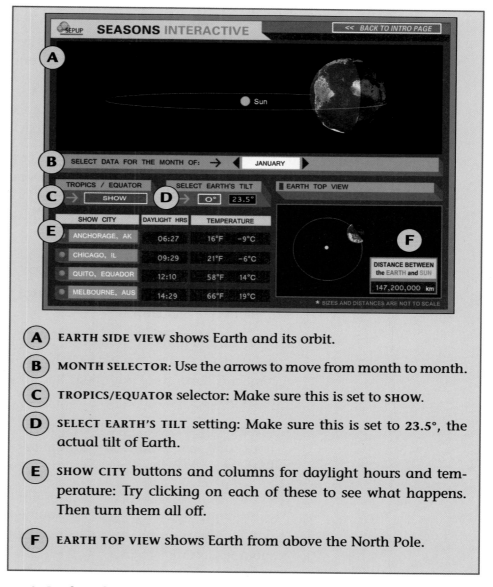

A) EARTH SIDE VIEW shows Earth and its orbit.

B) MONTH SELECTOR: Use the arrows to move from month to month.

C) TROPICS/EQUATOR selector: Make sure this is set to SHOW.

D) SELECT EARTH'S TILT setting: Make sure this is set to 23.5°, the actual tilt of Earth.

E) SHOW CITY buttons and columns for daylight hours and temperature: Try clicking on each of these to see what happens. Then turn them all off.

F) EARTH TOP VIEW shows Earth from above the North Pole.

4. Look at the EARTH TOP VIEW. Notice how the distance from Earth to the Sun is displayed in millions of kilometers at the bottom right corner.

5. Set the month to December, the beginning of winter. Record the distance from Earth to the Sun in the appropriate space on Student Sheet 76.1, "Earth 's Year Viewed from Space: Top View."

6. What do you think the distance from Earth to the Sun will be at the start of spring (March), of summer (June) and of fall (September)? Record your predictions in your science notebook.

7. Repeat Step 5 for March, June, and September to find out if your predictions are correct.

Part B: Analyzing Data on Earth's Tilt and the Seasons

8. Compare Student Sheet 76.2, "Earth's Year Viewed from Space: Side View" with the side view of the Sun and Earth at the top of your computer screen.

9. On the simulation, set the month for December, and click on the SHOW CITY button for Chicago.

10. Look at the top view and side view of Earth, and record each of the following on Student Sheet 76.2 for December in Chicago:

    • the position of Earth and direction of its tilt

    • the number of daylight hours

    • the average temperature

11. Repeat Step 10 three more times: once for March, once for June, and once for September.

12. What do you think the number of daylight hours and average temperature for Chicago would be in December, March, June, and September if Earth were not tilted? Record your ideas in your science notebook.

13. Change the tilt to 0°, and then describe what happens to daylight hours and temperature in Chicago as you change the months of the year and Earth revolves around the Sun.

14. Return the tilt to 23.5°. Now investigate Melbourne, Australia. Notice that Melbourne is in the Southern Hemisphere. Explore its daylight hours and average temperature as you change the months. Record:

    • its average daylight length in December and June

    • its average temperature in December and June

    • a description of the seasons in Melbourne, Australia and how they compare to seasons in Chicago

ANALYSIS

1. What motion of Earth causes the yearly cycle of the seasons?

2. Why does a year on Earth have 365¼ days?

3. In which month(s) is Earth:

   a. closest to the Sun?

   b. farthest from the Sun?

4. Based on what you have observed about the distance from Earth to the Sun, does the distance from Earth to the Sun determine the seasons? Explain the evidence for your answer.

5. In what month is the Northern Hemisphere most tilted *toward* the Sun?

6. In what month is the Northern Hemisphere most tilted *away* from the Sun?

7. Explain how the tilt of the Earth affects the seasons and daylight length.

EXTENSION

Graph the daylight length versus month for one of the cities presented in the simulation or for your city in the United States. Compare it to the graph you did in Activity 75, "Sunlight and Seasons." How are the graphs similar? How are they different?

MODELING

In the last activity, you used a computer simulation to investigate why there are seasons on Earth. Like any model, the simulation has some strengths and weaknesses. It shows the orbit and tilt of Earth to help you understand the seasons. But it doesn't show the correct relationship between the size of the Earth and Sun or the distance between them. It also might give you the incorrect idea that Earth's tilt causes one hemisphere to be significantly nearer to the Sun. Let's take a closer look at the ways in which the tilt of Earth makes a difference.

CHALLENGE

Why does the tilt of Earth lead to different surface temperatures?

This globe, called the Unisphere, was built for the 1964 World's Fair in Queens, New York. Like most globes, it shows Earth's tilt.

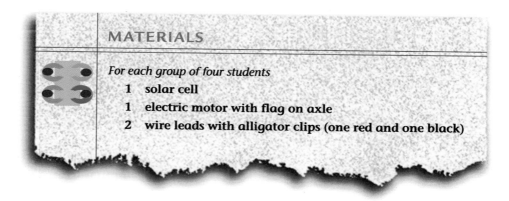

MATERIALS

For each group of four students

1   solar cell
1   electric motor with flag on axle
2   wire leads with alligator clips (one red and one black)

PROCEDURE

1. Work with your group to set up the solar cell. Use the diagrams at left as a guide.

2. Hold the solar cell so it directly faces the Sun, as shown in Position A below. Describe in your notebook what happens to the motor.

3. Gradually tilt the solar cell so that it still gets sunlight but does not directly face the Sun, as shown in Position B below. Describe in your notebook what happens to the speed of the motor.

4. Tilt the solar cell back to directly face the Sun. Keeping it directly facing the Sun, move it closer to and farther from the Sun. Describe what happens to the speed of the motor.

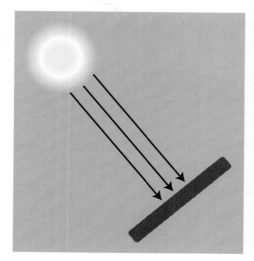

Position A

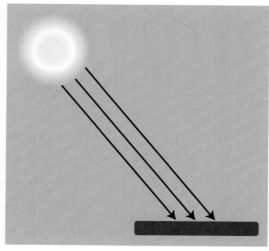

Position B

ANALYSIS

1. When your teacher tilted a portion of the globe directly into light from a flashlight, what happened to the light striking the globe?

2. When you tilted the solar cell from Position A to Position B, what effect did it have on the speed of the motor attached to the solar cell?

3. What does this tell you about the amount of the Sun's energy transferred to the solar cell in the two different positions? Be sure to give a complete explanation.

4. Why is the Northern Hemisphere warmer when it is tilted toward the Sun?

5. In Australia, it is summer in December and winter in July. Why is this?

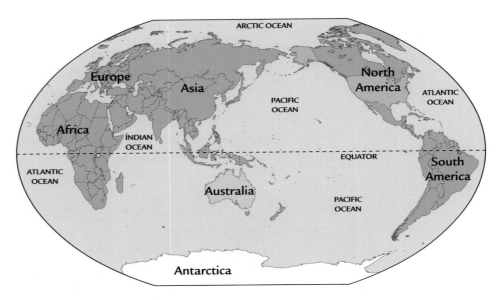

6. **Reflection:** How did each of the following models help you understand how Earth's tilt causes the seasons?

   • the computer model

   • the globe and a flashlight

   • the solar cell and motor

READING

It takes much longer for Earth to revolve around the Sun than to rotate on its axis. The period of time it takes for Earth to completely circle the Sun is called an Earth year—what we know simply as a year. During each year, the cycle of the seasons takes place.

Emily's cousin Charlotte from Australia came to visit her in June. One day, Emily took Charlotte to meet Tyler.

"This is so strange," Charlotte said. "At home, it's almost winter. Here it's hot and the flowers are blooming. I know it has something to do with the Northern and Southern Hemispheres, but I don't completely understand it."

Tyler went into his room and grabbed a globe. "Don't worry," he said, "Emily and I can explain."

CHALLENGE

How do the rotation and revolution of Earth explain the length of a year and the seasons?

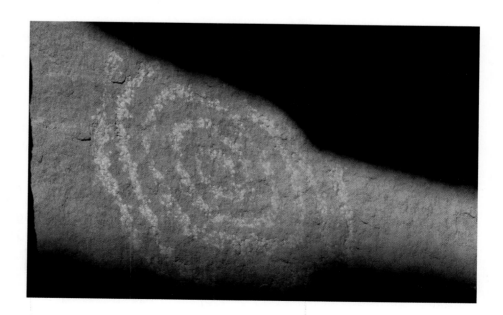

A spiral rock marking is lit by the morning sun on the longest day of the year. Ancient Pueblo people may have made such carvings to mark the seasons.

Earth viewed from space in July. Compare the amount of snow in the Northern and Southern Hemispheres in this photo to the one on the next page.

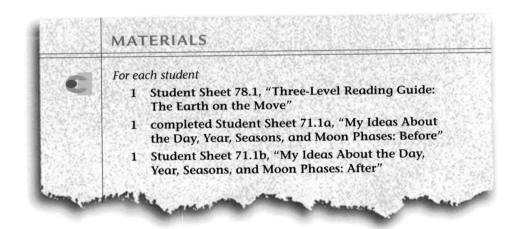

MATERIALS

For each student

1   Student Sheet 78.1, "Three-Level Reading Guide: The Earth on the Move"

1   completed Student Sheet 71.1a, "My Ideas About the Day, Year, Seasons, and Moon Phases: Before"

1   Student Sheet 71.1b, "My Ideas About the Day, Year, Seasons, and Moon Phases: After"

READING

Use Student Sheet 78.1, "Three-Level Reading Guide: The Earth on the Move" to guide you as you complete the following reading.

Earth's Year and the Seasons

As Earth orbits the Sun, the seasons change, but that does not mean Earth's orbiting causes the seasons. To understand seasons, you must consider both Earth's motion around the Sun and Earth's tilt.

Also, you might have thought that seasons are caused by changes in the distance between Earth and the Sun. This explanation could make

Earth viewed from space in January. Compare this with the photo on the facing page. Notice that there is more snow in North America, but less snow in the mountains of South America, where it is summer in January.

sense because Earth's orbit is an ellipse, not a perfect circle—that means that sometimes Earth is closer to the Sun than at other times. However, you learned in the last activity that this idea doesn't fit the evidence that scientists have collected.

The computer simulation showed that Earth is about 6 million km closer to the Sun in December than it is in June, and yet Chicago has much warmer weather in June than in December. If closeness of Earth to the Sun explained the seasons, both the Northern and Southern hemispheres would have winter in June and July and summer in December and January!

If the seasons are not caused by changes in Earth's distance from the Sun, what does cause them? The computer simulation showed that the seasons are related to Earth's tilt. During the time of year when the Northern Hemisphere is tilted toward the Sun, the Northern Hemisphere, which includes the United States, experiences summer. The seasons in the Southern Hemisphere are opposite from the seasons in the Northern Hemisphere. This is because the Southern Hemisphere is tilted away from the Sun when the Northern Hemisphere is tilted toward the Sun, as shown in Figure 1 on the next page. Australia and much of South America and Africa have winter from June through September, when the United States has summer!

Figure 1: Earth's Tilt

*This diagram shows that when one hemisphere is tilted toward the Sun, the other is tilted away from the Sun. (Size and distance are **not** to scale.)*

Earth's Tilt and the Light from the Sun

Why does Earth's tilt make such a difference? There are two reasons. The first reason is that the tilt puts part of Earth into the Sun's rays at a more direct angle than other parts.

When a part of Earth tilts toward the Sun, the Sun is higher in the sky and its rays hit that section of Earth at a higher angle. The higher the angle of the Sun's rays, the closer together they are when they hit Earth's surface. The closer together the rays are, the more effective they are at heating up the Earth. So, since the Northern Hemisphere is most tilted toward the Sun during June, that is when the United States experiences the beginning of summer. You observed the effect of sunlight striking a surface at a higher angle when you held your solar cell directly facing toward the Sun. The solar cell received more energy, which made the motor turn faster.

When you tilted the solar cell at an angle to the Sun's rays, it received less energy, which made the motor slow down. When you did this, you were modeling the change in the angle of the Sun's rays from summer to winter. Figure 2 below shows why the angle of the Sun's rays hitting Earth's surface in summer and winter affects the amount of energy hitting the surface.

Figure 2: Angle of Sunlight at Earth's Surface

When the sunlight strikes Earth's surface at a lower angle, as on the right, the Sun's energy is spread out more and is less effective in heating the Earth.

summer

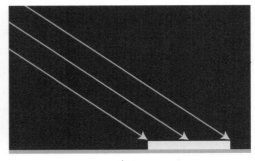

winter

Earth's Tilt and Daylight Length

The second reason why the tilt makes such a difference is its effect on the length of daylight. Figure 3 shows how Earth's tilt causes longer summer days in the United States. More hours of daylight in summer allow more time for the Sun's rays to heat the Earth. The longest day and highest angle of sunlight occur around June 21. However, the warmest days usually come later in the summer because heat builds up over time. The opposite occurs in winter. The shortest days and lowest angle of sunlight occur around December 21. But it continues to get colder after that, as heat is gradually lost.

If Earth were not tilted, most places would have very little difference in average daily temperature over the year. You saw this in the computer simulation when you set Earth's tilt to "0°." But if Earth tilted even more, the difference in temperature and daylight hours between summer and winter would be more extreme.

Figure 3: Seasons and Day Length
*In the summer, Chicago's day is longer than its night because the Northern Hemisphere is tilted toward the Sun. (Sizes and distances are **not** to scale.)*

Ancient Cultures and the Seasons

Ancient people knew the Sun and the seasons were important in their lives. For example, it was important for them to know when to plant crops. If they planted too early, a cold spell might kill the crops. If they planted too late, the plants might not have a long enough growing season. They needed to plant the seeds at just the right time of year so that the crops could grow during the long and sunny days of summer. Evidence gathered from ancient structures suggests that as long as 5,000 years ago, people made careful observations of the Sun's position and the shadows cast by the Sun. They used their observations to predict the seasons and know when to plant and harvest their crops. They also held celebrations at different times of the year, based on the Sun's position.

ANALYSIS

1. Rotation and revolution are both motions of the Earth.

   a. How does each of these motions help us mark time?

   b. In your science notebook, create a larger version of the Venn diagram shown below. Compare and contrast the rotation and the revolution of the Earth by recording the unique features of each phenomenon on the far side of each circle. Record common features of Earth's rotation and revolution in the space where the circles overlap. Hint: Think about what you have learned about these motions in the last few activities.

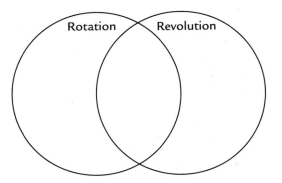

2. Prepare a labeled diagram that includes a caption that explains to Emily's cousin Charlotte how Earth's tilt and its revolution around the Sun cause each of the following:

   a. changes in the angle of sunlight hitting the Earth's surface

   b. the seasons in the Southern Hemisphere to be opposites of the seasons in the Northern Hemisphere

3. **Reflection:** Review your ideas about the seasons that you recorded on Student Sheet 71.1a, "My Ideas About the Day, Year, Seasons, and Phases of the Moon: Before." How have your ideas about the reasons for the seasons changed since you began this unit?

EXTENSION

Visit the *Issues and Earth Science* page of the SEPUP website to research structures built by ancient cultures to indicate the position of the Sun and predict the seasons. You can also find links to animations that explain the seasons.

FIELD STUDY

One sunny Saturday Emily was talking to Tyler on the telephone. As she looked out the window, she noticed the Moon in the sky.

"Hey Tyler," she said, *"It's daytime and I can see the Moon, but I can see only part of it. Not that long ago, it was a full Moon and it was only out at night. I'm going to keep track of the Moon's phases for a while to see what will happen next."*

As you made your observations of the Moon in the last few weeks, you probably noticed that the Moon seemed to change shape. The differ-

ent shapes of the Moon visible from Earth are called the **phases** (FAY-zes) of the Moon. For example, when the Moon looks like a completely lighted circle, it is called the **full Moon.** When it is dark and not visible, it is called the **new Moon.**

The changing phases of the Moon have fascinated people for thousands of years. Before artificial lighting, a full Moon allowed people to see at night. Many cultures have used the Moon's changing phases for measuring time. People who lived near an ocean wanted to know about the Moon's cycle because it helped them predict the tides.

CHALLENGE

How can we predict changes in the Moon's appearance?

Full moon rising over a lake shortly after sunset.

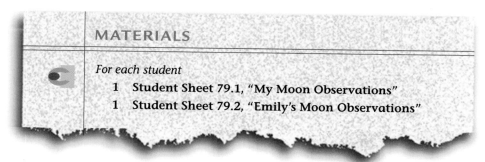

MATERIALS

For each student

1   **Student Sheet 79.1, "My Moon Observations"**
1   **Student Sheet 79.2, "Emily's Moon Observations"**

PROCEDURE

1. Review your data from your own observations of the Moon that you recorded on Student Sheet 79.1, "My Moon Observations."

2. Look for a pattern in the phases of the Moon. Record your ideas about the pattern in your science notebook.

3. Review Emily's data on Student Sheet 79.2, "Emily's Moon Observations."

4. Compare and contrast Emily's data with your data. Record in your science notebook the similarities and differences that you find.

5. In the circles on Student Sheet 79.2 for May 11, 22, and 28, draw the shape of the Moon you predict will be visible on those days.

6. Predict the date for the next full Moon for the June calendar on Student Sheet 79.2. Draw it on the calendar.

7. The phase when the Moon is not visible at any time of the day or night is called the new Moon. On Student Sheet 79.2, write the word "new" on the day(s) you predict the new Moon will occur.

ANALYSIS

1. Explain how you made your predictions for Procedure Steps 6 and 7.

2. In 2004, there was a full Moon on May 4. In 2005, there was a full Moon on May 23. Why doesn't the full Moon fall on the same day every year?

3. Predict the date of the next first quarter Moon for the June calendar on Student Sheet 79.2. Explain how you made your prediction.

4. Summarize the complete cycle of the Moon's phases in words and with a labeled diagram.

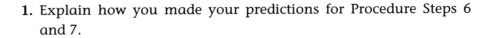

5. About how many days does a complete cycle of the Moon's phases take?

MODELING

In the last activity, you investigated the cycle of the Moon's phases. This is called the **lunar** (LOO-nur) **cycle**. To help you understand what causes the phases of the Moon, in this activity you will observe a model of the Sun, Earth, and Moon in space. Scientists build and use models to try to explain what they observe in nature. Often they find that the simplest models best explain what they see.

You will use a light to model the Sun, because the Sun produces its own light, and a ball to model the Moon, which does not produce light. Moonlight is actually sunlight that is reflected off the surface of the Moon! If the Moon produced light, it would always look like a full circle.

CHALLENGE

What causes the lunar cycle we observe from Earth?

PHASE

Sunday	Monday	Tuesday	Wednesday	Thursday	Friday	Saturday
Waxing crescent						First quarter
Waxing gibbous						Full
Waning gibbous						Third quarter
Waning crescent						New

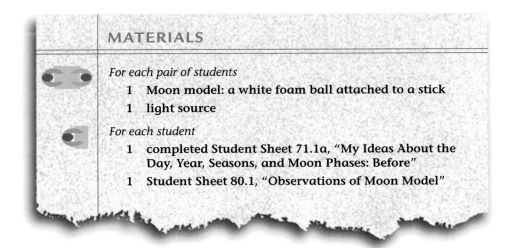

MATERIALS

For each pair of students

  1 Moon model: a white foam ball attached to a stick

  1 light source

For each student

  1 completed Student Sheet 71.1a, "My Ideas About the Day, Year, Seasons, and Moon Phases: Before"

  1 Student Sheet 80.1, "Observations of Moon Model"

PROCEDURE

Part A: Demonstration Model

1. Your teacher will do a demonstration with a ball that represents the Moon and a lightbulb that represents the Sun. You will represent a person looking at the sky from the Earth. Watch the demonstration and sketch your observations on Student Sheet 80.1, "Observations of Moon Model."

2. Answer Analysis Questions 1–3.

Part B: Students' Model

3. With your partner, use the Moon model to explore and understand the phases of the Moon.

4. Be sure to figure out why we sometimes see a crescent Moon, quarter Moon, or gibbous Moon. Draw sketches in your science notebook to show the position of the light, the white ball, and yourself when you see each of these three phases.

5. Answer Analysis Questions 4 and 5.

ANALYSIS

1. What fraction of the ball was always lit up by the lightbulb in the model shown by your teacher?

2. What fraction of the Moon is always lit up by the Sun?

3. Why can't you see the new Moon?

4. What motion causes the Moon to change phases?

5. What phase of the Moon is represented in each of the diagrams below?

   a.  b.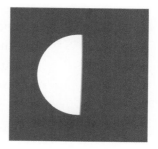

COMPUTER SIMULATION

Just as Earth revolves around the Sun, the Moon revolves around Earth. The seasons occur at different points in Earth's orbit around the Sun. The phases of the Moon occur at different points in the Moon's orbit around Earth.

Just as half of Earth is always lighted by the Sun and half is in darkness, half of the Moon is always lighted by the Sun and half is in darkness. In the last activity, you used a model to observe how the revolution of the Moon around Earth causes you to see different portions of the lighted half of the Moon. In this activity, you will use a computer simulation that provides a different model for understanding the phases of the Moon.

CHALLENGE

How does the Moon's revolution around Earth cause the Moon's phases?

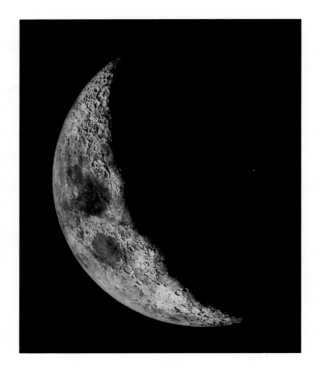

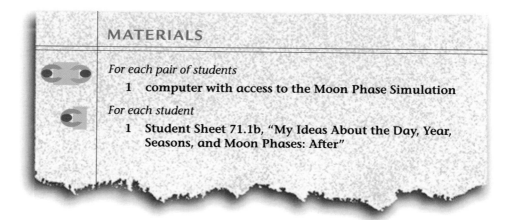

MATERIALS

For each pair of students
  1 computer with access to the Moon Phase Simulation

For each student
  1 Student Sheet 71.1b, "My Ideas About the Day, Year, Seasons, and Moon Phases: After"

PROCEDURE

Part A: Exploring the Simulation

1. Open the Moon Phase Simulation on your computer.

2. Make sure your POINT OF VIEW is TOP VIEW. If it isn't, change it so that it is.

3. Identify the Sun, Earth, and Moon.

4. Click on ANIMATE and describe any changes that occur. Click on STOP to pause the motion.

Part B: Observing the Phases

5. Change the POINT OF VIEW to BOTH VIEWS. Make sure your MOON PHASE is 0.0. If it isn't, change it by highlighting the number, typing in 0.0., and pressing RETURN.

6. Look carefully at the objects in the black box. Make a labeled sketch of them in your science notebook. Title your sketch with a) the moon phase number and b) the name of the phase.

7. Change the moon phase number to 0.25, and press the RETURN key. Make a titled and labeled sketch as you did in Step 6.

8. Repeat Step 7 until you have made sketches for the phase numbers 0.5, 0.75, and 1.0.

9. Click on ANIMATE, and describe what happens. Click on STOP to pause the motion.

ANALYSIS

1. In the simulation, what do the dark and light halves of Earth and the Moon represent?

2. Why are the lighter colored halves of the Moon and Earth always shown facing the Sun?

3. Compare your Part B sketches for MOON PHASE 0.0 and MOON PHASE 1.0. Explain why these phases have different numbers but look the same.

4. Compare this computer model to the physical model your teacher showed you in Activity 80.

   a. What are the advantages and disadvantages of using the ball and light to represent the Moon and Sun?

   b. What are the advantages and disadvantages of the computer model?

5. Write a description and draw pictures that you could use to explain the reason for the phases of the Moon to a friend.

6. **Reflection:** How have your ideas about the reason for the phases of the Moon changed since you began this unit?

EXTENSION

Visit the *Issues and Earth Science* page of the SEPUP website for links to information about eclipses of the Sun and Moon.

In August, Tyler went to visit his cousins who lived near the ocean in Tidal Town. After lunch on his second day there, his cousin Morgan took him to Sandy Beach. "Today is a great day for the beach," said Morgan. "The tide will be really low early this afternoon, so there will be a lot of room on the beach for us to play ball and run around."

At the beach, they spread out a blanket, played catch, and splashed around in the water. But in the late afternoon the tide began to come in, with the ocean covering up more and more of the beach. "Time to move our blanket way back," said Morgan. "High tide will be really high today."

"Do you know why the tides are extremely high and low today?" Tyler asked.

"I know it has something to do with the Moon," Morgan answered. "Right next to the tide information in the Tidal Town News are pictures of the Moon." That night they searched the Internet and found data on the Moon and tides for Sandy Beach. Then they started to look for a relationship between the tides and the Moon.

CHALLENGE

What is the relationship between the phase of the Moon and extreme tides?

Compare the water level at low and high tide in this bay in New Brunswick, Canada.

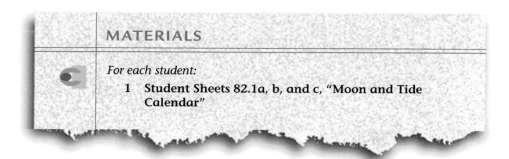

MATERIALS

For each student:

1 Student Sheets 82.1a, b, and c, "Moon and Tide Calendar"

PROCEDURE

1. Table 1 below shows the data about the Moon and tides that Tyler and Morgan found for the day when they went to Sandy Beach and for another day about a week earlier.

2. Record in your science notebook:

   a. How many high tides occur each day?

   b. How many low tides occur each day?

   c. Which day shows more extreme tides (higher high tides and lower low tides)?

Table 1: High and Low Tides for Two Days in August				
Day	**High Tide or Low Tide?**	**Tide Time**	**Height (feet)**	**Moon Phase**
August 7	high	12:10 a.m.	2.6	quarter
	low	6:16 a.m.	0.5	
	high	12:18 p.m.	2.2	
	low	6:36 p.m.	0.2	
August 14	low	12:26 a.m.	−0.2	full
	high	7:02 a.m.	3.5	
	low	1:37 p.m.	−0.2	
	high	7:19 p.m.	2.3	

Tyler and Morgan realized that they had to look at the tide height and Moon phase for several months. They decided to look for the days with extreme tides and days with full Moons to see if they could find a connection. Their results are shown in Table 2 below.

Table 2: Moon and Tide Data for Five Months	
Sets of Extreme Tides (EXT)	**Full Moons (F)**
May 2–5	May 18
May 18–21	June 16
June 1–2	July 15
June 14–16	August 14
July 1–2	September 13
July 13–17	
July 28–30	
August 13–15	
August 28–30	
September 12–15	

3. Transfer the information in Table 2 to your Student Sheet:
   - Mark full Moon days with an "F."
   - Mark when you think there will be new Moon days with an "N."
   - Mark extreme tide days with an "EXT."

4. Record in your science notebook any patterns you see in the relationship between the tides and the Moon each month.

ANALYSIS

1. Use the information on your Student Sheet:

   a. to count the number of days between the full Moons and list them. **Hint:** You should list 4 numbers.

   b. to calculate the average number of days between full Moons.

   c. to use your average to predict the date of the next full Moon after the one on September 13.

2. Based on the data on your Student Sheet, how often do sets of extreme tides (both high and low) occur?

3. What is the connection between extreme tides and the phases of the Moon? Use the evidence from your calendar to support your answer.

EXTENSION

Visit the *Issues and Earth Science* page of the SEPUP website to view an animation of the tides.

When Tyler got home from vacation, he called his friend Emily. "Hey, Emily," he said, "I just realized that the cycle of the Moon is pretty close to one month. Do you think that one month is based on the Moon's cycle?"

Emily thought that was reasonable, since the year and the day are based on the Earth's movement. "Makes sense to me," she replied. "Maybe it's no coincidence that the words 'month' and 'Moon' sound a lot alike!"

By doing some research in the library, Emily and Tyler found out that many calendars have been created at different times by different cultures.

Some calendars have been closely linked to the changing light from the Sun, or the **solar** year. Others have been based on the Moon's cycle, or lunar cycle. Still others have been tied to both the Sun and Moon, and some are not related to either the Sun or the Moon. However, in each case, the calendar has met the needs of the society. You can see some examples on the next page.

CHALLENGE

Why are there many different calendars?

Calendars Used by Different Cultures

Chinese calendar

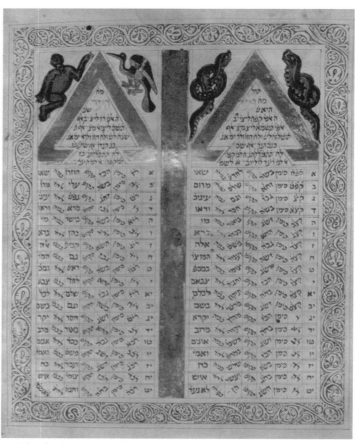

Jewish calendar

Muslim calendar

Aztec calendar

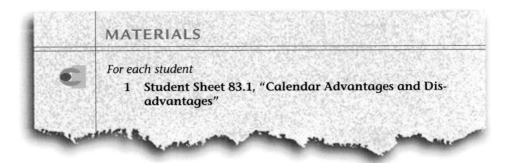

MATERIALS

For each student

1   Student Sheet 83.1, "Calendar Advantages and Disadvantages"

PROCEDURE

1. Review the proposals for three different calendars, A, B, and C on the following pages. Notice that each calendar shows the dates of the new Moon ●, the date of the shortest day of the year in the Northern Hemisphere (**W** for winter), and the date of the longest day of the year in the Northern Hemisphere (**S** for summer).

2. Use Student Sheet 83.1, "Calendar Advantages and Disadvantages," to prepare a list of the advantages and disadvantages of each calendar. Be sure to think about how the calendar fits with each of the following:

   - the cycle of the Moon's phases

   - the cycle of the year as Earth revolves around the Sun

   - the seasons

   - ease of use

3. Read "Place Descriptions" on page F-61.

4. Work with your group to answer Analysis Questions 1–3 for each place.

5. Be prepared to explain your answers for Analysis Question 3 to the class.

6. After the discussion of Analysis Question 3, complete the rest of the Analysis Questions as directed by your teacher.

Calendar Proposal A

We should have a calendar based on the Sun and the 365¼-day year. We will divide the year into 13 equal months of 4 weeks, or 28 days each. Every month in a year will start on a Sunday. Since 13 months times 28 days is only 364 days, we will add one day at the end for a New Year's Eve holiday. Every fourth year (leap year) the holiday will last for two days. These extra days will not be called by the usual day-of-the-week names. They will be New Year's Eve 1 and New Year's Eve 2.

Month 1								**Month 2**								**Month 3**						
Su	M	Tu	W	Th	F	Sa		Su	M	Tu	W	Th	F	Sa		Su	M	Tu	W	Th	F	Sa
1	2	3	4	5	6	7		1	2	3	4	5	6	7		1	2	3	4	5	6	7
8	9	●10	11	12	13	14		8	9	10	●11	12	13	14		8	9	10	11	12	●13	14
15	16	17	18	19	20	21		15	16	17	18	19	20	21		15	16	17	18	19	20	21
22	23	24	25	26	27	28		22	23	24	25	26	27	28		22	23	24	25	26	27	28

Month 4								**Month 5**								**Month 6**						
Su	M	Tu	W	Th	F	Sa		Su	M	Tu	W	Th	F	Sa		Su	M	Tu	W	Th	F	Sa
1	2	3	4	5	6	7		1	2	3	4	5	6	7		1	2	3	4	5	6	7
8	9	10	11	12	13	●14		8	9	10	11	12	13	14		8	9	10	11	12	13	14
15	16	17	18	19	20	21		15	●16	17	18	19	20	21		15	16	●17	18	19	20	21
22	23	24	25	26	27	28		22	23	24	25	26	27	28		22	23	24	25	26	27	28

Month 7								**Month 8**								**Month 9**						
Su	M	Tu	W	Th	F	Sa		Su	M	Tu	W	Th	F	Sa		Su	M	Tu	W	Th	F	Sa
1	2	3	[S]4	5	6	7		1	2	3	4	5	6	7		1	2	3	4	5	6	7
8	9	10	11	12	13	14		8	9	10	11	12	13	14		8	9	10	11	12	13	14
15	16	17	18	●19	20	21		15	16	17	18	19	●20	21		15	16	17	18	19	20	21
22	23	24	25	26	27	28		22	23	24	25	26	27	28		●22	23	24	25	26	27	28

Month 10								**Month 11**								**Month 12**								**Month 13**						
Su	M	Tu	W	Th	F	Sa		Su	M	Tu	W	Th	F	Sa		Su	M	Tu	W	Th	F	Sa		Su	M	Tu	W	Th	F	Sa
1	2	3	4	5	6	7		1	2	3	4	5	6	7		1	2	3	4	5	6	7		1	2	3	4	5	6	7
8	9	10	11	12	13	14		8	9	10	11	12	13	14		8	9	10	11	12	13	14		8	9	10	11	12	13	14
15	16	17	18	19	20	21		15	16	17	18	19	20	21		15	16	17	18	19	20	21		15	16	17	18	[W]19	20	21
22	●23	24	25	26	27	28		22	23	24	●25	26	27	28		22	23	24	25	●26	27	28		22	23	24	25	26	27	●28

New Year's Eve 29
Leap Year New Year's Eve 30

● = New Moon   [S] = Summer Solstice   [W] = Winter Solstice

Calendar Proposal B

We should have a calendar based on the Moon's cycle to determine the length of each month and the Earth's revolution around the Sun to determine a year. Since the Moon's cycle is approximately 29.5 days, the months will alternate between 29 days and 30 days. Each year will have 12 (six 29-day and six 30-day) of these normal months. That will account for 354 out of 365¼ days. Every year will end with a 13th short month of 11 days (12 days in leap years) to fill out the year.

Month 1
Su M Tu W Th F Sa
1 2 (3) 4 5 6 7
8 9 ⑩ 11 12 13 14
15 16 17 18 19 20 21
22 23 24 25 26 27 28
29

Month 2
Su M Tu W Th F Sa
1 2 3 4 5 6
7 8 9 ⑩ 11 12 13
14 15 16 17 18 19 20
21 22 23 24 25 26 27
28 29 30

Month 3
Su M Tu W Th F Sa
1 2 3 4
5 6 7 8 9 ⑩ 11
12 13 14 15 16 17 18
19 20 21 22 23 24 25
26 27 28 29

Month 4
Su M Tu W Th F Sa
1 2 3
4 5 6 7 8 9 ⑩
11 12 13 14 15 16 17
18 19 20 21 22 23 24
25 26 27 28 29 30

Month 5
Su M Tu W Th F Sa
1
2 3 4 5 6 7 8
9 ⑩ 11 12 13 14 15
16 17 18 19 20 21 22
23 24 25 26 27 28 29

Month 6
Su M Tu W Th F Sa
1 2 3 4 5 6 7
8 9 ⑩ 11 12 13 14
15 16 17 18 19 20 21
22 23 24 [S] 26 27 28
29 30

Month 7
Su M Tu W Th F Sa
1 2 3 4 5
6 7 8 9 ⑩ 11 12
13 14 15 16 17 18 19
20 21 22 23 24 25 26
27 28 29

Month 8
Su M Tu W Th F Sa
1 2 3 4
5 6 7 8 9 ⑩ 11
12 13 14 15 16 17 18
19 20 21 22 23 24 25
26 27 28 29 30

Month 9
Su M Tu W Th F Sa
1 2
3 4 5 6 7 8 9
⑩ 11 12 13 14 15 16
17 18 19 20 21 22 23
24 25 26 27 28 29

Month 10
Su M Tu W Th F Sa
1
2 3 4 5 6 7 8
9 ⑪ 11 12 13 14 15
16 17 18 19 20 21 22
23 24 25 26 27 28 29

Month 11
Su M Tu W Th F Sa
1 2 3 4 5 6
7 8 9 10 ⑪ 12 13
14 15 16 17 18 19 20
21 22 23 24 25 26 27
28 29

Month 12
Su M Tu W Th F Sa
1 2 3 4 5
6 7 8 9 10 11 ⑫
13 14 15 16 17 18 19
20 21 22 23 24 25 26
27 28 29 30

Month 13
Su M Tu W Th F Sa
[W] 2 3
4 5 6 7 8 9 10
11 [⑫] (leap year)

● = New Moon   [S] = Summer Solstice   [W] = Winter Solstice

Calendar Proposal C

We should have a calendar based exactly on the cycle of the Moon. We can use a computer to predict the date of the new Moon each month for the coming year. The date of the new Moon will be the first of the month. The full Moon will always fall within one day of the 15th of the month. After 12 months, we will start a new year. Each year will be about 354 days long.

Month 1	Month 2	Month 3
Su M Tu W Th F Sa	Su M Tu W Th F Sa	Su M Tu W Th F Sa
●1 2 3 4 5 6 7	●1 2 3 4 5 6	●1 2 3 4
8 9 10 11 12 13 14	7 8 9 10 11 12 13	5 6 7 8 9 10 11
15 16 17 18 19 20 21	14 15 16 17 18 19 20	12 13 14 15 16 17 18
22 23 24 25 26 27 28	21 22 23 24 25 26 27	19 20 21 22 23 24 25
29	28 29 30	26 27 28 29 30

Month 4	Month 5	Month 6
Su M Tu W Th F Sa	Su M Tu W Th F Sa	Su M Tu W Th F Sa
●1 2 3 4	●1	●1 2 3 4 5 6
5 6 7 8 9 10 11	2 3 4 5 6 7 8	7 8 9 10 11 12 13
12 13 14 15 16 17 18	9 10 11 12 13 14 15	14 15 16 17 18 19 20
19 20 21 22 23 24 25	16 17 18 19 20 21 22	21 22 23 24 25 [S]27
26 27 28 29	23/30 24 25 26 27 28 29	28 29

Month 7	Month 8	Month 9
Su M Tu W Th F Sa	Su M Tu W Th F Sa	Su M Tu W Th F Sa
●1 2 3 4 5	●1 2 3	●1 2
6 7 8 9 10 11 12	4 5 6 7 8 9 10	3 4 5 6 7 8 9
13 14 15 16 17 18 19	11 12 13 14 15 16 17	10 11 12 13 14 15 16
20 21 22 23 24 25 26	18 19 20 21 22 23 24	17 18 19 20 21 22 23
27 28 29 30	25 26 27 28 29	24 25 26 27 28 29

Month 10	Month 11	Month 12
Su M Tu W Th F Sa	Su M Tu W Th F Sa	Su M Tu W Th F Sa
●1 2 3 4 5 6 7	●1 2 3 4 5	●1 2 3 4
8 9 10 11 12 13 14	6 7 8 9 10 11 12	5 6 7 8 9 10 11
15 16 17 18 19 20 21	13 14 15 16 17 18 19	12 13 14 15 16 17 18
22 23 24 25 26 27 28	20 21 22 23 24 25 26	19 20 21 22 23 24 25
29 30	27 28 29	26 27 28 [W]

● = New Moon   [S] = Summer Solstice   [W] = Winter Solstice

Place descriptions

Tropicala is an island near the Equator. There are no noticeable seasons—it is warm and breezy all year. The people who live in Tropicala get their food from three sources. They pick fruits and greens from many kinds of plants that grow wild on the island all year. They gather oysters and clams that are easy to find only when the tide is extremely low. There aren't many animals on the island, but there is one animal that can be hunted when it searches for food at night. Moonlit nights are best for hunting, as bright torches or other lights scare the animals.

Storm Island has a cool and windy climate, with severe rainstorms every winter. The island has two main areas that the residents call East End and West End. Most people live on the rocky East End and have farms on West End, where the soil is excellent for growing crops. The growing season is short on Storm Island, so the residents grow cool weather crops, such as potatoes, carrots, and lettuce. They have to be careful to plant after the last frost of spring and harvest before the first frost of fall. Extremely high tides are a problem, because they flood the lowland that connects East End and West End.

Riverland is in the desert near a large river. The climate is very hot and dry all year. The river's floodplain is the only fertile land for growing crops. The crops are planted when all danger of flooding has passed in the late fall and harvested before flooding begins in the early summer. It is very important for the residents of Riverland to predict when the flooding will begin each fall and to know when the danger of flooding has passed in the spring.

ANALYSIS

1. How do the lives of people in each place depend on the yearly cycle of the seasons?

2. How do the lives of people in each place depend on the lunar cycle?

3. For each place:

    a. State which calendar (or calendars) would be most helpful for the people who live there.

    b. Give your reasons for your decision.

PROPOSED INTERNATIONAL CALENDAR

Month 1						
Su	M	Tu	W	Th	F	Sa
1	2	**10**	4	5	6	7
8	9	10	11	12	13	14
15	16	17	18	19	20	21
22	23	24	25	26	27	28
29	30					

Month 2						
Su	M	Tu	W	Th	F	Sa
	1	2	3	4	5	
6	7	8	**9**	10	11	12
13	14	15	16	17	18	19
20	21	22	23	24	25	26
27	28	29	30			

Month 3						
Su	M	Tu	W	Th	F	Sa
				1	2	3
4	5	6	7	8	**9**	10
11	12	13	14	15	16	17
18	19	20	21	22	23	24
25	26	27	28	29	30	31

Month 4						
Su	M	Tu	W	Th	F	Sa
1	2	3	4	5	6	**7**
8	9	10	11	12	13	14
15	16	17	18	19	20	21
22	23	24	25	26	27	28
29	30					

Month 5						
Su	M	Tu	W	Th	F	Sa
	1	2	3	4	5	
6	**7**	8	9	10	11	12
13	14	15	16	17	18	19
20	21	22	23	24	25	26
27	28	29	30			

Month 6						
Su	M	Tu	W	Th	F	Sa
				1	2	3
4	5	**6**	7	8	9	10
11	12	13	14	15	16	17
18	19	20	**S**	22	23	24
25	26	27	28	29	30	31

Extra Day
| 32 | (Leap Year Day)

Month 7						
Su	M	Tu	W	Th	F	Sa
1	2	3	4	**5**	6	7
8	9	10	11	12	13	14
15	16	17	18	19	20	21
22	23	24	25	26	27	28
29	30					

Month 8						
Su	M	Tu	W	Th	F	Sa
	1	2	3	**4**	5	
6	7	8	9	10	11	12
13	14	15	16	17	18	19
20	21	22	23	24	25	26
27	28	29	30			

Month 9						
Su	M	Tu	W	Th	F	Sa
				1	2	3
4	5	6	7	8	9	10
11	12	13	14	15	16	17
18	19	20	21	22	23	24
25	26	27	28	29	30	31

Month 10						
Su	M	Tu	W	Th	F	Sa
1	2	**3**	4	5	6	7
8	9	10	11	12	13	14
15	16	17	18	19	20	21
22	23	24	25	26	27	28
29	30					

Month 11						
Su	M	Tu	W	Th	F	Sa
	1	**2**	3	4	5	
6	7	8	9	10	11	12
13	14	15	16	17	18	19
20	21	22	23	24	25	26
27	28	29	30			

Month 12						
Su	M	Tu	W	Th	F	Sa
				1	**2**	3
4	5	6	7	8	9	10
11	12	13	14	15	16	17
18	19	20	21	**W**	23	24
25	26	27	28	29	30	31

| 32 | (New Year's Eve Day)

● = New Moon   **S** = Summer Solstice   **W** = Winter Solstice

GUIDELINES FOR INTERNATIONAL CALENDAR

- Each year will be based on 4 equal business quarters. Each quarter will have exactly 91 days divided into 13 weeks, or 3 months.

- The first, second, and third months in a quarter will have 30, 30, and 31 days respectively.

- Each year will begin on Sunday, January 1.

- Each quarter begins on Sunday and ends on Saturday.

- The calendar stays in step with the Sun by ending the year with a 365th day following December 31 each year. This additional day, December 32, is called New Year's Eve Day, (not Sunday or any of the other usual days of the week). New Year's Eve Day is a worldwide holiday.

- In leap years, an extra day is added at the end of June, following June 31. It will be June 32, and it will be called Extra Day (not Sunday or any of the other usual days of the week). Leap Year Day will also be a worldwide holiday.

4. Look at the "Proposed International Calendar" on the opposite page.

   a. Is this calendar based more on the cycle of the Moon or on the cycle of the Sun?

   b. Discuss with your group the convenience of this calendar for the people of the world in terms of:

   - the cycle of the year and the seasons
   - the cycle of the Moon's phases
   - international business and trade
   - cultural factors, such as holidays and celebrations
   - ease of use

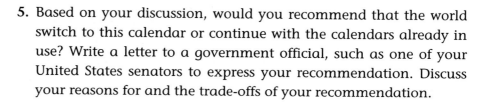

5. Based on your discussion, would you recommend that the world switch to this calendar or continue with the calendars already in use? Write a letter to a government official, such as one of your United States senators to express your recommendation. Discuss your reasons for and the trade-offs of your recommendation.

EXTENSION

Visit the *Issues and Earth Science* page of the SEPUP website to investigate calendars used by other cultures.

Every planet rotates on its axis and revolves around a star. However, the time it takes for each planet to rotate and revolve can be very different from the other planets' times. Some planets have a tilted axis, while others do not. These characteristics determine each planet's day length, year length, and seasons. In addition, some planets have no moons, while others have one or many moons, which may be larger or smaller than Earth's Moon.

Tyler was thinking about everything he had learned about the motions of Earth and the Moon and how they affect life on Earth. He started to daydream about what it would be like on another planet and realized that without Earth's day–night cycle and seasons, life would be very different. He began to imagine all sorts of strange planets . . .

CHALLENGE

What would the day length, year length, seasons, and tides be like on another planet?

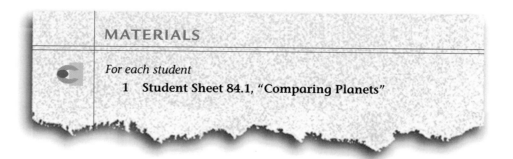

MATERIALS

For each student
   1 **Student Sheet 84.1, "Comparing Planets"**

PROCEDURE

1. Your teacher will assign you one of the planets in the table below. Assume that:

   • Your planet is like Earth in every way, except for the differences in the table.

   • Your planet orbits a star (sun) similar to Earth's Sun.

   • Your planet's moon, if it has one, is similar to Earth's Moon.

2. Work with your group to review the data for your planet in the table below. This shows ways that your planet may be different from Earth.

Data for Earth and 10 Imaginary Planets											
	Planet Earth	A	B	C	D	E	F	G	H	I	J
Rotation Period (in Earth days)	10	10	0.5	1.12	2	3	− 0.8*	1.2	4	40	80
Revolution Period (in Earth days)	365.25	100	600	400	80	600	350	900	160	80	80
Axis tilt (degrees)	23.5°	20°	5°	60°	15°	90°	20°	0°	3°	0°	15°
Number of Moons	1	1	0	1	1	0	1	1	0	1	1

* A negative sign means the planet rotates clockwise when viewed from its north pole, unlike Earth, which rotates counterclockwise.

3. Use the data to determine and record in your science notebook each of the following for your planet:

- day length (complete day–night cycle) in hours (multiply days by 24)

- average number of daytime and nighttime hours

- year length in Earth days

- year length in the planet's days (divide its revolution period by its rotation period and then subtract 1)

- whether it has seasons and what they are like

- whether the planet will have tides, and if yes:

  —will they be similar to, stronger than, or weaker than tides on Earth?

  —will there be extreme tides?

4. Describe in your science notebook what it would be like to live on the planet.

5. With your group, prepare a presentation to explain and model your planet's day, year, seasons, and tides to the class. Explain what it would be like to live on the planet. Your presentation must include a chart or poster.

6. View the other groups' presentations and record unusual features of each planet on Student Sheet 84.1, "Comparing Planets."

ANALYSIS

1. **a.** Create a concept map that includes each of the following 10 words:

axis	phase
day	rotate (or rotation)
Earth	seasons
Moon	Sun
orbit	year

b. Add at least four more words that relate to this unit to your concept map. Choose words that show important things that you have learned.

INDEX

CREDITS

ISSUES

Earth Science

& EXPLORING THE SOLAR SYSTEM

SCIENCE
EDUCATION FOR
PUBLIC
UNDERSTANDING
S E P U P PROGRAM

UNIVERSITY OF CALIFORNIA AT BERKELEY
LAWRENCE HALL OF SCIENCE LHS

LaB-aiDS®
INCORPORATED
RONKONKOMA, NEW YORK

This book is part of SEPUP's middle school science course sequence:

Issues and Earth Science

Studying Soils Scientifically
Rocks and Minerals
Erosion and Deposition
Plate Tectonics
Weather and Atmosphere
The Earth in Space
Exploring the Solar System

Issues and Life Science

Experimental Design: Studying People Scientifically
Body Works
Cell Biology and Disease
Genetics
Ecology
Evolution
Bioengineering

Issues and Physical Science

Studying Materials Scientifically
The Chemistry of Materials
Water
Energy
Force and Motion

Additional SEPUP instructional materials include:
CHEM-2 (Chemicals, Health, Environment and Me): Grades 4–6
SEPUP Modules: Grades 7–12
Science and Sustainability: Course for Grades 9–12
Science and Global Issues Biology: Course for Grades 9–12

 This material is based upon work supported by the National Science Foundation under Grant No. 0099265. Any opinions, findings, and conclusions or recommendations expressed in this material are those of the authors and do not necessarily reflect the views of the National Science Foundation.

For photo and illustration credits, see page G-72, which constitutes an extension of this copyright page.

SEPUP
Lawrence Hall of Science
University of California at Berkeley
Berkeley CA 94720-5200

e-mail: sepup@berkeley.edu
Website: www.sepuplhs.org

Published by:

17 Colt Court
Ronkonkoma NY 11779
Website: www.lab-aids.com

A Letter to *Issues and Earth Science* Students

As you examine the activities in this book, you may wonder, "Why does this book look so different from other science books I've seen?" The reason is simple: it is a different kind of science program, and only some of what you will learn can be seen by leafing through this book!

Issues and Earth Science uses several kinds of activities to teach science. For example, you will observe and test the properties of soil, rocks, and minerals. You will examine a model of the way water moves earth materials to change the surface of the land. You will conduct a computer simulation to investigate the causes of earthquakes and volcanoes. A combination of experiments, readings, models, debates, role plays, and projects will help you uncover the nature of science and the relevance of science to your interests.

You will find that important scientific ideas come up again and again in different activities throughout the book. You will be expected to do more than just memorize these concepts: you will be asked to explain and apply them. In particular, you will improve your decision-making skills by using evidence to weigh outcomes and to decide what you think should be done about the scientific issues facing our society.

How do we know that this is a good way for you to learn? In general, research on science education supports it. In particular, the activities in this book were tested by hundreds of students and their teachers, and then modified on the basis of their feedback. In a sense, this entire book is the result of an investigation: we had people test our ideas, we interpreted the results, and we then revised our ideas! We believe the result will show you that learning more about science is important, enjoyable, and relevant to your life.

SEPUP Staff

ISSUES & EARTH SCIENCE PROJECT

Director (2003–2006): Barbara Nagle
Director (2001–2002): Herbert D. Thier
Coordinator: Janet Bellantoni

UNIT G AUTHORS

Janet Bellantoni
Daniel Seaver
Barbara Nagle

OTHER CONTRIBUTORS

Lee Amosslee, Kathaleen Burke, Ryan Chinn, Kevin Cuff, Asher Davison,
Sara Dombkowski, Gayle Gutierrez, Kate Haber, Laura Kretschmar,
Donna Markey, Linda Mead, Mike Reeske, Suzanne Scott

CONTENT AND SCIENTIFIC REVIEW

Isabel Hawkins, Research Astronomer, Space Sciences Laboratory, University
of California at Berkeley, Berkeley, California *(Space Exploration)*

William Prothero, Professor of Geological Science, University of California at
Santa Barbara, Santa Barbara, California *(Complete course)*

Greg Schultz, Education/Outreach Scientist, Space Sciences Laboratory,
University of California at Berkeley, Berkeley, California *(The Earth in Space,
Space Exploration)*

PRODUCTION

Production Coordinator: Ayse Frosina
SEPUP Publications Coordinator: Miriam Shein
Design and Composition: Seventeenth Street Studios
Photo Research: Seventeenth Street Studios
Editor: Trish Beall
Administrative Assistance: Roberta Smith, Ezequiel Gonzalez

Field Test Centers

The classroom is SEPUP's laboratory for development. We are extremely appreciative of the following center directors and teachers who taught the program during the 2003–04 and 2004–05 school years. These teachers and their students contributed significantly to improving the course.

ATLANTA, GEORGIA
Geeta Verma, *Center Director*

Felecia Bell, Wanda Ellis, Lillian Harris, Patricia Lewis, Millicent McCaskill, Demetra McCoy, Melanie Robinson, Nicole Satchell

BUFFALO, NEW YORK
Kathaleen Burke, *Center Director*

Delores Anderson, Dianne Johnson, Deborah Kimble, Steven Koch, Corean Lofton

DALY CITY, CALIFORNIA
Andrew Coblentz, *Center Director*

Andrew Coblentz, Ken Klein, Catherine Macay, Benjamin Moser, Lucy Schoening

GREELEY-EVANS, COLORADO
Ray Tschillard, *Center Director*

Joann Angus, Djems Domerson, Nick Durham, Christina Kauffman, Jason McLaughlin, Gemarie Romero, Ruby Sabzevari, Mark Wiegers

LEMON GROVE, CALIFORNIA
Samantha Swann, *Center Director*

Jennifer Bates, Jim Haynes, Linda Schultz, Patti Sherillo, John Tessier

PINELLAS COUNTY, FLORIDA
Dr. Chin-Tang Liu and Nancy Stitt, *Center Directors*

Shirley Green, Lisa Mackey, Jennifer Sinphay, Nancy Stitt

WAKE COUNTY, NORTH CAROLINA
Michael Tally, Kim Gervase, and Catherine Norris, *Center Directors*

James Akins, Jon Corcoran, Karen Farnham, Jennifer Koch, Carla Steger

WINSTON-SALEM/FORSYTH COUNTY, NORTH CAROLINA
Jim Bott, *Center Director*

Amelie Bartolino, Ed Beiles, Mary Kay Bell, John Cardarelli, Megan Clayton, Jennifer Sasser, Barbara Strange, Jane Trace

VISTA, CALIFORNIA
Donna Markey, *Center Director*

Amy Alexander, Melissa Boeche, Nicole Buchanan, Dorothy Jones, Stacy Robe, Zamaria Rocio

Contents

Exploring the
Solar System

G

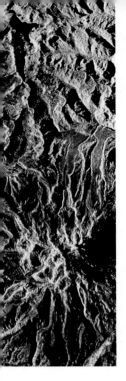

Exploring the Solar System

When Dean went over to Anya's house one day after school, he noticed a long cylinder on a stand in a corner of her back porch. "What's that?" he asked Anya.

"It's a telescope I built with my grandfather," she answered. "He was always going to the observatory, and finally he decided to build a telescope for himself. We put it together last summer."

"Wow," said Dean, "Can I look through it?"

Anya laughed. "Sure, but we might want to wait until it's dark. Maybe you can stay for dinner and do some stargazing with us."

Later, as they helped set up the telescope outside, Anya pointed to a small light in the sky and said, "See that bright spot next to the Moon? That's the planet Mars. "

Dean asked, "How do you know it's a planet and not a star?"

"Well, it looks a little brighter," said Anya, "and it doesn't flicker or twinkle like a regular star. If you look carefully, you can see it's a slightly different color than the stars around it."

Then Anya aimed the telescope at Mars. "Come take a look, Dean. We'll be able to see a lot more with the telescope."

• • •

What kinds of objects are in outer space? Which ones can you see without a telescope? What can we learn about faraway objects with a telescope?

In this unit, you will investigate some objects in space. You will learn what size they are, and how far they are from Earth. You will learn about the ways people explore outer space—whether from Earth or from a spacecraft—and what space exploration may be like in the future.

People have always wanted to explore space. At first they just used their eyes, then telescopes, and then spacecraft and other tools. **Spacecraft** include rockets, satellites, probes, space capsules, space stations, and space shuttles. Some spacecraft have people aboard, but most do not. The first spacecraft, a satellite called Sputnik, was built and launched into orbit in 1957 by the Soviet Union. Since then, several nations and private businesses have put thousands of spacecraft of all kinds into orbit. The launches have cost billions of dollars, and while many have been successful, some have not. Some missions have even ended in disaster.

CHALLENGE ➡

When did some of the great advances in space exploration occur?

Soviet Union leaders stand in front of a model of Sputnik III.

An astronaut climbs down a lunar module.

Space Shuttle Atlantis takes flight.

Two modules of the International Space Station are put together during an astronaut's space walk.

A supply vehicle leaves the International Space Station.

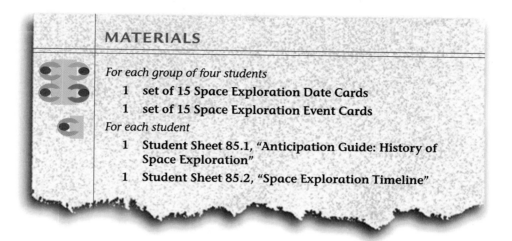

MATERIALS

For each group of four students

1   set of 15 Space Exploration Date Cards
1   set of 15 Space Exploration Event Cards

For each student

1   Student Sheet 85.1, "Anticipation Guide: History of Space Exploration"

1   Student Sheet 85.2, "Space Exploration Timeline"

PROCEDURE

Use Student Sheet 85.1, "Anticipation Guide: History of Space Exploration" to prepare for the following activity.

1. Place the Space Exploration Date Cards in order in a column, with the earliest year at the top and the most recent at the bottom.

2. Carefully read all 15 Space Exploration Event Cards.

3. Work with your group to put the Space Exploration Event Cards in the order in which the events occurred. Place each Event Card to the **left** of the Date Card showing the year in which you think the event occurred.

4. Using the letters and dates on the cards, write this order of events in your science notebook putting the most recent event at the top.

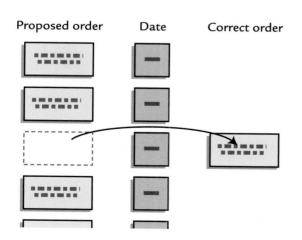

Proposed order   Date   Correct order

5. Your teacher will provide a clue to help you place one of the cards. Use this clue to move one of the Space Exploration Event Cards to the **right** of the Date Card, as shown in the diagram at left. Moving an Event Card to the right means it is next to the correct Date Card.

6. Re-order your Event Cards on the left of the Date Cards as necessary, based on the new information.

7. Repeat Steps 5 and 6 until you have moved as many Event Cards as possible to the right side of the Date Cards.

8. Compare your timeline to the one provided by your teacher. For any cards still on the left side of the Date Cards, move them to the right side of the correct Date Cards.

9. When all Events are in the correct order, copy all the Events onto Student Sheet 85.2, "Space Exploration Timeline."

ANALYSIS

1. Which of the Space Exploration Event Cards that did not have dates did you place:

   a. closest to the correct date?
   Explain how you made your decision.

   b. farthest from the correct date?
   Explain how you made your decision.

2. Why do you think many space exploration events occurred between 1960 and 1980?

3. **Reflection:** If you had to choose a place in space to explore, what would it be? Explain why you chose this place.

Space exploration has always been aided by the work of astronomers. An **astronomer** is a scientist who studies objects and events beyond the Earth's atmosphere, such as the composition or movement of stars and planets. A **star** is a huge ball of gas that gives off heat and light. A **planet**, which is smaller than a star, revolves around a star and reflects that star's light.

Although many objects in the night sky can be seen with the "naked eye," that is, without telescopes or binoculars, telescopes help astronomers make more detailed observations of space objects. For example, for a long time people thought they saw oceans and lakes on the Moon. Using telescopes, astronomers realized that these were fields of hardened volcanic lava.

CHALLENGE

What can you observe about objects in space?

PROCEDURE

1. Each photograph on the next page shows a space object as seen through a powerful telescope. In your science notebook, make a table like the one below.

Observing Space Objects

Space Object Number	Observations	Category
1		
2		
3		
4		
5		
6		

2. Carefully examine the six space objects shown. Look for ways to tell the objects apart.

3. Discuss your observations with your partner, and then record them in the "Observations" column of your table. Leave the "Category" column blank for now.

4. Discuss your observations with the other pair in your group. Review the tables together, and add any new observations about the space objects.

5. In your group of four, decide whether you think the space objects are planets, stars, or "other." Record your ideas in the "Category" column of the table.

6. Describe in your science notebook how you selected the category for each object in the photographs.

Space Objects

1

2

3

4

5

6

ANALYSIS

1. Which objects were most difficult to categorize? Explain what made it difficult.

2. What other observations or information about the objects would help you identify them more easily?

3. What technological inventions have helped us describe and identify space objects?

EXTENSION

On a clear night take Student Sheet 86.1, "Night Sky Observations," a pencil, and a flashlight, and go outside. Find a place where you have a good view of the sky and you are as far away as possible from any lights. Look carefully at the sky, and find five bright, but different, objects. Use the information on the next page to guide your observations. Record your observations on your Student Sheet. Look at those same objects on five different nights and identify how they have changed.

Field Study
of the Night Sky

The objects described below are visible with the "naked eye," and can usually be seen on a dark clear night.

Stars are the most common object we see in the night sky. The light from a star comes from so far away that it acts as a single ray of light. Stars seem to "twinkle" because the Earth's atmosphere refracts, or redirects, the ray of light. Stars appear to move together across the sky during the night.

Planets may be difficult to distinguish from stars. If an object in the sky looks similar to a star but doesn't twinkle as much or looks fuzzier, it is likely to be a planet. Planets appear as disks when magnified with binoculars or a telescope. Although much smaller than stars, they can appear larger because they are much closer to Earth.

Earth's Moon looks like the largest object in the night sky because it is the closest object to Earth. The phase of the Moon changes during the lunar cycle. Other planets have moons but they are too small or too distant to be seen without a telescope.

Satellites and jets move quickly across the night sky and often appear to blink regularly. Sometimes they can look very similar to each other. Most satellites take about 90 minutes to orbit the Earth, so if the object you are observing comes back along the same path in that time, it is probably a satellite.

Meteors are small, bright objects that speed across the sky for a few seconds and appear to leave a trail. Meteors are often mistakenly called "shooting stars" or "falling stars" but they are not stars at all. Meteors are pieces of rock that are falling through the atmosphere and usually burn up before they hit the ground. Meteors that reach Earth's surface are called meteorites.

Galaxies are collections of billions of stars. When conditions make one or more of them visible, each galaxy appears as a fuzzy patch of sky. Only a few galaxies can be seen with the naked eye because most are too distant. Our galaxy, sometimes called the Milky Way, is shaped like a disc. When we look out along the plane of the disk, we are looking toward billions of distant stars that appear as a hazy band of light.

READING

The development of the telescope over the past 400 years has allowed astronomers to see more and more details in known space objects. It has also helped them discover objects that are smaller or farther away from Earth. In the early 1600s, telescopes helped astronomers better distinguish the objects they had already seen in the **Solar System.** The Solar System is the collection of space objects that includes the Sun, its planets, their moons, and other smaller objects. With every new telescope advancement, we have learned more about the regions beyond Earth and the Solar System.

CHALLENGE

How has the telescope helped astronomers see space objects?

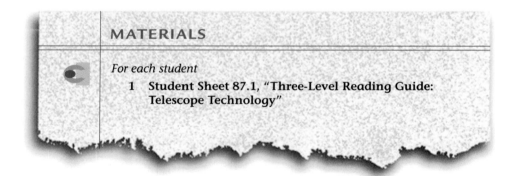

MATERIALS

For each student

1   Student Sheet 87.1, "Three-Level Reading Guide: Telescope Technology"

READING

Use Student Sheet 87.1, "Three-Level Reading Guide: Telescope Technology" to guide you as you complete the following reading.

Galileo's Telescope

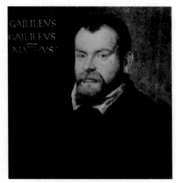

A portrait of Galileo Galilei (1564–1642).

You may have heard that Galileo invented the telescope in the 1600s, but this is not true. In fact, many people made telescopes in the early 1600s to help ship captains find their way and see other ships at sea, but Galileo was the first to use a telescope to observe the sky. He improved it by increasing the strength of its magnifying lenses (the glass pieces that make objects appear larger). Using a telescope that had two one-inch-wide lenses he discovered that there were many moons orbiting Jupiter. This was a big leap forward for the science of astronomy. Another of the important observations Galileo made with his telescope showed that the Moon was not smooth as people thought, but its surface was rough and uneven.

Galileo's telescope with which he discovered four of Jupiter's moons.

Hale's Telescope

George Hale at his desk in 1906.

The power and quality of telescopes improved quickly, and by 1900, astronomers depended on them. Although their telescopes could show space objects hundreds of times bigger than could be seen with the naked eye, some twentieth century scientists wanted to look farther into space. George Ellery Hale was one of those scientists. An ambitious man, he built the now-famous Mount Wilson Observatory in Pasadena, California in 1904. Risking his reputation and a lot of money, in 1906 he ordered the making of a 100-inch telescope that would see far beyond the Solar System. Besides needing a new observatory and special machinery, his telescope would need the largest solid glass mirror ever made. Hale wasn't even sure if that could be done.

Engineers polish the glass of the 100-inch mirror before it is put in the telescope at the Mt. Wilson Observatory.

The project, from the very beginning, met problem after problem. The massive 4,100 kg (9,000 pound) mirror was made in France of wine-bottle glass. It took a year for the glass-makers to build the mold needed to form the mirror. When the mirror arrived in Pasadena in 1908, there were bubbles in the glass, which made it defective. Another mirror was built the next year, but it broke as it cooled. A third mirror was made, but it was too thin. Although some people said the first mirror was useless, Hale decided to use it anyway. That meant five years worth of grinding and polishing the glass before it could become part of the telescope. In the scientific community, doubts about Hale's effort grew as the years passed.

When the mirror was finally ready, it was very carefully trucked up the side of Mt. Wilson at 1 mph, with the help of 200 men. On November 1, 1917, 11 years after the project began, the 100-inch telescope was first aimed at Jupiter. Once the telescope was installed, it was clear that Hale's gamble had paid off. It showed stars as brilliant points of light. Hale's 100-inch telescope produced excellent results, and it remained the largest telescope in the world for 40 years. For decades, the famous astronomer Edwin Hubble used the telescope to measure very distant objects and to find the speed at which they move.

Astronomer Edwin Hubble looks through the eyepiece of the 100-inch telescope.

Leavitt's Observations

Meanwhile on the other side of the country, astronomers in Cambridge, Massachusetts were using other kinds of powerful telescopes to advance their science. One of these astronomers was Henrietta Leavitt, who, like Hubble, aimed a telescope beyond the Solar System.

Henrietta Leavitt created a way of measuring distances to stars that are very far away.

When Leavitt graduated from college in 1895, she went to work, first as a volunteer and then later as a paid staff member, at the Harvard College Observatory. Her work there was interrupted for several years by an illness that left her deaf.

When Leavitt went back to work in 1902, she was assigned the job of cataloging Cepheids (se-FAY-ids), which are stars that regularly brighten and dim. She observed more than 20 of these unusual stars using telescope photographs of stars outside of our galaxy. Several years before Hale's 100-inch telescope began working, Leavitt graphed her data and discovered a pattern. The Cepheids that appeared brightest took longer to cycle from bright to dim and then bright again. Her data allowed her to determine that a Cepheid's actual brightness was related to its distance from Earth. She was able to find the distance to a nearby **galaxy**, a collection of billions of stars. To do this, she only needed to find a Cepheid star in that galaxy and then use it as a cosmic tape measure. This was a scientific breakthrough because until then no one had been able to estimate such large distances.

Leavitt's brilliant career was cut short when she died of cancer at age 53. Some scientists think that, had she lived, she might have received a Nobel Prize.

The Hubble Space Telescope

The Hubble Space Telescope has been orbiting Earth since 1990.

Using both Hale's telescope and Leavitt's measuring method, Edwin Hubble soon made startling discoveries about the movement of galaxies. Because of his major contributions to the field of astronomy, the 200-inch Hubble Space Telescope was named in his honor. This telescope is currently orbiting Earth and looking deeper into space than any telescope has done before. It provides data and images of space objects that could not be gathered from within Earth's atmosphere.

Although the Hubble Space Telescope has been successful, it has a major drawback: a telescope orbiting in space is difficult to repair. Since it was sent into orbit on a space shuttle in 1990, astronauts on shuttles have visited it several times to perform routine service and repairs.

ANALYSIS

1. How has the invention of the telescope helped scientists understand objects in the sky?

2. Choose at least two of the four scientists presented in the reading. Describe how they contributed to astronomy.

3. **Reflection:** If you had access to a powerful telescope, what space object would you want to observe? Explain.

EXTENSION

Investigate the life and work of a famous astronomer. Start at the *Issues and Earth Science* page of the SEPUP website.

Many kinds of objects in the sky can be observed with the naked eye and with telescopes. In this activity you will further investigate objects in space, mostly those found in our own Solar System. Our Solar System, with its one star, is just one tiny part of our galaxy. Our galaxy is only one of billions of galaxies.

CHALLENGE

What types of objects are found in space?

This galaxy made up of billions of stars forms a spiral shape.

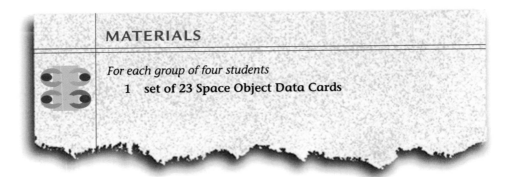

MATERIALS

For each group of four students
1   set of 23 Space Object Data Cards

PROCEDURE

1. Spread your Space Object Data Cards out on a table.

2. Read each card carefully, noting the similarities and differences among the objects.

3. With your group of four, classify the Space Objects into 5 to 10 groups that have similar features. Work together to agree on a classification system.

    • Listen to and consider explanations and ideas of other members of your team.

    • If you disagree with your team members about how to classify a space object, explain why you disagree.

4. In your science notebook, list the common features of each group of space objects. Then write down the numbers of the objects that belong to each group. Label your classification system, "Our Classification System."

5. Discuss with the class your group's classification system. Observe the similarities and differences between your system and the others.

6. Get a set of Classification Cards from your teacher. Each card represents a group of space objects as classified by astronomers. Based on the information described on the Classification Cards, place each Space Object Data Card under one of the Classification Card categories.

7. In your science notebook, list the common features of each category of space objects as described on the Classification Cards. Then list the objects that belong to each set. Label this classification system, "Astronomers' Classification System."

8. With your group, compare the two classification systems. Describe how the systems are:

   • similar

   • different

9. Record your group's ideas in your science notebook.

ANALYSIS

1. How did your group classify the objects? Describe your system.

2. List the seven major objects described in the Astronomers' Classification System. For each classification, write down at least two of the major features of that category.

3. Carefully read the article below.

   a. Why was Pluto's classification changed?

   b. Do you agree with the changes made by the International Astronomical Union? Explain your choice using evidence from the article.

AUGUST 25, 2006

Pluto Demoted!

Prague, Czech Republic —Today the International Astronomical Union, a group of more than 9,000 astronomers around the world, voted to change the definition of a planet. Scientists met to settle the debate over the classification of Pluto and other solar system objects. The result of the vote is that Pluto, discovered in 1930 and designated our ninth planet, is no longer a planet. Pluto is round and orbits the Sun, as required by the definition. However, it does not qualify as a planet because the area around its orbit is not clear of other objects.

The new definition of a planet also settles the debate about Eris (for-merly known as Xena), discovered in 2003. Eris is round and orbits the Sun. It is slightly larger in diameter and three times as far from the Sun as Pluto. The old definition said that a planet was any round object orbiting the Sun that is made of rock or gas and has a diameter equal to or larger than Pluto. If the old classification system were used consistently, Eris, Pluto, and another object named Ceres would all be planets.

The scientists were faced with a difficult choice. Either they had to add more planets to our solar system or they had to reclassify Pluto and similar objects. Currently there are dozens of objects like Pluto, Eris, and Ceres. Scientists predict that hundreds more will be discovered in the future.

The new classification system makes Pluto, Eris, and Ceres "dwarf planets," which is a new category. Objects that orbit the Sun but are not planets or dwarf planets are now called Small Solar System Bodies. Although the new definitions settled the debate about Eris, the new classification system is being criticized. Shortly after the vote was taken, 300 astronomers signed a statement saying they would not use the new definitions. They do not like that the new classification depends on how an object moves (namely, that the area around its orbit is clear of other objects) instead of on its properties. Furthermore, the definitions do not always work outside our Solar System.

INVESTIGATION

Planets have many features in common. For example, all planets are spherically shaped and each orbits a star. But each planet in our Solar System also has many other characteristics that make it different from the others.

Imagine that sometime in the future, people travel to all the planets in the Solar System. Imagine you are living in this time, and some of your friends are away on trips into outer space. You have received messages from your friends on other planets, but there is a problem with some of them. Four of your friends forgot to say what planet they are visiting.

CHALLENGE

What features make each planet unique?

MATERIALS

For each student
  1   **Student Sheet 89.1, "Planet Information"**

PROCEDURE

1. Read the four messages from space shown on the next page.

2. Choose one of the messages and carefully compare the descriptions in it with the information provided on Student Sheet 89.1, "Planet Information."

3. With your partner, decide which planet that message was sent from.

4. In your science notebook:

   • Record the name of the person who sent the message and the name of the planet he or she was visiting.

   • List the evidence in the message that helped you decide which planet the message came from.

5. Repeat Steps 2–4 for the other three messages.

ANALYSIS

1. Write a message from a planet in our Solar System other than the ones already used in the four messages presented in this activity. In your message describe several features that would help someone else identify the planet.

Interplanetary Message

The temperature is so extreme here! During the day, the Sun looks huge and bright, and so it's very, very hot outside. When it is night, it gets really, really cold. Nighttime is always pitch black because there is no Moon. I guess it is kind of like living at the North or South Pole during summer or winter. There are no clouds, wind, or any kind of weather. Thank goodness we brought our own oxygen so we can breathe. I'm glad I brought my space hiking books because there are lots of large craters, kind of like the Moon. I visited one yesterday that is the size of Texas!

Kayla

Interplanetary Message

I can't believe I finally got here! It took close to 10 years to make the trip. I'm glad to be here during this planet's summer, but it's still below −130°C. And, because the planet is tipped on its side, the Sun doesn't shine at all in winter, which lasts more than 7,500 Earth days. The Sun is shining now, but it's not very big, bright, or warm. I'm not sure how long I'll be here, because one year on this planet takes a lifetime, but it's weird because one day is so short.

Not having a solid surface to walk on is kind of tricky, so I spend most of my time on the spacecraft. They say there are a bunch of moons, but I've only seen five. I think the others must be pretty small. I can see some faint gray lines that go all the way across the sky. I'm not sure what they are—I'll have to keep looking.

Ronin

Interplanetary Message

There is so much iron here! The other day, I made the mistake of getting caught in a dust storm. The red dust coming off all the rocks completely blocked my view, and I was lost for a while. The day length is similar to back home, but even in the summer it is still cold. It's like Earth's South Pole in winter, but there is no snow. There is a lot of trash and equipment from previous explorations. It was quite a quick trip here, so I'll be home soon.

Len

P.S. I forgot to tell you that it's kind of spooky having more than one moon zipping across the sky.

Interplanetary Message

This place is so bizarre because it has no solid surface! It is a huge ball of gas, and our space hotel hovers above it. Going out for a walk is certainly not an option. We saw this place that has a huge red hurricane almost three times the size of Earth. It has 400 mph winds that have been blowing for centuries. That's over twice the speed of the winds from the strongest hurricanes on Earth. The atmosphere is constantly swirling and has a lot of hydrogen and helium.

Last night I saw four big moons, which are easy to see, and many little ones that I can't tell apart. It's easy to stay up all night long to watch them because a full night is only about 5 hours long. The daylight time is only 5 hours long, too, so a full day lasts only 10 hours. I can also see a few faint rings when I look out into the sky during the day.

Eva

MODELING

When you look into the night sky, most of the objects other than the Moon appear to be about the same size. They also look like they're all about the same distance from Earth. They are neither. Although early astronomers' observations gave people some idea of how big and how far away the planets are, it took the invention of telescopes, satellites, and rockets, to make accurate measurements.

In this activity, you will use a **scale**—a ratio between the actual size of an object and its size in a model—to turn scientific measurements into an accurate model showing the distances of the planets from the Sun.

CHALLENGE

How far away are other planets in the Solar System?

A model, such as this one of a skyscraper, helps people visualize something that is very large or small.

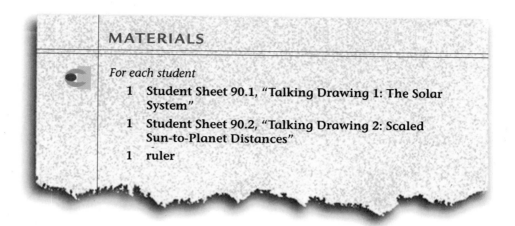

MATERIALS

For each student

1 Student Sheet 90.1, "Talking Drawing 1: The Solar System"

1 Student Sheet 90.2, "Talking Drawing 2: Scaled Sun-to-Planet Distances"

1 ruler

PROCEDURE

Use Student Sheet 90.1, "Talking Drawing 1: The Solar System" to prepare you for the following activity.

Part A: Distances in the Solar System

1. Using the data in Table 1 below and a scale of **1 cm = 200,000,000 km**, calculate the relative distances of the planets from the Sun.

   Hint: To calculate the distance in centimeters (cm), you will need to divide the planet's distance from the Sun in kilometers (km) by the scale.

Table 1: Planets' Distance from the Sun	
Planet	**Approximate Distance from the Sun (km)**
Mercury	58,000,000
Venus	108,000,000
Earth	150,000,000
Mars	227,000,000
Jupiter	778,000,000
Saturn	1,429,000,000
Uranus	2,869,000,000
Neptune	4,505,000,000

2. Record the results of your calculations in the table on Student Sheet 90.2, "Scaled Sun-to-Planet Distances." Round your answers to the nearest 0.1 centimeter.

3. Using the information you just calculated, make a scaled drawing of the distances on Student Sheet 90.2. Measuring from the center of the Sun, draw an X on the line where each planet is located. Record the name of each planet next to its location on the line.

Part B: Diameters in the Solar System

4. Look at the diameters of the planets shown in Table 2 below.

Table 2: Diameters of the Planets	
Planet	**Diameter (km)**
Mercury	5,000
Venus	12,000
Earth	13,000
Mars	7,000
Jupiter	143,000
Saturn	120,500
Uranus	51,000
Neptune	49,500

5. In your group, discuss the following questions about making a scale model of the planets' diameters.

   • Is the scale used in Part A (1 cm = 200,000,000 km) a useful scale for drawing the diameters of the planets? Explain why or why not.

   • The Sun has a diameter of 1,390,000 km. Is the scale used in Part A (1 cm = 200,000,000 km) a useful scale for drawing the diameter of the Sun? Explain why or why not.

   • Using a piece of regular notebook paper and a pencil, can you draw a picture that uses the same scale to accurately show the diameter of the Sun, the distances from the planets to the Sun, and the diameters of the planets?

6. Carefully examine each of the following models of the Solar System. With your group, discuss what is accurate and what is *not* accurate in each image. Record your ideas in your science notebook.

1

2

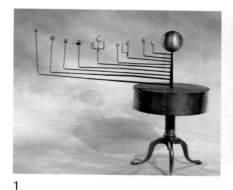

3

4

Models of the Solar System

ANALYSIS

1. Astronomers often measure distances in the Solar System using a unit called the **astronomical unit** (AU). One AU is about 150,000,000 km—the distance between Earth and the Sun.

    a. Why do you think the AU is used to measure distance in the Solar System?

    b. Why do you think the AU is not used to measure distances on Earth?

2. What are the main advantage(s) and the main disadvantage(s) of drawing a picture of the Solar System on a piece of regular notebook paper?

PROJECT

In the previous activity, you drew a scaled diagram of the Sun-to-planet distances in the Solar System. On the same diagram, the scaled size of Earth would be much too small to see. We need to use a different scale when comparing the sizes of different planets.

CHALLENGE

How can you make a scale model showing the sizes of all of the planets?

MATERIALS

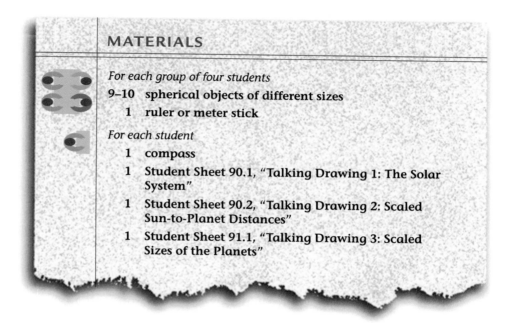

For each group of four students

9–10 spherical objects of different sizes
   1 ruler or meter stick

For each student

   1 compass
   1 Student Sheet 90.1, "Talking Drawing 1: The Solar System"
   1 Student Sheet 90.2, "Talking Drawing 2: Scaled Sun-to-Planet Distances"
   1 Student Sheet 91.1, "Talking Drawing 3: Scaled Sizes of the Planets"

PROCEDURE

Part A: Determining a Scale

1. In your science notebook, make a table like the one below.

Diameter of the Planets

Planet	Actual Diameter of Planet (km)	Scaled Diameter of Planet (cm)	Diameter of Model Object (cm)
Mercury	5,000		
Venus	12,000		
Earth	13,000		
Mars	7,000		
Jupiter	143,000		
Saturn	120,500		
Uranus	51,000		
Neptune	49,500		

2. With your group, decide on a scale for the diameter of the planets. You will use this scale to find objects that represent the size of the planets. Complete Steps 2a–e to make the scale.

   a. Decide how many kilometers a single centimeter will represent. This is the scale.

   b. Convert the diameters of the smallest and largest planets using the scale.

      Hint: Divide the diameter in km by the scale in km to get the diameter in cm.

   c. If either of the scaled diameters is too big or too small for the ordinary spherical objects you have at school and at home, try creating another scale.

   d. Repeat Steps 2a–c until the group agrees that the scale for the size of the smallest and largest planets is reasonable.

   e. Record the scale in your science notebook.

3. Using the scale you made and the data in the table, calculate the scaled diameters of all the planets and record these in your table.

Part B: Making the Model

4. With your group, use your work from Part A to create an accurate model of the planets using round objects you find at home and school. Gather objects that will show the size of each planet compared to sizes of the other planets.

5. Measure the actual diameters of the objects and record them in your table.

ANALYSIS

1. How accurate is your model? Compare the scaled size of each planet to the size of the object you used to show it in your model.

2. The diameter of the Sun is about 1,390,000 km.

   a. Use your scale to convert this diameter to your model.

   b. What object could be used in the model to represent the Sun?

3. Complete Student Sheet 91.1, "Talking Drawing 3: Scaled Sizes of the Planets."

    a. Find a scale that allows you to accurately draw the smallest and largest planets on the paper.

    b. Record the scale on the Student Sheet.

    c. Convert all the diameters of the planets to the model, and record them in the table.

    d. Use a compass to draw the scaled planets as circles inside circles with all planet centers being Point C. To draw each planet, adjust the compass to one half the planet's diameter.

    e. Label each planet with its name and actual diameter.

4. Compare your drawing on Student Sheet 90.1, "Talking Drawing 1: The Solar System," with your drawings on Student Sheet 90.2, "Talking Drawing 2: Scaled Sun-to-Planet Distances," and Student Sheet 91.1, "Talking Drawing 3: Scaled Sizes of the Planets." Describe how your understanding of the Sun-to-planet distances and sizes of the planets has changed.

EXTENSION

With your class, make a physical model of the Solar System that shows both the Sun-to-planet distances and the sizes of the planets.

92 The Nearest Star: The Sun

READING

Without the energy we receive from the Sun, Earth would be a cold, dark, and lifeless place. The Sun provides energy for the growth of plants that support life on Earth and the energy that drives the winds, ocean currents, and the water cycle.

Since ancient times, people have recognized the importance of the Sun as a source of warmth and light. The Sun played a central role in the myths of nearly every ancient culture. People observed the Sun in the sky and used its changing positions to predict seasonal events, such as when to plant and harvest crops.

CHALLENGE

How is the Sun different from other objects in the Solar System?

This 13th century temple in Konarak, Orissa, India is dedicated to the Sun God Surya.

READING

The Sun is a Star

Listen as your teacher reads aloud.

Stop when you see this yellow pencil and close your book.

Write down the main ideas you just heard.

Among the many billions of stars in our galaxy, the Sun is average in size and temperature. When you look at the night sky with your naked eye from anywhere on Earth, you can see up to 8,000 stars. With a telescope you will see many more. Still others can only be detected with other technologies. These have also helped astronomers learn about the composition of the Sun.

The Sun's composition is very different than that of Earth or the other planets, except Jupiter. It is mostly hydrogen and helium mixed together in a high-temperature gas. It varies from 5,000° C at the surface to more than 10,000,000° C at the center. Dark spots on the surface of the Sun, called sunspots, are a little cooler than the rest of the surface.

The Sun, like other stars, releases huge amounts of heat and light energy. This energy is produced by nuclear reactions at the Sun's center. A **nuclear reaction** involves a change in the nuclei (the center) of atoms. In the Sun, these nuclear reactions convert hydrogen to helium through a process known as nuclear fusion. In **nuclear fusion**, smaller atoms combine to form larger atoms. Nuclear fusion reactions release a very large amount of energy in comparison to other kinds of reactions. A hydrogen bomb, the most powerful type of nuclear bomb, uses nuclear fusion to produce more than enough energy to destroy an average sized city. Each second the Sun produces as much energy as millions of hydrogen bombs.

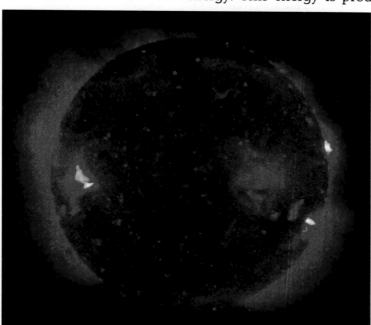

The Sun is the star that is closest to Earth.

The Sun has been producing energy from fusion for 5 billion years. When the hydrogen in the Sun, its nuclear fuel, runs out, it will stop releasing heat and light. But this won't happen anytime soon. The Sun is only about halfway through its 10-billion-year-long life cycle.

How Far and How Big?

If the Sun is an average-sized star, why does it appear so much larger than other stars? Because, of course, it is much closer. To imagine how much closer, you have to think in terms of very large numbers. The Sun is about 150 million km away from Earth, but our next closest star is more than *40 million million* km away or more than 250,000 times farther away.

That the Sun is about 150 million km away means it's far enough that it takes eight minutes for light to travel from the Sun's surface to Earth. If you traveled to the Sun in a regular passenger jet, the trip would take about 20 years!

Peppercorn (Earth)

Bowling ball (Sun)

The size of the Sun is hard to grasp, because it is almost never shown to scale in diagrams. Its diameter is about 1,390,000 km, almost 110 times that of Earth. More than one million Earths could fit inside the Sun. Even Jupiter, the largest planet, is only one-tenth the size of the Sun. If you use a peppercorn to represent Earth as shown at left, the Sun would be about the size of a bowling ball. Using this scale, you would have to place these items about 25 meters (the length of most public swimming pools) apart to show the distance between them.

A researcher in Antarctica sets up a recorder that measures the duration of sunlight.

The Sun at the Center

Today, scientists accept that the Sun is at the center of the Solar System. But early scientists thought that the Sun and other planets orbited Earth. In about 260 BCE, a Greek astronomer and mathematician named Aristarchus may have been the first to argue that Earth orbits the Sun. Most people ignored his ideas for a very long time because other well-known scientists did not accept them. Then, in the 1500s, Polish astronomer Nicolaus Copernicus noticed that he could not explain all his observations of planetary motion by using models with Earth at the center.

Copernicus realized that he could create a simpler model to explain his observations. In his model, shown below, you can see how it revived Aristarchus' idea that Earth and the other planets orbit the Sun. In the 1600s, the Italian astronomer Galileo used his telescope to make many observations that led him to support Copernicus' model. By 1700, most scientists agreed that the Sun was at the center of the Solar System. The model of the Solar System used today includes the planets circling the Sun, and also uses mathematical formulas to help predict the motion of the planets.

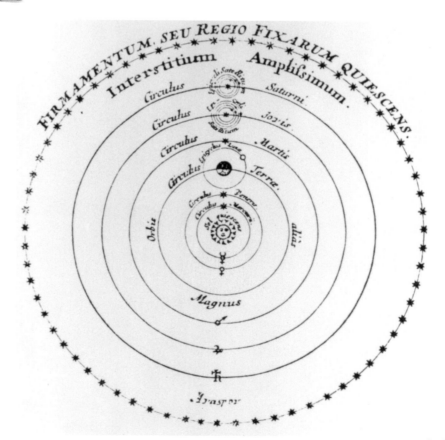

This drawing of Copernicus' model of the Solar System shows the Sun and the planets known at the time. It in written in Latin. Sol means Sun and Terra means Earth.

ANALYSIS

1. How would you explain to a fourth grader why the Sun looks so much bigger than other stars?

2. What is the source of the Sun's energy?

3. **a.** Is the following statement true or false?

   If you used an apple to represent the Sun, you would need to use a grape to represent Earth at the same scale.

   b. Explain your answer.

4. What characteristics of the Sun would make it a difficult place to explore or visit?

5. Why do you think it took a long time for people to accept that Earth and planets orbit the Sun?

No astronaut has ever been to the surface of another planet. In fact, no manufactured object has come within a thousand kilometers of most planets. Some of the planets are so covered with clouds or are so far away, that even the most powerful telescopes can't provide a very good view of them. Yet there are many images of the planets available. Scientists use different kinds of remote sensing methods to gather information about objects that we can't see or that are very distant. **Remote sensing** refers to any procedure that provides information about an object without us touching or directly observing the object.

You and your fellow scientists are using a remote-sensing instrument to get information about the distance from a spacecraft to the surface of a planet. The measurements it takes from space are being sent back to Earth. You would like to use these measurements to make a picture of the surface of the planet.

CHALLENGE

How can you get a picture of a surface you can't see?

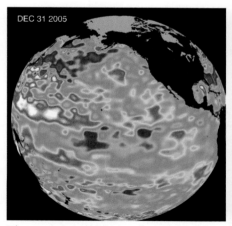

The remote sensing image above shows changes in the height of Earth's ocean. Purple means a drop in ocean height. Green is normal. Red means increased height.

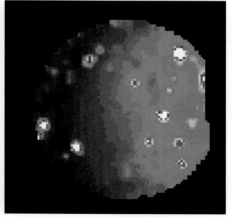

This remote sensing image shows temperature on the surface of Io, Jupiter's largest moon. Red and white show hotter areas. Blue areas are colder. The red spots are volcanoes.

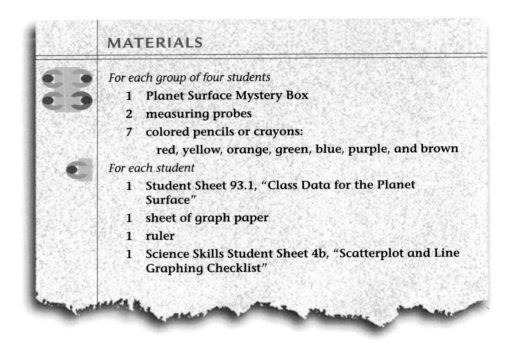

MATERIALS

For each group of four students

- 1 Planet Surface Mystery Box
- 2 measuring probes
- 7 colored pencils or crayons:
  red, yellow, orange, green, blue, purple, and brown

For each student

- 1 Student Sheet 93.1, "Class Data for the Planet Surface"
- 1 sheet of graph paper
- 1 ruler
- 1 Science Skills Student Sheet 4b, "Scatterplot and Line Graphing Checklist"

PROCEDURE

Part A: Sensing the Surface

1. In your science notebook, make a table like the one below.

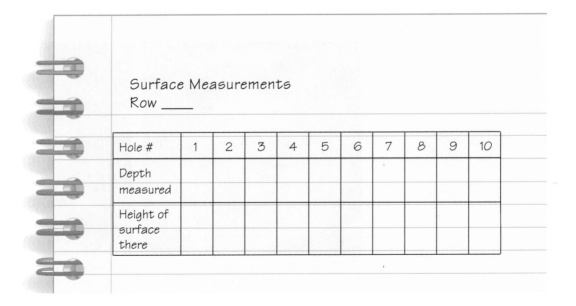

Surface Measurements
Row _____

Hole #	1	2	3	4	5	6	7	8	9	10
Depth measured										
Height of surface there										

2. Your teacher will assign your group one of the rows A–H of the box to investigate. Record the letter of the row in your table. One pair will measure Holes 1–5 in the row. The other pair will measure Holes 6–10 in the row.

3. At each hole, use the probe to measure the depth at that location. Round the measurement to the nearest 0.5 cm, and record it in your table.

   Hint: Make your measurement as soon as your probe touches the surface. Do not slide it farther into the box.

4. Calculate the height of the surface directly beneath each hole by subtracting the depth from the height of the box. Since the height of the box is 10 cm,

   10 cm − depth of hole = height of surface at that location

   Record the results in the bottom row of your table.

5. In your science notebook, use your data to make a line graph of what is inside the box. Label the graph, "Heights in Row ___," inserting the letter for the row you measured.

   Hint: On the horizontal axis, put the data for the hole number. On the vertical axis, put the data for the surface height beneath the hole.

6. In your group discuss the shape of the planet's surface. Describe your part of the surface of the planet based on your data. Record the description in your science notebook.

Part B: Sharing the Data

7. Share your data with the rest of the class. Record all the data on the top half of Student Sheet 93.1, "Class Data for the Planet Surface."

8. Use the key to complete the bottom half of Student Sheet 93.1. Color each square with the appropriate color for its height. In this way, your class data creates a false-color topographical map.

9. Using your false-color topographical map, describe the shape of the surface in the box. Record your ideas in your science notebook.

ANALYSIS

1. In a false-color topographical map, does it matter which color is used for each height?

2. Compare the graph you made in Part A to the false-color topographical map you made in Part B. Did the additional data from your classmates change how you visualized the surface of the planet? Explain how.

3. Look at the maps below. Both are maps of the same area. Map A is a false-color topographical map, and Map B is a lined topographical map.

   a. Describe the surface shown in the map.

   b. What are the advantages of the false-color topographical map?

   c. What are the advantages of the lined topographical map?

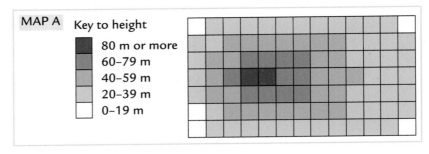

MAP A Key to height
- 80 m or more
- 60–79 m
- 40–59 m
- 20–39 m
- 0–19 m

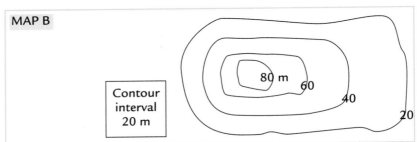

MAP B

Contour interval 20 m

80 m 60 40 20

INVESTIGATION

Remote sensing is a way to measure things that are difficult to see or touch. Scientists may not use wooden probes like the one you used in the last activity, but they use similar methods. For example, one remote sensing method is radar, which uses light waves to explore the surface of an object. The waves are sent toward a distant object, they bounce back, or reflect, from the object, and the roundtrip data is collected. Waves that take longer to return have traveled farther than those that returned sooner.

Waves also change when they are reflected from different materials, such as Earth's forests or rivers. Scientists have programmed computers to analyze the data from the reflected waves and make pictures, maps, and graphs. Because radar can be far away from the object, it is used to get information about hard-to-get-to places such as rain clouds and other planets.

CHALLENGE

What does remote sensing tell us about the surface of Earth and other planets?

This false color map of the New York metropolitan area was taken from a space shuttle using radar.

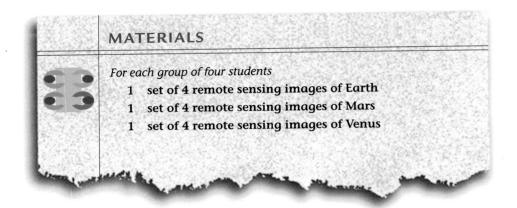

MATERIALS

For each group of four students

1 set of 4 remote sensing images of Earth
1 set of 4 remote sensing images of Mars
1 set of 4 remote sensing images of Venus

PROCEDURE

1. Look carefully at Image 1 for Earth, Mars, and Venus, and identify features that are common to all three planets.

2. In your science notebook, list the features that the three planets have in common. Label the list, "Common Features: Image 1."

3. Repeat Steps 1 and 2 for Images 2–4 for all three planets.

4. In your science notebook, make a table like the one below.

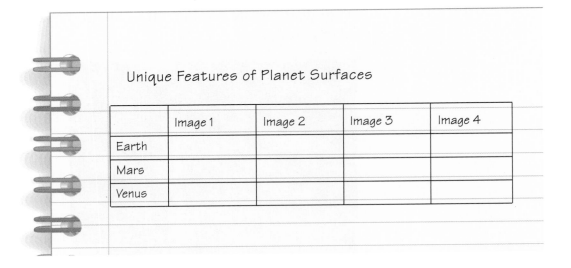

Unique Features of Planet Surfaces

	Image 1	Image 2	Image 3	Image 4
Earth				
Mars				
Venus				

5. Again look carefully at Image 1 for Earth, Mars, and Venus. This time try to find features that make each planet different from the other two. These are its *unique* features.

6. Record those unique features of the planets in your table.

7. Repeat Steps 5 and 6 for Images 2–4 for all three planets.

ANALYSIS

1. What information about the planets that was collected through remote sensing devices:

   a. is shown by these images?

   b. is *not* shown by these images?

2. In these images, how is the surface of Earth:

   a. similar to the other two planets?

   b. different from the other two planets?

3. Look at the image below, made by remote sensing. Can you tell from the surface features what planet it shows? Explain why or why not.

4. How could remote sensing be used to help prepare for a mission to another planet?

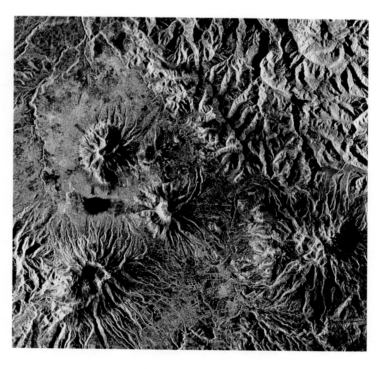

A **force** is any push or pull. The force due to gravity interests astronomers because it is most noticeable with big objects, like stars, and reaches over long distances, such as those between the planets. **Gravity** is a natural phenomenon that causes any two objects to be pulled together. Isaac Newton's inquiry into the effects of gravity led him to determine the universal law of gravitation, which relates the force of gravity to distance and **mass.** Mass is the measurement of the amount of matter or stuff that makes up an object.

Imagine that you are a scientist who has been receiving information from a spacecraft exploring Saturn's rings. The rings reach out from Saturn for 300,000 km and contain particles of ice and rock that range in size from as tiny as a sand grain to as big as a house. Your remote sensing device got information about some of the objects in one of the rings.

CHALLENGE

What determines the amount of gravitational force between objects?

Although they look solid from Earth, Saturn's rings are actually made up of a large number of small particles each in its own orbit.

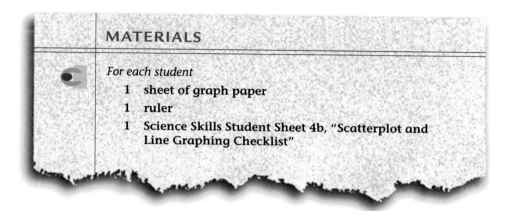

MATERIALS

For each student
1 sheet of graph paper
1 ruler
1 Science Skills Student Sheet 4b, "Scatterplot and Line Graphing Checklist"

PROCEDURE

1. The table below shows the gravitational force between Saturn and some particles in Saturn's rings. All of the particles are the same distance, 180,000 km, from Saturn's center.

Table 1: Mass and Gravitational Force Data	
Mass of Ring Particle (kg)	**Gravitational Force Between Saturn and Ring Particle (in 10,000 N)**
2	23
3	35
4	47
5	58
6	70
7	82
8	93
9	105

2. Use the data in the table to make a graph of the relationship between mass and gravitational force. Label your graph "Mass and Gravitational Force."

   Hint: Put the data for mass on the horizontal axis and the data for gravitational force on the vertical axis.

3. Look at your graphed data, and record in your science notebook any relationship you notice.

4. The table below shows the gravitational force between Saturn and some ring particles that are at different distances from the planet. All of the particles have a mass of 1 kg.

Table 2: Distance and Gravitational Force Data	
Distance of 1-kg Ring Particle from Center of Saturn (in 1,000 km)	Gravitational Force Between Saturn and 1-kg Ring Particle (in 10,000 N)
100	38
120	26
130	22
150	17
180	12
200	9
220	8
250	6
280	5

5. Use the data on the table to make a graph of the relationship between distance and gravitational force. Label your graph "Distance and Gravitational Force."

   Hint: Put the data for distance on the horizontal axis and the data for force on the vertical axis.

6. Look at your graphed data, and record in your science notebook any relationships you notice.

ANALYSIS

1. Compare your two graphs. Identify and explain any:

   a. similarities

   b. differences

2. Look at the pictures of the two planets below. Their diameters are the same, but Planet B has twice the mass of Planet A. Which one would you expect to have a stronger pull of gravity on its surface? Explain.

Planet A   Planet B

3. Look at the picture below of astronauts at different distances from a planet. In which position, A or B, would there be a stronger gravitational pull between the astronaut and the planet? Explain.

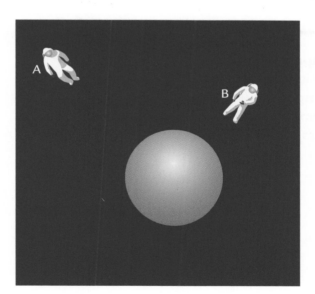

4. Your friend tells you that if you double the distance of a spacecraft from a planet, the gravitational pull is one half as strong. Do you think this is correct? Cite evidence from this investigation to support your position.

EXTENSION

Jupiter has about 300 times the mass of Earth. But gravity at its "surface" is only about three times the gravity on Earth's surface. Look at the Space Object Data Cards for Jupiter and Earth, shown below. Can you explain why the gravitational pull at Jupiter's "surface" is only about three times as much as Earth's?

Space Object 5 (Jupiter)

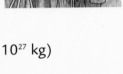

Shape: round
Orbits: the Sun
Composition: gaseous
Diameter: 143,000 km
Mass: 1,900,000,000,000,000,000,000,000,000 kg (1.9×10^{27} kg)
Other: Has rings

Space Object 11 (Earth)

Shape: round
Orbits: the Sun
Composition: rocky
Diameter: 12,800 km
Mass: 6,000,000,000,000,000,000,000,000 kg (6.0×10^{24} kg)

READING

The force of gravity holds us on Earth and helps objects in space stay in orbit. The planets in the Solar System could not continue to orbit the Sun without the force of gravity. Astronauts need to know a lot about gravity when they travel in space because they often orbit Earth. Those controlling the flight of any spacecraft must consider the effects of gravity from Earth and other planets on the spacecraft's course and safety.

CHALLENGE

How does gravity affect space travel?

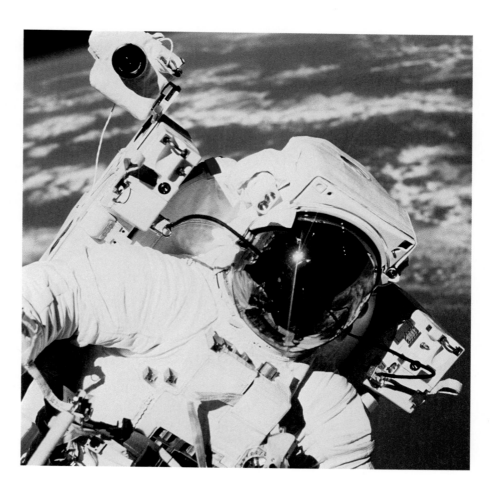

The pull of gravity between this astronaut and Earth keeps him in orbit.

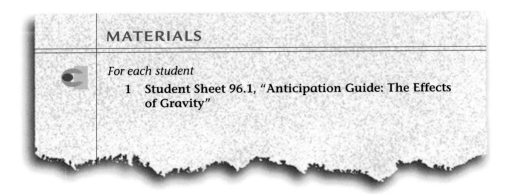

MATERIALS

For each student

1 Student Sheet 96.1, "Anticipation Guide: The Effects of Gravity"

READING

Complete Student Sheet 96.1, "Anticipation Guide: Gravity" to help prepare for the following reading.

Direction of Gravity

Gravity is a force that pulls any two objects toward each other. You are familiar with gravity as the force that pulls things down toward Earth.

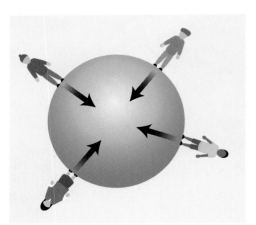

But when considering Earth as a planet, which direction is "down?" Look at the diagram at left, which shows people standing on the surface of the Earth. "Down" is a different direction at different locations on the surface, but "down" is always the direction toward the center of Earth. Gravity always pulls the center of two objects toward each other.

STOPPING TO THINK 1

Argentina and Japan are on exactly opposite sides of the globe. Is "down" in Japan the same direction as "down" in Argentina? Explain.

Strength of Gravity—Mass and Distance

The strength of the force of gravity between two objects depends on the mass of the two objects and the distance between them.

All things with mass exert a gravitational pull on other objects with mass. The more mass an object has, the stronger it pulls. Earth is the most massive object near us, and so it has a strong attractive force. This is why things fall down toward Earth, specifically the center of Earth.

But, strange as it may sound, while Earth pulls on an object near it, the object also pulls Earth. When an object falls to the ground, even a paper clip, for example, Earth is pulled toward the falling object. This is because the falling object has mass, and any object with mass exerts a gravitational force on any other object. In the case of an object falling to Earth, however, the Earth moves much less than the object does, because Earth has so much more mass than the falling object.

The force of gravity near other planets is different than it is near Earth because each planet has a different mass. An object's **weight** on Earth is the pull of gravity between it and Earth. If the object is on another planet or moon, its weight is the force of gravity between it and the planet or moon. For example, Jupiter's gravitational pull is stronger than Earth's because Jupiter has more mass than Earth. A 10-kg rock on Earth would still have 10 kg of mass near Jupiter, but the rock's weight would be three times greater near Jupiter.

STOPPING TO THINK 2

Why do astronauts have the same mass on the Moon as they do on Earth, but weigh less on the Moon?

The reduced weight of this astronaut made him bounce when he walked on the Moon. In this television picture from a Moon landing, the astronaut jumped high as he saluted the flag.

Across a very long distance, gravity pulled these two galaxies toward each other.

When an object near Earth drops, it falls toward Earth instead of toward a more massive object, such as Jupiter or the Sun. This means the force of gravity must be determined by something more than mass. As you saw in the last activity, the farther away an object is from a planet, the weaker the gravitational force between them. The opposite is also true—the closer two objects are, the stronger the gravitational force between them. You may not have realized it, but you weigh slightly less when you are in an airplane flying high above Earth because you are farther from the center of Earth. A 150-pound person weighs about one-half pound less while flying in an airplane. Similarly, since the Sun is so far away, its gravitational pull on objects near Earth is not as strong as Earth's, even though it has much more mass than Earth.

Although the pull of an object's gravity decreases as you move farther away from it, gravity never entirely disappears. There is always a gravitational attraction between the centers of two objects, no matter how far apart they are. The long reach of gravity is an important consideration for space travel. When a spacecraft is launched, it only needs to use fuel until it gets so far away from Earth that Earth's gravity has very little effect on it. Beyond that point, it travels without using any fuel at all (except when it needs to slow down or turn). If it gets close enough to another planet, the Moon, or the Sun, the gravitational force between the two will increase and the spacecraft will be pulled toward that object.

STOPPING TO THINK 3

a. Would you expect to weigh more on an ocean beach or on top of a mountain? Explain.

b. Outside the Solar System is there any gravitational pull from the Sun?

Gravity and Orbiting Objects

Since Earth's gravity pulls everything down toward its center, why don't satellites and even the Moon come crashing down to Earth? Strange as it may seem, gravity helps satellites and the Moon stay in orbit around Earth.

Imagine throwing a ball as fast as you can. It might go 30 meters before it hits the ground. The ball curves as it falls because the force of gravity is pulling it down as it travels. Next, imagine that you have a cannon on the top of a tall tower as in the diagram below. Your cannonball might go quite a distance before it hits the ground (Path A). Now, imagine that you have a cannon that can fire a cannonball faster. It would travel much farther before falling to the ground (Path B). If you could keep firing cannonballs at higher and higher speeds, eventually one would go fast enough that it would "fall" all the way around Earth, but never hit the ground (Path C). An orbiting object is being pulled down by gravity, but it is going fast enough that it never actually hits the ground. If a satellite, or even the Moon, were not moving fast enough, it would begin to spiral back to Earth.

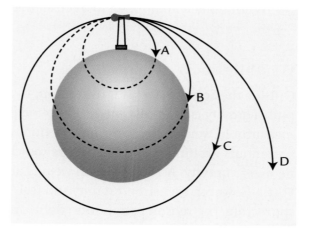

A & B: Speed too slow:
Satellite falls back to Earth because "orbit" is too small.

C: Speed just right:
Satellite stays in orbit around Earth.

D: Speed too fast:
Satellite goes beyond orbit and does not return.

When a spacecraft is launched, launch speed is very important. If the speed is too low, it will fall back to Earth like the cannonball in Path A. If the speed is just right, it will go into orbit. If the speed is greater than what is needed for the spacecraft to get into orbit, it can break away from Earth's gravity. This is how spacecraft are sent to the Moon, Mars, or farther.

A rocket is launched from the Kennedy Space Center, Cape Canaveral, Florida.

STOPPING TO THINK 4

What is likely to happen to a rocket that takes off at a slow speed?

Weightlessness

Outside the Solar System, far away from the Sun and any planets, the pull of gravity is so small that a 150-pound person would not have any measurable weight at all. So far, no human has ever gone that far. Astronauts orbiting around Earth are too close to Earth to experience near-zero gravity. A 150-lb person weighs about 136 lbs while orbiting Earth. However, an astronaut may still feel "weightless" in an orbiting spacecraft. The reason astronauts "float" in space is not because they there is no force of gravity. Instead, they "float" because they are moving in an orbit. As they move along the path of the orbit, the spacecraft and the astronauts on board are constantly falling towards Earth due to the pull of gravity. This free falling makes astronauts appear to be floating.

The astronauts' weightlessness is the same as you feel for a moment when you're on a rollercoaster and your car plunges down a steep slope. Both your body and the rollercoaster car are free-falling together, just like the astronaut in a spacecraft. You can experience "weightlessness" yourself if a gravitational force pulls on you but you are not held up by a surface, as shown below.

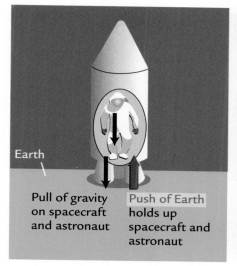

On Earth's surface, the Earth pushes the spacecraft and astronaut up just as much as the gravitational force pulls them down.

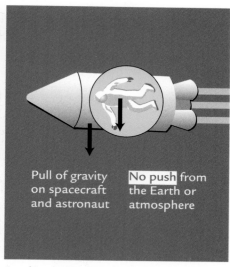

In orbit, the Earth and its atmosphere are not pushing up. The spacecraft and astronaut fall freely and experience "weightlessness."

STOPPING TO THINK 5

How is going over the top of a rollercoaster like experiencing "weightlessness" in space?

ANALYSIS

Object	Mass*
Mercury	0.055
Venus	0.86
Earth	1.00
Mars	0.11
Jupiter	318
Saturn	95
Uranus	14.5
Neptune	17.2
Sun	330,000
Moon	0.01

relative to Earth

1. Choose one of the objects listed in the table to the right. Describe how astronauts' weights might change if they visited the object.

2. Your friend tells you that there is no gravity in the space shuttle, which orbits at 400 km (250 miles) above Earth. Do you agree or disagree? Explain.

3. What do you think would happen to a satellite in orbit if it suddenly stopped? Explain.

ROLE PLAY

The National Aeronautics and Space Administration (NASA) has a yearly budget of about $15 billion for space exploration. Although this is a lot of money, it is not enough to fund every project that NASA scientists propose. To help NASA administrators decide which exploration projects to fund, they sometimes listen to recommendations from a panel of space flight experts.

CHALLENGE

What types of space exploration should NASA fund?

"There is nothing like take-off. It's terrifying, exhilarating, emotional. When the two rockets on either side ignite, you know you are going someplace! If you aren't scared, you don't understand what's about to happen." Sally Kristen Ride, the first American woman in space.

"When the images came down and we could see horizon all the way around, that was every bit as exhilarating as getting to the top of any mountain I've climbed on Earth." Chris Leger, Mars Rover engineer.

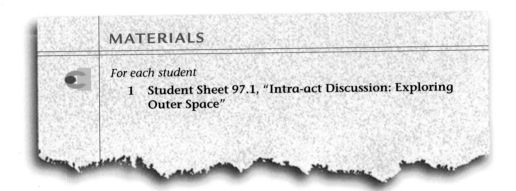

MATERIALS

For each student
1   **Student Sheet 97.1, "Intra-act Discussion: Exploring Outer Space"**

PROCEDURE

1. Assign one of the following roles to each person in your group.

    - Greta Puzon, administrator

    - Kato Barre, astronaut

    - Wanda Keller, aerospace engineer

    - Dr. Owen Rowley, NASA medical doctor

2. In your group, read the role-play aloud. As you read, think about what each character is saying.

3. Discuss which types of space exploration should take place in the future.

4. Mark whether you agree or disagree with the statements on Student Sheet 97.1, "Intra-act Discussion: Exploring Outer Space." Predict what you think other members of your group will say.

5. Discuss the statements with your group. Have each person share his or her opinion about each statement and explain why he or she agreed or disagreed.

EXPLORING OUTER SPACE

Greta: Good morning. I've asked you to come here today to talk about which types of space exploration missions we should include in this year's budget.

Before we begin, please introduce yourself and tell us a little about your background. Kato, will you begin?

Kato: Good morning. I am Kato Barre, an American astronaut. I have spent 184 days on the International Space Station. While in space, I conducted biology and physics experiments in a reduced-gravity environment.

Wanda: Hello. My name is Wanda Keller, and I am an aerospace engineer who specializes in space rover design. I design, build, and test robotic vehicles that will one day visit the surfaces of other planets.

Owen: And I am Owen Rowley, a medical doctor for NASA's astronaut program. I am part of a medical team that watches the health of the astronauts from the beginning of their training, through their flights, and for some time after they have returned safely to Earth. I also conduct medical research based on data collected from human space flights.

Greta: Thank you for the introductions. Kato, as someone who has traveled in space, would you tell us about the most exciting part of that experience?

Kato: Ah, I would have to say that seeing the beautiful blue Earth from such a great distance was a tremendous personal experience. In terms of science, we learned a lot about the effects of a "weightless" environment by being in space. We learned, for example, how muscles lose mass and bones get weaker when they don't have to work against the same force of gravity we have on Earth.

Greta: Humans have been in orbit around Earth and have walked on the Moon. The space shuttle orbits about 350 miles above the surface of

Planet Earth as viewed from space.

Earth, and the Moon is about 239,000 miles from Earth. Wanda, do you think we will see a piloted space flight to somewhere farther—namely, another planet?

Wanda: Yes, I hope so. Although Venus is closer, Mars would be the most likely planet for a piloted visit. In comparison to the Moon, Mars is almost 150 times as far away, at 35 million miles when it is closest to Earth. Right now, it is not possible for humans to take such a long trip through space. Our technology cannot yet support and protect humans on such a long trip.

Kato: I'd like to expand on that. Part of the challenge of a long trip to a planet is that supplies could not be sent to the faraway spacecraft. Everything needed for the entire mission would have to be packed on board. This extra cargo weight demands that we have stronger, heavier rockets and more fuel to power them. This adds more risk and cost to the mission.

Owen: Not to mention the risk to the astronauts' health because of such a long mission. Without the protection of an atmosphere, astronauts are exposed to a tremendous amount of harmful radiation from the Sun. Solar shields on space suits and radiation-resistant materials block out only a portion of the radiation from the Sun.

In addition, as Kato described, muscles and bones weaken. Even the heart, which is a muscle, gets weaker because it is not constantly working against as much gravity. Exercise helps the astronauts minimize this effect but, even so, on a long trip they still lose strength. The longer the mission, the greater the permanent loss.

Greta: Are you saying you don't think piloted flights are worth the dangers they present to people?

Owen: No, not at all. Even though there are dangers involved to individuals, the work of scientists and

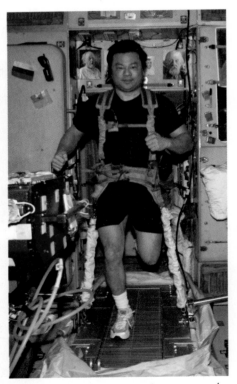

An American astronaut exercises on a treadmill using a bungee cord harness aboard the International Space Station.

engineers in space exploration has given us a tremendous amount of scientific information. Technology for the space program has been led to improvements in such medical devices as pacemakers, ultrasound, and CT scanners. These tools have advanced the treatment of disease, and have helped many lives here on Earth.

Kato: I agree. There is certainly more risk and cost involved when you send humans into space. But throughout history, women and men have gone on dangerous adventures and taken extreme risks.

A Japanese astronaut participates in a space suit fit check.

Wanda: I don't think we need to take those risks. Satellites and probes can travel greater distances for longer periods of time than astronauts can. And we are constantly improving the types of instruments that are placed on rovers, landers, and satellites to collect data.

Greta: But can instruments take the place of humans conducting complicated experiments?

Wanda: Well, let me respond with an example. The rovers that went to Mars have a rock abrasion tool (RAT), which works like a robot. Scientists on Earth can make the rover drive up to a rock on Mars and extend the RAT to drill into the surface. The rover then takes a picture of the inside of the rock, which is then sent to Earth for analysis. We haven't been able to send an actual geologist to the surface of Mars, but these pictures are getting us close.

Kato: Unpiloted missions certainly make sense for exploring the outer planets. Even if we were able to send a piloted craft to the outer Solar System, it would be decades before a human could reach Pluto. Unpiloted missions allow us to gather information for many more years and from much more distant parts of the Solar System, because we don't have to bring them home.

Greta: What types of missions would you like to see NASA fund in the future?

Owen: I think it's important to develop technology that will allow us to travel farther and live in harsh environments unlike those on our own planet. I hope that someday spacecrafts will carry humans to greater distances in space and also help us conduct more research on the human body. In this way, piloted space exploration helps both research on space and people here at home.

Kato: We have not landed on the Moon since 1972. I think we should again send missions to the Moon and build a complete space station there. This would allow astronaut crews to spend extended time in space and possibly use the Moon as a launching pad for explorations to other planets, like Mars.

Wanda: Unpiloted space flight is the future for exploring other planets. Although astronauts can perform complex experiments that machines cannot, it is simply not efficient or worth the risk. For less money and less development time, unpiloted spacecraft can perform important tests about the composition, gravity, and environment of other planets.

Greta: I want to thank you for taking the time to come together to share your expertise with us. I will use your information to help me put together this year's proposed budget.

In 2004, this probe left the Cassini spacecraft, entered Saturn's atmosphere, and parachuted to its surface.

ANALYSIS

1. Construct two tables in your science notebook like the ones below. Use the information presented in the role-play to complete the tables on the advantages and disadvantages of:

   a. unpiloted space exploration

   b. piloted space exploration

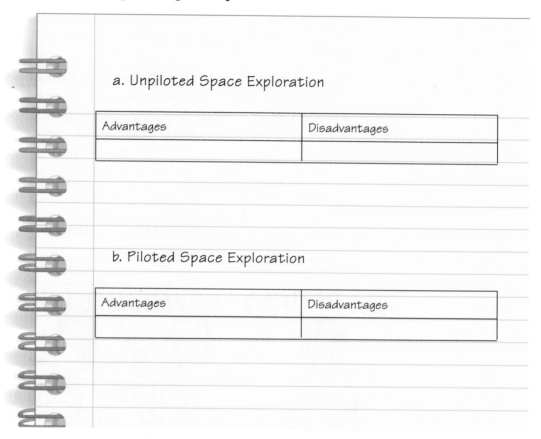

a. Unpiloted Space Exploration

Advantages	Disadvantages

b. Piloted Space Exploration

Advantages	Disadvantages

2. **Reflection:** If you had the opportunity, would you go on a mission into outer space? Explain why or why not.

EXTENSION

Visit the *Issues and Earth Science* page of the SEPUP website for links to information about what it would be like to travel into space as an astronaut. Describe the living conditions in a spacecraft. What does it take to become an astronaut?

There has been a lot of debate about whether piloted spacecraft should return to the Moon or travel even farther to other planets. After nearly 50 years of spaceflight, the future of space exploration remains uncertain. Now that you know much more about the Solar System and space exploration, you are better able to make an informed decision about future space missions.

You and your classmates are participating in a National Government Council meeting to discuss this year's budget for space exploration. The government has set aside money to pay for one new space mission. As members of the Council, you have to decide which mission to fund.

CHALLENGE

What kinds of future space missions should we conduct?

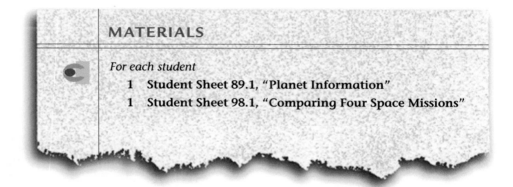

MATERIALS

For each student
1   Student Sheet 89.1, "Planet Information"
1   Student Sheet 98.1, "Comparing Four Space Missions"

PROCEDURE

1. Read about four proposed space missions on the next page.

2. Review Student Sheet 89.1, "Planet Information."

3. Use Student Sheet 89.1, and anything else you have learned in this unit to evaluate the missions with your group. Discuss how you think the money should be spent by studying the following about each mission:

   • what scientists can learn on the mission

   • what makes the mission interesting

   • special challenges to the mission

4. Compare the missions by completing Student Sheet 98.1, "Comparing Four Space Missions." In the last column of the table, rank on a scale of 1 to 4 how much you support each mission, with 1 indicating the most support and 4 indicating the least support.

5. With your group of four students, come to an agreement about which mission the money should fund. Support your ideas with the information about the planets and the missions.

   • Remember to listen to and consider the ideas of other members of your group.

   • If you disagree with others in your group, explain why you disagree.

6. Present your recommendation to the class.

Mission Proposal A

Destination: Kuiper Belt

Type of mission: unpiloted

Estimated travel time (one way): 16 years

Unlike previous missions to the outer Solar System, the spacecraft for this one will carry a lander that will go to Pluto and take samples of the surface rocks. The spacecraft will also have the best remote sensing instruments possible. The instruments will send back information on all the planets the spacecraft passes along the way. The spacecraft will continue into the Kuiper Belt and visit other objects beyond Pluto. The data gathered could help us better understand what it is like at the edge of the Solar System.

Mission Proposal B

Destination: Mars

Type of mission: piloted

Estimated travel time (one way): 8 months

This mission is different than previous missions to Mars because it will be piloted. Mars is Earth's closest neighbor in the Solar System so it is reasonable for a piloted flight to get there. Mars is the most important place to visit because it has the possibility of having supported life. It may have had water in the past. The best way to find out as much as we can is to send people there and bring rock samples back to Earth.

Mission Proposal C

Destination: Titan, Saturn's largest moon

Type of mission: unpiloted

Estimated travel time (one way): 4 years

Titan has an atmosphere, and some people suspect it may even have water. The mission's rover will explore the surface of Titan and look for water. And since Titan orbits Saturn, the instruments on the lander will use remote sensing to provide detailed pictures and composition data of Saturn and its rings. As a "gas planet," Saturn doesn't have a solid surface. The pictures would help us know what a gas planet looks like up close.

Mission Proposal D

Destination: the Moon

Type of mission: piloted

Estimated travel time (one way): 10 hours

The goal of this mission is to establish a base on the Moon. Before sending astronauts on a long mission to another planet, we need to make sure that they will be as safe as possible. The base on the Moon will allow us to test out new equipment in a lower-gravity situation. It will also let us learn more about the effects on the body of living in space for a long time. This will prepare us for piloted missions to farther places, and may provide a place for future colonization.

ANALYSIS

1. What other information do you wish you had known before making a final decision?

2. Write a letter to the National Government Council stating your recommendation for which of the four missions to fund. Convince the council with evidence you gathered in this activity and unit. Be sure to present the trade-offs of your recommendation.

EXTENSION

Space missions that are going on now are described on the NASA website. Research one of these current missions. Describe the goals of the mission, the spacecraft, measuring devices used, and what scientists are learning during the exploration.

INDEX

CREDITS

Abbreviations: t (top), m (middle), b (bottom), l (left), r (right), c (center)

All illustrations by Seventeenth Street Studios / Valerie Winemiller.

Cover (front): volcano: Photodisc / Getty Images; magnifiers and rocks: LabAids®, Inc.; (back): student hands: Lab-Aids®, Inc.

"Problem Solving" icon photo: ©Thom Lang / Corbis
"Talking It Over" icon photo: ©Michael Keller / Corbis

UNIT G
Unit Title (G1) Photodisc / Getty Images; Unit opener (G2, G3) tl: Cassini Imaging Team, Cassini Project, NASA; tr: Photodisc / Getty Images; ml, mr: NASA; b: NASA / JPL-Caltech / Cornell; G4 tl: Keystone / Stringer / Getty Images; tr, bl, bc, br: NASA; G9 all: Photodisc / Getty Images; G13 tl: SPL / Photo Researchers, Inc.; tr: Gianni Tortoli / Photo Researchers, Inc.; b: Courtesy of the Archives, California Institute of Technology; G14 t: Courtesy of the Archives, California Institute of Technology; b: Margaret Bourke-White / Time & Life Pictures / Getty Images; G15 t: Harvard College Observatory / Photo Researchers, Inc; b: NASA; G17 Photodisc / Getty Images; G24 Spencer Grant / Photo Researchers, Inc.; G27 tl: ©Corbis; tr: Antonio M Rosario / The Image Bank / Getty Images; bl: Photodisc / Getty Images; br: Space Frontiers / Getty Images; G32 John Henry Claude Wilson / Robert Harding World Imagery / Getty Images; G33 Photodisc / Getty Images; G34 British Antarctic Survey / Photo Researchers, Inc.; G35 Dr. Jeremy Burgess / Photo Researchers, Inc.; G37 l: NASA / JPL Ocean Surface Topography Team; r: NASA / JPL / University of Arizona; G41 NASA / JPL; G43 Photodisc / Getty Images; G44 Photodisc / Getty Images; G49 Photodisc / Getty Images; G51 NASA; G52 NASA / The Hubble Heritage Team / STScI / AURA; G54 NASA; G57 l: Frederic Lewis / Getty Images; r: NASA / JPL; G59 Photodisc / Getty Images; G60 NASA; G61 NASA G62 NASA / JPL; G66 t: Dr. R. Albrecht, ESA / ESO Space Telescope European Coordinating Facility / NASA; b: Photodisc / Getty Images; G67 t: NASA, ESA and Erich Karkoschka (University of Arizona); b: Photodisc / Getty Images.

ISSUES
&Physical Science

ENERGY

SCIENCE™
EDUCATION FOR
PUBLIC
UNDERSTANDING
PROGRAM

UNIVERSITY OF CALIFORNIA AT BERKELEY
LAWRENCE HALL OF SCIENCE

LAB-AIDS
INCORPORATED
RONKONKOMA, NEW YORK

This book is part of SEPUP's middle school science course sequence:

Issues and Earth Science

Studying Soils Scientifically
Rocks and Minerals
Erosion and Deposition
Plate Tectonics
Weather and Atmosphere
The Earth in Space
Exploring the Solar System

Issues and Life Science

Experimental Design: Studying People Scientifically
Body Works
Cell Biology and Disease
Genetics
Ecology
Evolution
Bioengineering

Issues and Physical Science

Studying Materials Scientifically
The Chemistry of Materials
Water
Energy
Force and Motion

Additional SEPUP instructional materials include:
CHEM-2 (Chemicals, Health, Environment and Me): Grades 4–6
SEPUP Modules: Grades 7–12
Science and Sustainability: Course for Grades 9–12
Science and Global Issues Biology: Course for Grades 9–12

This material is based upon work supported by the National Science Foundation under Grants No. 9252906 and No. 0099265. Any opinions, findings, and conclusions or recommendations expressed in this material are those of the authors and do not necessarily reflect the views of the National Science Foundation.

SEPUP
Lawrence Hall of Science
University of California at Berkeley
Berkeley CA 94720-5200

e-mail: sepup@berkeley.edu
Website: www.sepuplhs.org

Published by:

17 Colt Court
Ronkonkoma NY 11779
Website: www.lab-aids.com

A Letter to *Issues and Physical Science* Students

As you examine the activities in this book, you may wonder, "Why does this book look so different from other science books I've seen?" The reason is simple: it is a different kind of science program, and only some of what you will learn can be seen by leafing through this book!

Issues and Physical Science uses several kinds of activities to teach science. For example, you will observe and test the properties of elements and compounds. You will model the atoms and molecules that make up these substances. You will design and conduct investigations to explore energy transfer. You will investigate the motion of a cart on a ramp, and apply what you learn to the physics of automobile accidents and safety features. A combination of laboratories, investigations, readings, models, debates, role plays, and projects will help you uncover the nature of science and the relevance of physical science to your interests.

You will find that important scientific ideas come up again and again in different activities throughout the book. You will be expected to do more than just memorize these concepts: you will be asked to explain and apply them. In particular, you will improve your decision-making skills by using evidence to weigh outcomes and to decide what you think should be done about the scientific issues facing our society.

How do we know that this is a good way for you to learn? In general, research on science education supports it. In particular, the activities in this book were tested by hundreds of students and their teachers, and then modified on the basis of their feedback. In a sense, this entire book is the result of an investigation: we had people test our ideas, we interpreted the results, and we then revised our ideas! We believe the result will show you that learning more about science is important, enjoyable, and relevant to your life.

SEPUP Staff

ISSUES & PHYSICAL SCIENCE PROJECT

Director (2003–2007): Barbara Nagle

Director (2001–2002): Herbert D. Thier

Unit D Authors

Janet Bellantoni
Lee Trampleasure
Donna Markey
Daniel Seaver

OTHER CONTRIBUTORS

Kathy Burke, Sara Dombkowski, Kate Haber, Manisha Hariani, Laura Lenz, Barbara Nagle

We would also like to thank everyone who contributed to the first edition of *Issues, Evidence, and You,* especially Robert Horvat, Mark Koker, Mike Reeske, Stephen Rutherford, Herbert D. Thier, and Mark Wilson and staff from the Berkeley Evaluation and Research (BEAR) Center, Graduate School of Education, University of California at Berkeley.

CONTENT AND SCIENTIFIC REVIEW

Dr. Chinh Nguyen, Lick-Wilmerding High School, San Francisco, California

Dr. Scott Randol, Lawrence Hall of Science, University of California, Berkeley

PRODUCTION

Production Coordinator: Ayse Frosina
SEPUP Publications Coordinator: Miriam Shein
Design and Composition: Seventeenth Street Studios
Photo Research: Seventeenth Street Studios
Editing: Trish Beall
Administrative Assistance: Roberta Smith, Ezequiel Gonzalez

FIELD TEST CENTERS

This course is a revision of *Issues, Evidence and You.* The following centers participated in field testing the original course or the revised materials. We are extremely grateful to the center directors and teachers who taught the program. These teachers and their students contributed significantly to improving the course.

IEY CENTERS

Alaska: Donna York (Director), Kim Bunselmeyer, Linda Churchill, James Cunningham, Patty Dietderich, Lori Gillam, Gina Ireland-Kelly, Mary Klopfer, Jim Petrash, Amy Spargo

California–San Bernardino County: Dr. Herbert Brunkhorst (Director), William Cross, Alan Jolliff, Kimberly Michael, Chuck Schindler

Contents

Energy

D

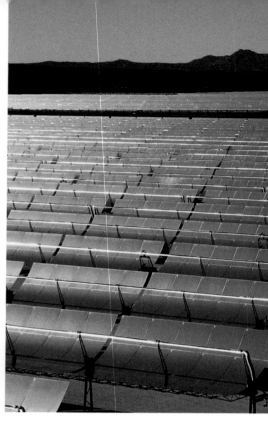

Energy

Van watched Diego take a strange palm-sized device out of his backpack. "Hey Diego, what is that?"

"It's my solar charger. My cell phone is dead and I need to recharge it."

As Diego unfolded a small plastic case with black panels inside it, Van said, "*That* can charge a phone? Wow, that's cool. How does it work?"

"Well, these solar panels absorb the Sun's energy and make electricity out of it," explained Diego as he connected the charger to his cell phone. "It's great because I don't have to plug the phone into the wall. I can charge it outside."

"Looks expensive," said Van. How'd you get it?"

"It didn't cost that much so I bought it with my allowance. I found it on-line one day when I was supposed to be doing my homework. Compared with plugging the phone into the wall, it cost money to start. But soon it saved more money than I paid and from now on it won't cost anything to charge my phone. The sun gives free energy! My parents like that they don't pay to charge my phone on their electric bill."

"Does it run on batteries?" asked Van.

"No, it runs on sunlight," said Diego. "It works pretty well and is better for the environment."

Van wasn't exactly sure what Diego meant when he said that the solar panels were better for the environment. He wondered why it made a difference where the electricity came from. He wondered how the energy supplied by the sun was the same or different than the energy supplied by a battery.

• • •

In this unit, you will learn about the transfer and transformation of energy in our everyday lives. By exploring how energy can be used more efficiently at home, you will learn the answers to some puzzling questions: Where does all the energy around us come from? Are there different types? Does it ever run out? How does it get from one place to another?

Yasmin and her mother examined the form that came with their new water heater. "Look," said Yasmin, "We can get a huge rebate!"

Her mother looked more carefully at the paper. "You're right, our water heater qualifies because it is more energy efficient than our old one."

As Yasmin's mother sat down and started to fill out the form, Yasmin read over the accompanying flyer. Something caught her attention again. "Mom, did you know that there is a free service that will come here and tell us how to save even more energy?"

"Oh that would be great," said Yasmin's mother. "Last winter we had a pretty high electricity bill. I don't want to waste my hard-earned money if I don't have to."

CHALLENGE   **What does it take to reduce energy use in a home?**

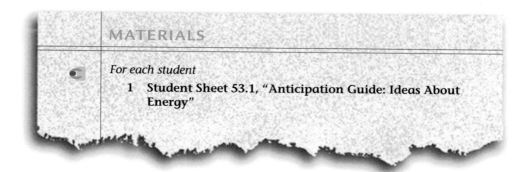

MATERIALS

For each student

1   Student Sheet 53.1, "Anticipation Guide: Ideas About Energy"

PROCEDURE

1. In your group, brainstorm a list of typical household activities where you see energy in use.

2. Put your list in order, from the most to least energy used in a typical home during one year.

3. Look at the table on the next page related to two homes that are similar in size but located in different parts of the country.

4. For each of the home features, explain as best you can how that feature is related to the energy consumption in the home.

5. Compare the data for Home A and Home B on the next page. For each home feature, decide which house you think consumes less energy. Record your ideas for each home in your science notebook.

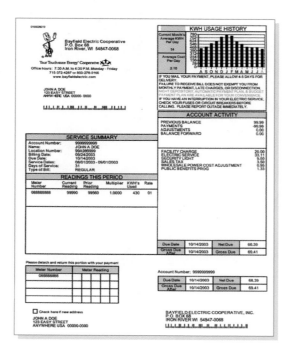

Local utility companies charge residents monthly for electricity and other energy uses.

Comparing Energy Use in Two Similar Homes		
Home feature	**Home A, Texas**	**Home B, New York**
Heating source	Oil	Natural gas
Cooling source	Electricity	Electricity
Insulation	Ceiling	Exterior walls, ceiling
Window type	10 single pane	5 single pane, 3 double pane
Window treatment	Reflective film	No treatment
Hot water heater	Electric	Natural gas
Air conditioning	Central	1 high-efficiency window unit
Appliances	3 high efficiency, 3 not high efficiency	5 high efficiency
Lightbulbs	10 incandescent	3 incandescent, 8 compact fluorescent
Nearby vegetation	Grass	Tall shrubbery, maple trees

Home A, Texas

Home B, New York

ANALYSIS

1. How do the climates of the two home locations influence the energy used in the homes?

2. In the context of this activity, what does the term "energy efficient" mean? Explain, and give an example from this activity.

3. If the people who live in homes A and B have similar lifestyles, which home do you think uses less energy in a year? Use data from the table to support your choice.

4. What could be done to reduce the energy needs of:

   a. Home A?

   b. Home B?

5. **Reflection:** What steps have you and your family taken to reduce energy use in your home?

LABORATORY

Yasmin spent part of the morning helping her mother install weather stripping at the bottom of the doors to the outside of their house. When they finished, they started talking about energy. Yasmin knew from school that **energy** can cause objects to change, move, or work. Yasmin's mom was thinking about how energy moved through the house. She told Yasmin that energy is observable when it moves from one place or object to another. "Like when the oil in the furnace is burned and energy is released. Or when I swing this hammer," she said. "The energy from my hand is transferred to the hammer and then to the nail."

Energy appears in many ways. **Potential energy** is stored energy that has not yet been used, such as energy stored in the oil in the furnace, the built-up electron charge on your clothes, or a rubber band that is fully stretched. When potential energy is due to an object's position above the earth, such as how high a hammer is held, it is called **gravitational potential energy**. When an object is moving, it has **kinetic energy**. For example, a faster-moving hammer has more kinetic energy when it hits a nail than a slower one.

CHALLENGE ⟹ **How does the height and mass of an object affect its gravitational potential energy?**

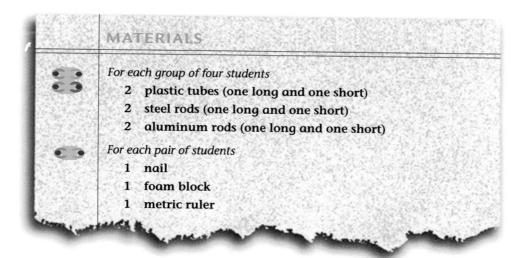

MATERIALS

For each group of four students

  2 **plastic tubes (one long and one short)**

  2 **steel rods (one long and one short)**

  2 **aluminum rods (one long and one short)**

For each pair of students

  1 **nail**

  1 **foam block**

  1 **metric ruler**

SAFETY

Nails are sharp and can cause injury if misused. Follow the safety precautions your teacher demonstrates.

PROCEDURE

1. Look at the metal rods. Record the similarities and differences between them in your science notebook. Be as specific as you can about each rod.

2. Look at the plastic tubes. Record the similarities and differences between them in your science notebook. Be as specific as you can about each tube.

3. Design an experiment that will determine which combination of plastic tubes (long, short) and metal rods (long, short) transfers the *most* and the *least* energy to the nail.

    When designing your experiment, think about these questions:

    What is the purpose of your experiment?

    What variable are you testing?

    What is your hypothesis?

    What variables will you keep the same?

    What is your control?

    How many trials will you conduct?

    Will you collect qualitative or quantitative data or both? How will the data help you form a conclusion?

    How will you record the data?

4. Record your hypothesis and your planned experimental procedure in your science notebook.

5. Make a data table that has space for all the data you need to record during the experiment.

6. Obtain your teacher's approval of your experiment.

7. Conduct your experiment, and record your results.

ANALYSIS

 1. Which combination of tube height and rod mass transferred the most and least energy to the nail? Explain the evidence you gathered to make this conclusion.

2. Where was the rod located when there was the most:

   a. gravitational potential energy?

   b. kinetic energy?

3. Do you think that all the energy from the rod transferred to the nail? Describe any evidence that showed it did or did not.

4. How do the following variables affect how much energy is transferred to the nail?

   a. Mass of the rod

   b. Height of the rod

   c. Shape of the rod

5. In the situation shown below, how much gravitational potential and kinetic energy does the block have at each position?

a. When released from rest:
   Potential energy = 100 J
   Kinetic energy   = _____

b. Halfway down:
   Potential energy = _____
   Kinetic energy   = _____

c. Just before it hits:
   Potential energy = 0
   Kinetic energy   = _____

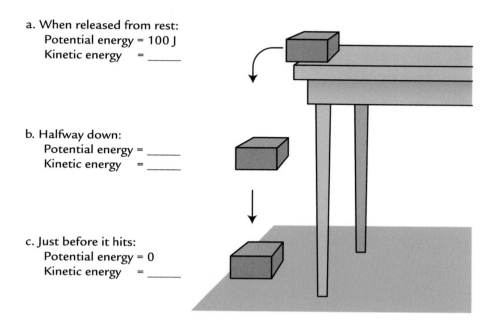

ROLE PLAY

Energy is **transferred** when it moves from one place to another, as in the last activity when the energy from the rod was transferred to the nail. Energy is **transformed** when it changes from one type to another. In the last activity, the gravitational potential of the rod when held up high was transformed into kinetic energy just before it hit the nail. In this activity, you will further explore the transformation of gravitational potential energy into kinetic energy.

The next day, Yasmin and her Uncle Raymond spent the day at the amusement park. They went there often because her uncle worked for the park. Of all the rides, Yasmin loved the roller coaster the most. That got her thinking. "Uncle Raymond," she said, "this roller coaster is kind of like the hammer and the nail. At the top of the hill there is a lot of potential energy in the cars and the passengers."

"That is right, Yasmin." Uncle Raymond said. "And as we move down the hill, the gravitational potential energy is transformed into kinetic energy. We move the fastest at the bottom where there is the most kinetic energy."

"Geeeez, there is energy everywhere," Yasmin said. Then she had an idea. "Uncle Raymond, would you be willing to come to school and talk to my class about energy and roller coasters?"

CHALLENGE **How is energy transformed on a roller coaster?**

MATERIALS

For each student

1   **Student Sheet 53.1, "Anticipation Guide: Energy Ideas,"
    from Activity 53, "Home Energy Use"**

1   **Student Sheet 55.1, "Talking Drawing: Roller Coaster
    Energy"**

PROCEDURE

*Use Student Sheet 55.1, "Talking Drawing: Roller Coaster Energy," to prepare
yourself for the role play.*

1. Assign one of the four roles to each person in your group.

2. Read the following role-play aloud as a group.

Roles:

Mateo Masoni, interviewer for the Student Science Hour

Raymond Li, engineer for Coasters Inc.

Dr. Sara Low, physics professor

Niki Jackson, amusement park director

It's a Thrill! Roller Coaster Energy

Mateo:	Welcome to the Student Science Hour. Today we have brought together a panel of experts who will help us explore the science behind roller coasters. What is responsible for the thrilling ride down a coaster? Energy!
	Panelists, please introduce yourselves, and describe your backgrounds.
Dr. Low:	Hello, my name is Sara Low. I am a physics professor at State University. Specifically, I study how energy transforms from one type to another.
Ms. Jackson:	My name is Niki Jackson. I am in charge of the amusement park. One of my responsibilities is to make sure the guests are safe while they are having a good time. I use my science and business background to help decide what types of coasters we should have in the park.

Mr. Li: And I'm Raymond Li. I'm an engineer for a company that designs and builds roller coasters. My expertise is in classic wooden coasters that are still in use and need to be maintained.

Mateo: I'm glad that you could take the time to join us today. Now let's talk about park rides. Ms. Jackson, I understand that some riders worry that roller coasters are dangerous. I mean, hanging hundreds of feet in the air cannot possibly be safe, right?

Ms. Jackson: Although roller coasters are designed to frighten passengers, they are statistically the safest ride in the park. Not to mention one of the most popular. A person has a one in one-and-a-half billion chance of being killed on a roller coaster. That mortality rate is lower than for children's wagons, chewing gum, golf, and folding lawn chairs.

Mr. Li: The safety of the riders is a very serious matter for roller coaster designers and engineers. Safety factors are built into every aspect of the coaster. Coasters are built much stronger than they need to be. We also duplicate the safety factors in case of failure. The majority of incidents at amusement parks result from unsafe behavior by the guests' or operators rather than the park's equipment. Although it rarely happens, people have died on a coaster due to a heart ailment they didn't know they had.

Ms. Jackson: Every day, safety experts go over every centimeter of track and examine each portion for wear and tear, or anything that could indicate a problem.

Mateo: Dr. Low, can you describe the energy transformations that are involved in a roller coaster?

Dr. Low: The cars, hooked together to form the train, are pulled up the first hill, known as the lift hill, by a cable or chain. The energy that runs the cable comes from traditional energy sources such as electricity. That energy is transformed into the motion that lifts the train and passengers. As the train travels up the lift hill, it gains gravitational potential energy. The higher it goes and the more massive the train and people in it, the more gravitational potential energy it will have at the top.

Mr. Li: I'd like to add that once the train reaches the peak of the first hill, the train is disengaged from the chain and no more energy is put into the train system until it reaches the end of the ride. Tall coasters give more exciting rides because they start with more gravitational potential energy.

Dr. Low: It's true that when the park compares roller coaster designs, the lift hill height is an important consideration.

Mateo: But energy must be involved after the first peak.

The Kingda Ka roller coaster in New Jersey is one of the tallest in the world. The first hill is 139 meters (456 feet) tall and its top speed is 57 meters/second (128 miles per hour).

Dr. Low: Oh yes. Energy is transformed throughout the ride. The gravitational potential energy of the train and passengers at the top of the hill becomes transformed into kinetic energy as it rolls down the first hill. At the bottom, the kinetic energy is the greatest and the train is moving the fastest.

Mateo: Then the coaster climbs the next hill. Mr. Li says energy is not added to the train, so how does it get up the next hill?

Dr. Low: The kinetic energy at the bottom of the hill sends it up the next hill. As it climbs the hill, the kinetic energy of the train is transformed back into gravitational potential energy. At the top of the next hill, most of the energy has been transformed into potential energy and the process starts over again. Coasters are a result of continuous energy transformations between gravitational potential energy and kinetic energy.

Mateo: I have noticed that on a roller coaster, the first hill is taller than all the others. Why is that?

Mr. Li: That is a good observation, Mateo. In fact, each hill the coaster travels up is smaller than the previous one. That is because every time gravitational potential energy is transformed into kinetic energy, some of it is also transformed into other types of energy. Some of the transformed energy heats up the wheels and tracks. Some more of the transformed energy results in the sound of the train riding on the track.

Mateo: I get it. If the next hill is too high, the train won't make it to the top because it has lost some energy.

Dr. Low: Well, yes. But to be accurate, the energy isn't lost. It is still there, but it is no longer kinetic or gravitational potential energy. It has been transformed into different types of energy during the process.

Mr. Li: A properly designed roller coaster has enough energy to complete the entire course without additional outside energy despite the reduction of available kinetic energy as it travels. At the end of the ride, brakes bring the train to a complete stop, and it is pulled back into the station by a cable.

Mateo: I have one last question for each of you. What is your favorite kind of roller coaster ride?

Mr. Li: I like wooden roller coasters. Although corkscrews and loops are much more difficult to build in wooden coasters, the wooden ones give a rougher ride, and, I think, a great sensation of being airborne. There is a lot of debate about which is better, wooden or steel coasters, but I definitely think the wooden ones have more character and provide the best ride.

The first hill of a roller coaster is always the tallest and the following hills decline in height.

Ms. Jackson: Our park has an inverted roller coaster where the train runs under the track instead of on top of it. That type is my favorite because your legs are exposed instead of your arms, which makes it feel really scary.

Dr. Low: I like coasters that are tall. By tall, I mean a tall lift hill. There is even one that that is over 120 meters, which is about 400 feet. All that energy means it hits 225 km/hr, or 140 mph, at the bottom of the first hill. It is a short ride, just two hills, but very thrilling.

Mateo: Unfortunately we have run out of time for the Student Science Hour. Thank you all for joining us today.

ANALYSIS

1. Look at the diagram of a roller coaster below. At which point does a train on this roller coaster:

   a. have the most gravitational potential energy? Explain your choice.

   b. have the most kinetic energy? Explain your choice.

   c. have both kinetic and gravitational potential energy? Explain your choice.

2. Kinetic energy is related to the speed of an object. In which place, Point E or Point F, is the train moving faster? Explain in terms of kinetic energy.

3. As the train travels on the track, the energy of the train changes back and forth from gravitational potential to kinetic. What other energy transformations occur as the train travels the track? Explain.

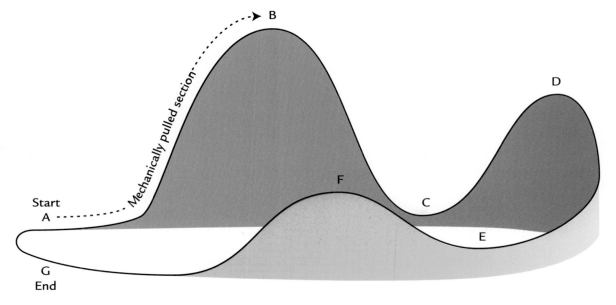

4. Why can't a roller coaster go up a hill that is higher than the hill it just came down?

EXTENSION

Learn more about roller coasters by visiting the *Issues and Physical Science* page of the SEPUP website.

INVESTIGATION

In the last activity, some of the kinetic energy of the train was transformed into thermal energy during the roller coaster ride. In this activity, you will explore a similar transformation. You will investigate the transformation of kinetic energy—in this case, moving metal pellets, or shot, in a vial—into heat. **Heat** is the movement of thermal energy from hot to cold. An object does not "have" heat. Rather, heat is the process of energy movement from a higher-temperature object to a lower-temperature object because of the temperature difference. **Temperature** is a measure of the average energy *per molecule* of a substance. Although related, temperature and heat are not the same thing. For example, a spoonful of water and a large pot of water both boil at the same temperature. However, the pot of boiling water has more total energy and releases more energy during cooling than the spoon-ful of water.

Although temperature and heat are not the same thing, they are related because temperature measurements are used to determine heating. In this activity, you will measure a change in temperature to indicate the trans-formation of energy. The change is due to friction, which heats up objects when they rub against each other.

CHALLENGE ⟹ **How can kinetic energy be transformed into another energy type?**

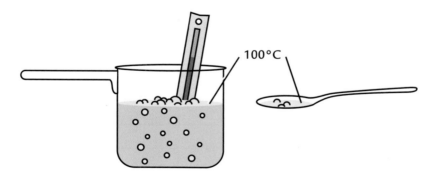

Boiling water in a pot and spoon are at the same temperature, but have different amounts of thermal energy.

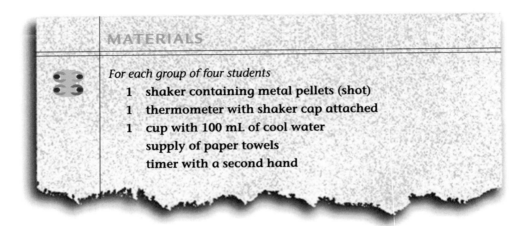

MATERIALS

For each group of four students

1 shaker containing metal pellets (shot)
1 thermometer with shaker cap attached
1 cup with 100 mL of cool water
   supply of paper towels
   timer with a second hand

PROCEDURE

1. Prepare a data table similar to the one below.

2. Take the room temperature with the thermometer, and record it in your science notebook.

3. Take the regular cap off the shaker and replace it with the one with the thermometer attached, making sure the thermometer bulb is surrounded by the pellets as shown on the next page.

Shot Shaker Data

Time (sec)	Trial	Initial temperature (°Celsius)	Final temperature (°Celsius)	Temperature change (°Celsius)	Average temperature change (°Celsius)
10	1				
10	2				
10	3				
20	1				
20	2				
20	3				
30	1				
30	2				
30	3				

The shaker assembly

4. Observe the initial temperature of the pellets. If the initial temperature is more than 2°C above room temperature, remove the inner vial containing the pellets and immerse it in cool water until the temperature is within 2°C of room temperature. Dry it off, and place it back inside the larger vial.

5. In your data table record the initial temperature of the pellets.

6. Exchange caps, and make sure the regular cap snaps tightly onto the shaker. Then, while holding the cap on with your thumb, shake the vial as fast as you can for 10 seconds.

7. Quickly exchange the regular cap for the one with the thermometer attached. Wait until the alcohol in the thermometer stops moving, and record the temperature.

   Hint: The thermometer reading rises slowly, so you may need to be patient to get an accurate reading.

8. Find the temperature change by subtracting the initial temperature from the final temperature. Record the temperature change in the data table.

9. Repeat Steps 4–8 for Trials 2 and 3.

10. Calculate the average temperature changes for the three trials, and record them in the table.

11. Repeat Steps 4–10, this time shaking the vial for 20 seconds.

12. Repeat Steps 4–10, this time shaking the vial for 30 seconds.

ANALYSIS

1. For each time interval, why did you perform three trials and then average the temperatures?

2. Describe any possible sources of error in your experiment, and explain how each may have affected your results.

3. Use evidence gathered in this investigation to describe the relationship between:

   a. shaking time and temperature change.

   b. shaking time and energy transfer.

4. Of the two descriptions below which, a or b, correctly describes the transformation of energy shown in the diagrams below? Explain your choice.

    a. potential energy ⟶ temperature

    b. kinetic energy ⟶ thermal energy

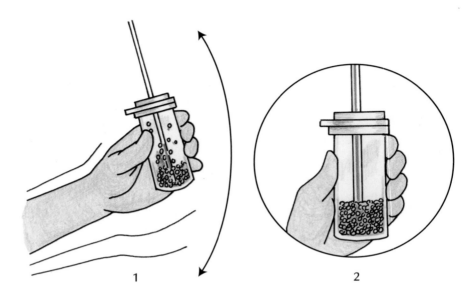

      1   2

READING

Energy is involved in everything that happens. We are aware of energy when it is released or absorbed. Examining the changes of energy in action has led to one of the most important scientific ideas central to all science disciplines.

CHALLENGE

What is the guiding principle behind the behavior of energy?

Energy, light, and sound are released when fireworks explode.

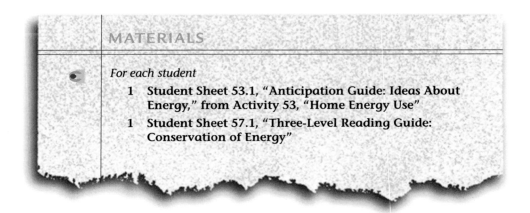

MATERIALS

For each student

1   Student Sheet 53.1, "Anticipation Guide: Ideas About Energy," from Activity 53, "Home Energy Use"
1   Student Sheet 57.1, "Three-Level Reading Guide: Conservation of Energy"

READING

Use Student Sheet 57.1, "Three-Level Reading Guide: Conservation of Energy" to guide you through the following reading.

ENERGY ACTION

Releasing Energy, Absorbing Energy

From our everyday experiences, energy seems to us like it is something that people consume. It often appears that energy is "used up" when, actually, it has not disappeared. Instead, energy is transferred and/or transformed into another energy type. For example, the energy in the food we eat food provides thermal energy for our bodies. Or the chemical energy in gasoline is released and transformed into the motion of the car. Everyday energy "consumptions" are really energy transformations in which energy is released.

Oil was formed over millions of years deep inside the earth from decayed plants and animals. The plants and animals absorbed energy from other sources such as food and sunlight.

Following energy as it is transferred and transformed shows us a chain of interactions that both release and absorb energy. Take oil, for example. Oil formed in the ground over millions of years from the decay of dead plants and small animals. The energy in the plants originally came from sunlight, which the plants transformed into chemical energy through the process of photosynthesis. The energy in the animals came from the food they ate. When oil in a furnace burns, the chemical potential energy in the oil is released as thermal energy which we feel as warmth.

The Law of Conservation of Energy

If you compared the amount of chemical potential energy of the oil in the furnace before it was burned to the amount of thermal energy coming out of the furnace, you would find they were different. There is less energy released from burning oil than there was chemical potential energy stored in it. What happened to the other energy? Not all of the chemical energy in the oil is transformed into thermal energy during the burning. Some was transformed into an energy type that's easy to overlook. In the case of the burner, a small amount of the chemical potential energy in the oil was transformed into light and some into sound, and some remained in the ash and was not released. Sometimes the "missing" energy from a process is called "lost energy." This lost energy has turned into another energy type that is not recognized or used. Sound and light may not be energy useful for heating in this example, but it must be considered part of the total energy released by the burning oil.

The total amount of energy in a system is the same before and after a transformation. Energy can be transferred or transformed, but cannot be lost or destroyed. This idea is known as the **Law of Conservation of Energy**. This means that the total amount of energy before something happens must be equal to the amount afterward, regardless of the process or energy types involved. The Law of Conservation of Energy doesn't say which kind of energy must be present before and after an event, just that the total energy doesn't change.

The Law of Conservation of Energy is one of the central principles in science and applies to many disciplines. For example, a biologist can apply this law when examining a food web. Biologists have tracked the amount of chemical energy in a producer, such as grass, through several consumers, such as a cow and a person. It appears that some of the chemical potential energy in all of the grass eaten by the cow is "lost" before the person drinks milk from the cow. However, a closer look reveals that this chemical energy was transformed into a variety of energy types, including the mechanical energy used by the cow to move around and the energy released by the cow's metabolism.

The Process of Heating

Thermal energy is almost always released during an energy transformation. For example, a lightbulb transforms electrical energy into light, but the system loses energy by heating. A hot lightbulb is evidence of this. When you drive a nail into a block, the nail becomes warm, indicating that some of the mechanical energy hitting the nail was turned into thermal energy. The process of heating, although useful in many situations and critical to life, is not always desirable. With the lightbulb, usually the desirable energy type is light, not thermal energy.

Thermal energy that is released during a transformation is not lost or destroyed but is dissipated, or spread out, which makes it hard to harness. Therefore, transforming thermal energy into other types of energy is

The interior of a motor.

Large generators at a hydroelectric power plant.

A Rolls Royce combustion engine is assembled.

more difficult than many other transformations. Even with the most innovative technology, only about 40% of thermal energy can be converted into useful mechanical energy. Similarly, it is difficult to convert thermal energy into chemical or electrical energy. Although many transformations release thermal energy, it can be a challenge to capture and use it.

Energy Efficiency

No energy transformations result in 100% useful energy, and people who are concerned with energy evaluate energy transformations by efficiency. **Efficiency** is the ratio of useful energy that is released to the total energy absorbed by the process. For example, a car's engine transforms the chemical potential energy of gasoline into other types of energy. About 74% of the energy in the gasoline is released by heating, but only the remaining 26% is transformed into motion from the engine. Although no energy is created or destroyed, the engine's efficiency is only 26%, or the portion of useful energy that was released. Interestingly enough, since the engine has to overcome air, road, and transmission resistance, it turns out that only about 3% of the original chemical potential energy actually moves the car.

Appliances and other devices are rated by the government for their energy efficiency. When a certain model of an appliance is described as "energy efficient," it usually means that it uses less energy than comparable models that produce the same result. For example, a newer refrigerator that has an "Energy Star" consumes less energy than older models of refrigerators consume to cool the same volume of food at the same temperature. By consuming less energy to do the same work, an Energy Star appliance increases efficiency.

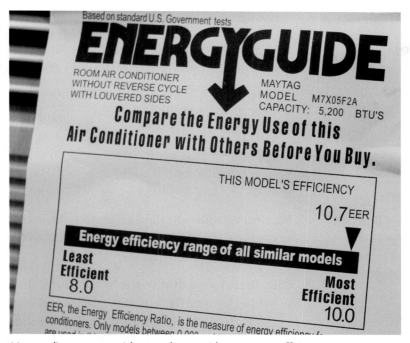

New appliances come with a tag that provides an energy efficiency rating.

An important idea that is related to efficiency is the term conservation. **Energy conservation** (not to be confused with the Law of Conservation of Energy) means to reduce, or "save," the total energy transformed in the first place. For example, someone who turns out lights when not using them is conserving energy. Keeping a lightbulb off when not in use is related to conservation because it will use less energy, or conserve energy. Another way to conserve energy is to use an energy-efficient device that uses less energy when it is on. Using energy efficiently saves energy resources, reduces environmental pollutants, and reduces cost. For these reasons, learning how to convert energy more efficiently is a major goal of technology and engineering.

ANALYSIS

1. Which of the following diagrams accurately applies the Law of Conservation of Energy to a toaster in use? Explain your choice.

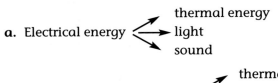

a. Electrical energy →
thermal energy
light
sound

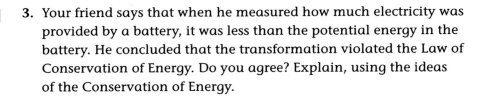

b. Chemical potential energy →
thermal energy
light

2. Your friend tells you that a "generator makes electricity." Do you agree or disagree with her statement? Explain why in terms of the Law of Conservation of Energy.

3. Your friend says that when he measured how much electricity was provided by a battery, it was less than the potential energy in the battery. He concluded that the transformation violated the Law of Conservation of Energy. Do you agree? Explain, using the ideas of the Conservation of Energy.

4. Which energy is often called the "graveyard of kinetic energy" and why?

5. What is the efficiency of an engine that gives off 70% thermal energy?

INVESTIGATION

Since energy is never created or destroyed, it is possible to follow energy transfer through many transformations. If you follow energy transformations far enough, you will find something interesting: most of the energy here on earth can be traced all the way back to the Sun. The Sun emits electromagnetic energy, or light, which is produced from nuclear reactions occurring in its center. When the Sun's energy reaches us here on Earth, it is transformed into many types of energy that sustain life.

CHALLENGE ➡ **Can you follow the transforming energy?**

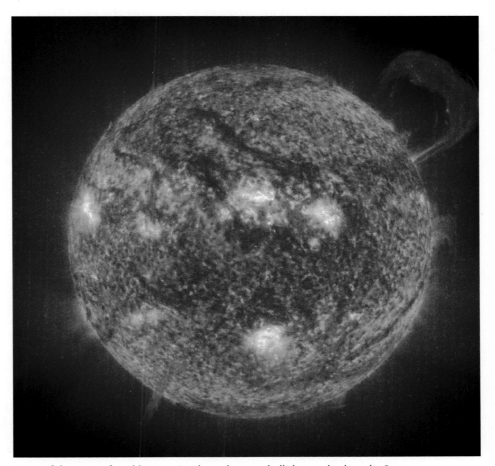

Most of the energy found here on Earth can be traced all the way back to the Sun.

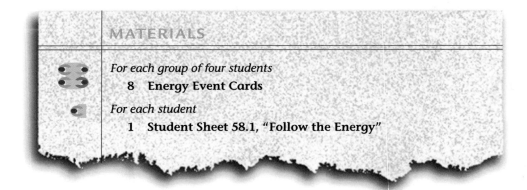

MATERIALS

For each group of four students
    8   **Energy Event Cards**

For each student
    1   **Student Sheet 58.1, "Follow the Energy"**

PROCEDURE

1. Look at the table that describes different types of energy found in nature or human inventions.

2. With your group, examine the eight Energy Event Cards, and compare them to the table on the next page.

3. Chose an Energy Event Card, and identify all the energy types involved in the transformation shown. Use Student Sheet 58.1, "Follow the Energy," to record the energy types before and after the transformation.

4. In the last column on Student Sheet 58.1, "Follow the Energy," write a complete sentence or two that describes the energy transformation shown on the Energy Event Card. Include all the energy types you listed.

5. Repeat Steps 3–4 for the other seven Energy Event Cards.

ANALYSIS

1. Copy the lists of words shown below.

List 1:	List 2:	List 3:
kinetic energy	chemical energy	fossil fuels
potential energy	potential energy	stored energy
light	nuclear energy	chemical energy
sound	thermal energy	absorb energy
		release energy

    a. Look for a relationship among the words in each list. Cross out the word in each list that does not belong with the others.

    b. Circle the word in each list that is a category that includes the others.

    c. Explain how the word you circled relates to the other words in the list, and how the word you crossed out does not fit in the list.

A Summary of Energy Types

Energy type	Name	Depends on	Description	Example
Potential energy	Chemical	Type of substance	Energy stored in the bonds of atoms	Energy stored in fossil fuels and food
	Elastic	Springiness of object	Energy stored by stretching or compressing	Energy stored in a stretched rubber band or compressed foam
	Electric (static)	Electron-charge buildup	Energy stored by the buildup of charges (electrons or ions)	Charge building up on person walking on a rug or combing fine hair
	Gravitational	Height and mass	Energy stored due to an object's mass and height	Energy stored due to the mass and position of a train on the top of a roller coaster or water at the top of a waterfall
	Nuclear	Stability of atom	Energy that is stored in the nucleus of atoms	Energy stored in uranium-238 atoms, energy stored in the nucleus of hydrogen atoms in the center of the Sun
Kinetic Energy	Electric (current)	Charge, conductivity	Movement of charge and energy from one place to another	Lightning, electricity through wires
	Light	Intensity and frequency	Energy transferred by the rapid movement of electromagnetic fields	Sunlight or X rays
	Motion (kinetic)	Mass, speed	Movement of an object from one place to another	Wind or a moving train
	Sound	Loudness	Energy transferred by the vibration of an object	Music in air or voices under water
	Thermal	Mass, material, and temperature	Energy transferred in transit from a hot to a cold object	Hot plate heating up water, or hot water cooling to room temperature

2. The diagram below shows the transfer of energy from the Sun all the way to a student using a computer. Using the table "A Summary of Energy Types" on the previous page, decide on the type of energy at each of the situations. There may be more than one energy type at each place.

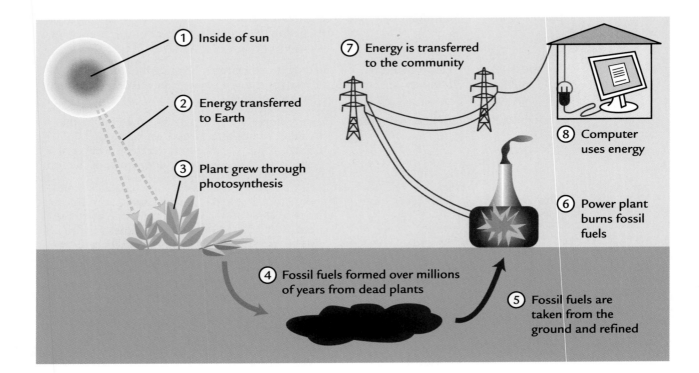

① Inside of sun

② Energy transferred to Earth

③ Plant grew through photosynthesis

④ Fossil fuels formed over millions of years from dead plants

⑤ Fossil fuels are taken from the ground and refined

⑥ Power plant burns fossil fuels

⑦ Energy is transferred to the community

⑧ Computer uses energy

LABORATORY

Mom, there is one thing I don't get about heat," said Yasmin. " I under-stand that heat is a transfer of energy from hot to cold. That makes sense when two things touch each other, like when a hot pack warms up my hands. But what about air? How can thermal energy move through nothing?"

"Well, air is not nothing," said her mother. "The energy is transferred when mole-cules bump into each other. It doesn't matter if the molecules are in a gas, like air, or in a liquid or a solid."

One of the ways that energy is transferred is by conduction. **Conduction** is the process by which energy is transferred directly when materials touch each other. Conduction is a result of electron and atomic collisions inside the materials. Any solid, liquid, or gas can transfer energy by conduction. Sometimes an object can change phase because it has absorbed energy by conduction, such as an ice cube that turns from solid to liquid when it melts in a drink. Materials that have a structure that easily allows energy transfer are called **conductors**. Examples of good conductors are copper and aluminum.

CHALLENGE

How can you increase the energy transferred to an ice cube?

Conduction in a gas.
The diagram shows the collision of a single hot atom (red) and cool atom (pink). As a result of the collision, some of the thermal energy from the hot atom is transferred to the cool one.

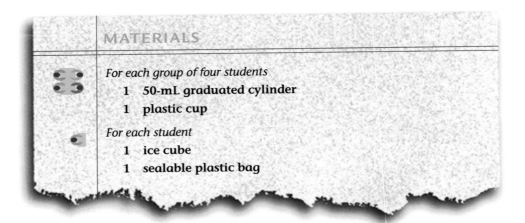

MATERIALS

For each group of four students

1   50-mL graduated cylinder
1   plastic cup

For each student

1   ice cube
1   sealable plastic bag

⚠ SAFETY

Do not put the ice or the bag in your mouth.

PROCEDURE

1. Review the Ice-Melting Rules shown below.

2. With your group, discuss the things you could do to melt as much of the ice cube as possible in the set timeframe. Record your ice-melting plan in your science notebook.

3. Your teacher will instruct you on how to get your ice cube. Then melt as much of it as you can in the time allowed.

4. When the contest is over, carefully pour the water from your plastic bag into the graduated cylinder, and record the volume of the water in your science notebook. Each member of your group will do this separately.

5. Record the volume of water your teacher obtained in the control bag.

Ice-Melting Rules

• Keep the ice cube in the plastic bag until the end of the contest.

• You may not put the ice or the bag in your mouth.

• Handle your bags carefully. A broken bag will disqualify you.

• Keep all water in the plastic bag. Water that spills or leaks out of the bag will not be measured.

• Watch carefully for your teacher's start and stop signals.

• As soon as the contest time is up, remove the remaining ice from the plastic bag, place it in the cup provided, and set it aside.

ANALYSIS

1. What volume of water did you collect? Compare your results with the control and with other students' results.

2. What did you do to maximize the rate at which your ice melted? Describe the techniques you used.

3. When melting the ice, how did you use:

   a. conduction?

   b. energy transformation(s)?

4. Which of your or your classmates' techniques seemed to transfer:

   a. the most energy?

   b. the least energy?

 5. List all of the variables that affected how fast the ice melted. Choose one of these variables, and design an investigation to test if changing this variable would affect the melting speed.

LABORATORY

Yasmin wanted to know what her mother was doing. It was a beautiful fall day, but instead of heading outside as usual, she was pulling out hammers, nails, masks, and a big roll of thick, cloth-like material. Uncle Raymond was on his way over, too. "Mom, what's going on?" Yasmin asked.

"I am going to insulate the house today," her mother said. "Last winter we had a pretty high electricity bill, so I want to reduce our energy bill by making the house more energy efficient. I don't want to waste my hard-earned money if I don't have to."

Yasmin looked over the items on the floor. She loved to build things. "Can I help, Mom?"

"Sure you can. Just make sure to put on long sleeves and a mask so you won't inhale fibers from the insulation."

Sometimes we need to minimize the transfer of energy. Materials that are poor conductors and, therefore, slow down the rate of energy movement are called **insulators**. Examples of insulators are wood, wool, and paper. In houses, insulating materials help to keep energy from transferring outdoors in the winter and from moving inside in the summer.

CHALLENGE ➡️ **How can you insulate an ice cube?**

This fiberglass insulation minimizes the heat transfer through the wall.

MATERIALS

For each group of four students

1   50-mL graduated cylinder
1   plastic cup

For each pair of students

1   ice cube
1   sealable plastic bag
1   empty 1.89-L (1/2-gal.) milk carton
    materials from home for preserving your ice cube

SAFETY

Do not put the ice or the bag in your mouth.

PROCEDURE

1. Review the Ice-Melting Rules in Activity 59, "Ice-Melting Contest," and "Additional Contest Rules" shown here.

2. Discuss with the class how to set up a control for this contest.

3. Work with your partner to design an insulating container for your ice cube. Discuss how you think your design will prevent energy transfer. Decide what materials you will need, and sketch your design in your science notebook.

4. With your teacher's permission, build the insulating container.

5. Your teacher will instruct you on how to get your ice cube. Then preserve as much ice as you can in the time allowed.

6. As your ice cube sits in its insulating container, read the article on the next page. Answer the questions with your partner.

7. When the contest is over, carefully pour the water from your plastic bag into the graduated cylinder, and record the volume of water in your science notebook. Each member of your group will do this separately.

8. Record the volume of water your teacher obtained in the control bag.

Additional Contest Rules

- Keep the ice and bag on the table until directed to start the contest.

- No commercial coolers or thermoses allowed.

ANALYSIS

1. What volume of water did you collect? Compare your results with the control and with other pairs' devices.

2. What did you do to decrease the rate at which your ice melted? Describe the materials and techniques you and your partner used.

3. Which among your and your classmates' techniques seemed to transfer:

    a. the most energy?

    b. the least energy?

4. Look carefully at the pictures of buildings below. In your science notebook, write a short description of each picture. Be sure to include:

    a. what material you think the house is made of.

    b. how well you think that material insulates from thermal energy transfer.

EXTENSION

Research the materials that are shown in the houses below, and use the information to rank the houses from the best to the worst insulated.

A

B

C

D

READING

Keeping Cool

It's the hottest day of the summer. Your friend comes to visit, and the two of you decide to get cold drinks from the refrigerator. Once you have them, you alternate between sipping the cool drink and holding it against your hot forehead. Because of conduction, some of the energy from your body transfers to the cool drink when it touches your forehead. It may feel like the cold is moving into your body, but in actuality, what you feel is the loss of the thermal energy that transfers to the drink. The drink gets warmer while your head gets cooler. The energy transfer cools your body, and it feels great.

Before the refrigerator was invented, people used iceboxes to transfer energy from food to ice. Iceboxes were usually made of wood and were lined with such insulating materials as cork, sawdust, and seaweed. Large blocks of ice placed in the icebox absorbed energy from the food that people put in the icebox. As more and more energy was transferred to the block of ice, it melted. A drip pan collected the melted water, and emptying it daily was a common kitchen chore. The ice had to be replaced every few days, creating business for companies that cut ice in the winter from northern lakes and rivers, and stored and delivered it. Eventually, commercial freezers made artificial ice for iceboxes.

The first iceboxes were developed in the mid 1700s but did not have widespread use until the 1900s. At the start of the 20th century, about half of homes in the United States had an icebox, and half had no cooled storage

Men cut large blocks of ice from a lake, 1942

Iceboxes required new ice every few days.

at all. Modern refrigerators started appearing in homes around 1915, and by 1944, 85% of American homes had one. Today, virtually all homes in the developed world have refrigerators. The invention of the refrigerator has allowed the modern family to preserve food products for much longer periods of time than was previously possible.

In a closed icebox, the ice is warmed as energy is transferred to it from the food. In a modern refrigerator, the air in the refrigerator absorbs the energy from the food. Then a special gas absorbs energy from the air in the refrigerator. That gas, known as a refrigerant, expands as it absorbs the energy. In order for the refrigerant to expand, however, it had to have been compressed in the first place. The initial compression of the refrigerant takes energy. The energy is usually provided through a motor. (This explains why refrigerators consume energy even though there is less energy in the inside air of the refrigerator than outside.) The energy from the refrigerant is transferred to the air immediately outside the refrigerator with fans. A simplified version of the refrigeration cycle is shown on next page.

It is important to note that the diagram shows the refrigerant circulating in this cycle and not the air inside the refrigerator. The refrigerant is a special gas that is housed in the machinery behind the refrigerator compartment. The gas never touches the food or the air in the compartment as it circulates. Only thermal energy is transferred from the food compartment to the refrigerant.

Refrigeration Cycle

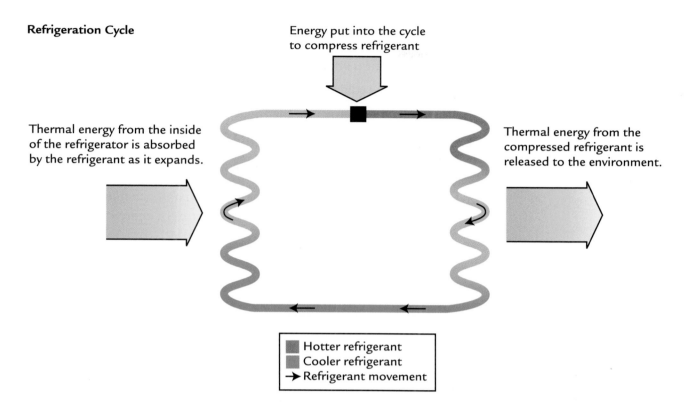

Energy put into the cycle to compress refrigerant

Thermal energy from the inside of the refrigerator is absorbed by the refrigerant as it expands.

Thermal energy from the compressed refrigerant is released to the environment.

Hotter refrigerant
Cooler refrigerant
→ Refrigerant movement

Air conditioners and refrigerators work on similar principles. In fact, air conditioning was developed in the early 1900s around the same time as refrigerators. Early air conditioners were made to improve industrial processes that need stable humidity and temperature, like printing, rather than for use in people's home. These days, air conditioning is commonplace in the United States in cars, houses, apartments, and commercial buildings to keep people comfortable.

Window-mounted room air conditioners, like refrigerators, have refrigerant flowing in the back of the device. In central air-conditioning systems the refrigerant equipment is usually located in an outdoor box next to the house or on the roof of the building. Fans in the air conditioner blow hot air away from the air conditioner and the cooled air toward the rooms to be cooled.

Both air conditioners and refrigerators work most efficiently when the volume of air they are trying to cool is well insulated. This prevents energy from moving into the space being cooled. For example, a refrigerator needs to be lined with insulating materials and have a good seal on the door. Air conditioners in a house should be in a well-sealed space that doesn't allow much energy to transfer through doors, walls, and windows.

The scientific understanding of energy transfer led inventors to develop solutions to the problems of controlling temperature. The development of the refrigerator and air conditioner has improved the quality of life and the way people live their everyday lives.

THINKING IT OVER

1. Which statement is scientifically accurate?

   a. "Don't let the cold energy out of the fridge!"

   b. "Don't let the energy into the fridge!"

   Explain your choice in terms of energy transfer.

2. Why is the air immediately around a refrigerator warm?

3. What happens if an air conditioner is used in a house that is not well insulated and not well sealed? Explain in terms of energy transfer.

LABORATORY

Yasmin, her Mom, and Uncle Raymond were at a restaurant having breakfast. Uncle Raymond complained that his coffee had cooled off. He asked the waiter for a "touch up" of hot coffee. The waiter filled Raymond's half-full cup of cool coffee with steaming hot coffee. Raymond knew that Yasmin was studying energy. He looked over at his niece. "Now, Yasmin," he asked, "Is my coffee too hot to drink?"

CHALLENGE

What happens to the energy when hot and cool water are mixed?

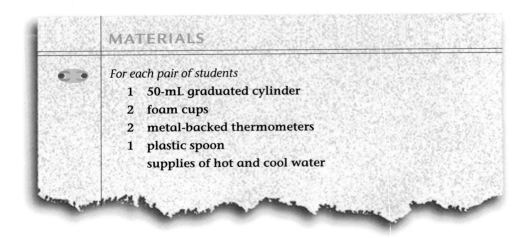

MATERIALS

For each pair of students

1   50-mL graduated cylinder
2   foam cups
2   metal-backed thermometers
1   plastic spoon
    supplies of hot and cool water

PROCEDURE

1. With your partner, consider what will happen if you mix each of the following:

Experiment 1: 60 mL of hot water (60°C) with 60 mL of cool water (20°C)

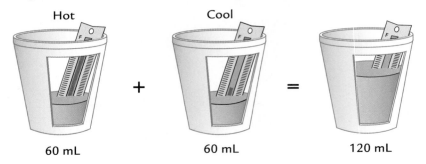

Hot   Cool

60 mL   +   60 mL   =   120 mL

Experiment 2: 60 mL of hot water (60°C) with 30 mL of cool water (20°C)

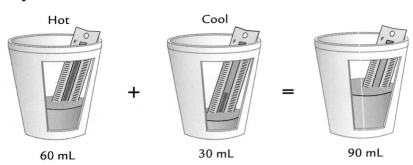

Hot   Cool

60 mL   +   30 mL   =   90 mL

Experiment 3: 30 mL of hot water (60°C) with 60 mL of cool water (20°C)

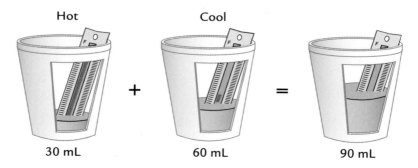

Hot   Cool

30 mL   60 mL   90 mL

2. Discuss what you think will happen to the energy and the temperature for each experiment. Record your predictions in your science notebook.

3. Make a table similar to the one below in your science notebook.

Mixing Water Data

Experiment	Water	Volume (mL)	Starting temperature (°C)	Final temperature (°C)	Temperature change (°C)
1	Hot	60			
	Cool	60			
2	Hot	60			
	Cool	30			
3	Hot	30			
	Cool	60			

4. With your partner, follow your teacher's instructions for obtaining 60 mL of cool water and 60 mL of hot water in each of your foam cups.

5. Measure the starting temperature of the cool and hot water. Record the temperatures in the table.

6. Quickly add the cool water to the hot water. Stir gently with a spoon until the temperature of the mixture remains steady. Record the final temperature in the data table.

7. Calculate the temperature change for the mixture. Record the change in the table.

8. Empty the cups and repeat Procedure Steps 4–7, but use the volumes for Experiment 2 and Experiment 3.

ANALYSIS

1. Were the results what you expected? Compare your and your partner's predictions to the actual results.

2. When you mixed equal volumes of hot and cool water, how did the final temperature compare to the starting temperatures?

3. When you mixed **un**equal volumes of hot and cool water, how did the final temperature compare to the starting temperatures?

4. For all the experiments, explain what happened to the thermal energy in the water when the hot and cool water were mixed.

5. In any of the experiments, would it have been possible for the final temperature to be greater than either of the initial temperatures?

6. Did any energy leave the cup-and-water system? Describe the evidence that supports your answer.

EXTENSION

Design an experiment to measure the temperature changes of hot and cool water that are not directly mixed, but instead are held next to each other. Use a plastic cup to separate the water, as shown in the diagram below. Before conducting the experiment, predict the temperature of the hot and cold water after a certain amount of time.

INVESTIGATION

When hot water melts an ice cube, some of the thermal energy of the liquid water is transferred to the ice through heating. This energy overcomes the forces between molecules in the ice. When enough energy has been transferred to the ice to create a phase change, the ice melts. The amount of thermal energy the ice absorbed while melting is equal to the thermal energy that the water released. This energy can be quantified by measuring the temperature change of the water and then using it to calculate the energy the water lost.

CHALLENGE ➡ **How much energy does it take to melt an ice cube?**

The ice cubes absorb thermal energy, which causes them to melt.

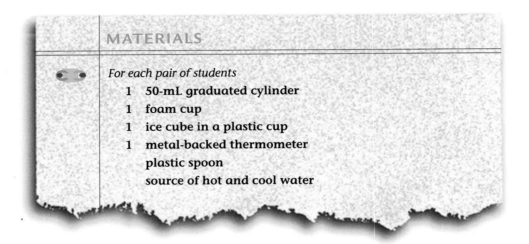

MATERIALS

For each pair of students

1   50-mL graduated cylinder
1   foam cup
1   ice cube in a plastic cup
1   metal-backed thermometer
    plastic spoon
    source of hot and cool water

SAFETY

Use caution when working with the hot water. If you spill any on your hand, hold your hand under cool water for five minutes.

PROCEDURE

1. Follow your teacher's directions for obtaining an ice cube and some hot water.

2. Put 100 mL of hot water into the foam cup.

3. Record the starting temperature of the hot water in your science notebook.

4. Immediately shake any water off of the ice cube, and place it in the hot water.

5. Gently stir until the ice is completely melted. Observe the cup carefully since it can be difficult to see the moment at which all the ice has melted.

6. As soon as the ice has melted, measure and record the final temperature of the water.

7. Calculate the change in the water temperature, and record it in your science notebook.

8. Calculate the amount of thermal energy lost by the water by using the formula below:

$$\text{energy released (°C g)} = \frac{\text{temperature change}}{\text{of water (°C)}} \times \frac{\text{mass of}}{\text{water (g)}}$$

Hint: 1 mL of water weighs 1 gram.

9. Record the energy lost by the water in your science notebook.

ANALYSIS

1. If the energy absorbed by the ice is exactly equal to the energy lost by the water, what was the amount of energy needed to melt the ice? Show your calculation.

2. Do you think *all* of the energy lost by the hot water was transferred to the ice? Explain.

3. Do you think that stirring the mixture had an effect on the melting of the ice? Explain why or why not.

4. Based on your answers to Analysis Questions 2 and 3, do you think your calculation of the heat energy absorbed by the ice is likely to be too high or too low? Explain.

5. How is the energy transfer in this experiment similar to the energy transfer that occurs in a house? Explain, and provide an example.

LABORATORY

Scientists use a device called a **calorimeter**, as shown below, to measure the amount of chemical potential energy there is in all sorts of materials. To determine the chemical energy of a material, scientists first measure the mass of a sample of the material. Then they place the sample in a sealed container called a bomb. They put the bomb in a well-insulated container filled with a known volume of water. An electrical spark from inside the bomb starts the sample burning. The water in the container absorbs the energy released by the burned sample. A thermometer measures the change in the temperature of the water. The potential energy of the original material is equal to the thermal energy transferred to the water.

In this activity, you will use a simple calorimeter to measure the amount of stored energy in a nut. When you eat a nut, or any other food, the potential chemical energy in it is released and used by your body. A calorimeter can determine the amount of stored energy in the nut, measured in calories. A **calorie** is the energy unit you explored in Activity 62, "Quantifying Energy"—it is the energy required to raise the temperature of one gram of water by 1°C. When describing the energy available in food, such as with the nut, the unit Calorie is used. A **Calorie**, with a capital C, is 1,000 calories.

CHALLENGE ➡ **How many Calories are in a nut?**

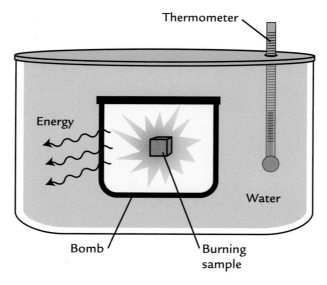

A bomb calorimeter.

MATERIALS

For each group of four students

 1 wire coat hanger, wrapped with aluminum foil
 1 aluminum beverage can
 1 nut
 1 SEPUP nut holder
 1 50-mL graduated container
 1 glass thermometer
    wooden matches or lighter
 1 cup of water
    tongs or potholder

For each student

 1 pair of safety goggles
 1 Student Sheet 53.1, "Anticipation Guide: Ideas About Energy," from Activity 53, "Home Energy Use"

SAFETY

Be sure to wear safety goggles during this investigation. Long hair must be tied back, and loose sleeves rolled up. If anything besides the nut starts to burn, inform your teacher immediately. **Be especially careful not to get clothing or your hair near the flame.** Make sure to keep a cup of water close by the experiment as a fire-safety precaution.

Notify your teacher if you are allergic to nuts.

The can may become quite hot. Carefully follow all instructions from your teacher.

PROCEDURE

1. Carefully place the nut on the nut holder.

2. Pour 100 mL of water into the can.

3. Set up your calorimeter with the can hanging from the bent coat hangar as shown on the next page. Position the bottom of the can so it will be in the flame of the burning nut, but not so low that it will put out the flame.

4. Just before lighting the nut, record the starting temperature of the water.

The calorimeter apparatus.

5. Light the nut. When it begins to burn, slide it under the can, and let it burn completely. If you think the nut stopped burning before all its energy was transformed, ask your teacher for advice on relighting it.

6. As soon as the nut stops burning, use the thermometer to stir the water gently inside the can, and record its final temperature.

7. Calculate the change in the water temperature, and record it in your science notebook.

8. Calculate, in calories, the amount of heat energy the water gained, by using this formula:

$$\text{energy released (calories)} = \frac{\text{temperature change}}{\text{of water (°C)}} \times \frac{\text{mass of}}{\text{water (g)}}$$

Hint: 1 mL of water weighs 1 gram.

9. There are 1,000 calories in 1 Calorie. Determine how many Calories were in the nut, and record it in your science notebook.

ANALYSIS

1. How many Calories were in your nut? Show your calculation.

2. Explain, in terms of energy transfer and transformation, what caused the temperature of the water to change.

3. Was all of the energy from the burning nut transferred to the water? If not, explain what happened to the energy that was not transferred to the water.

4. How would you improve the design of this calorimeter so that it would work better?

   a. Draw a detailed, labeled diagram of your improved calorimeter. Be sure that you could build it yourself, if you had the materials.

   b. Explain why your design is better than the one you used.

5. If you burned a puffed cheese snack of the same size as the nut, would you get the same result? Why or why not?

6. A curious student wanted to know if the calorimeter would work with different amounts of water. The table below shows the results from her burning three nuts of the same type and mass, but using varied amounts of water in the can. Explain from the table below whether the calorimeter measured the energy in the nut properly when used with each amount of water.

Nut Experiment Data		
Experiment	Mass of water (g)	Temperature change (°C)
Nut 1	200	19
Nut 2	100	39
Nut 3	50	77

EXTENSION

With your teacher's permission, measure the temperature change caused by burning a marshmallow or a puffed cheese snack.

Food nutrition labels are required to show information about the energy in the food, measured in Calories.

Nutrition Facts

Serving Size 1 cup (228g)
Servings Per Container 2

Amount Per Serving

Calories 250   Calories from Fat 110

	% Daily Value*
Total Fat 12g	**18%**
Saturated Fat 3g	**15%**
Trans Fat 3g	
Cholesterol 30mg	**10%**
Sodium 470mg	**20%**
Potassium 700mg	**20%**
Total Carbohydrate 31g	**10%**
Dietary Fiber 0g	**0%**
Sugars 5g	
Protein 5g	

Vitamin A	**4%**
Vitamin C	**2%**
Calcium	**20%**
Iron	**4%**

* Percent Daily Values are based on a 2,000 calorie diet. Your Daily Values may be higher or lower depending on your calorie needs.

	Calories:	2,000	2,500
Total Fat	Less than	65g	80g
Sat Fat	Less than	20g	25g
Cholesterol	Less than	300mg	300mg
Sodium	Less than	2,400mg	2,400mg
Total Carbohydrate		300g	375g
Dietary Fiber		25g	30g

READING

Now that Yasmin understood that energy can be measured, she started paying more attention to amounts of energy in her daily life. For example, she noticed that in addition to paying for heating the house with natural gas, her parents get a bill every month for the amount of electricity the family uses. When Yasmin took a household energy survey, she found that electricity was in almost constant use. She wondered where all that electrical energy came from.

Electrical energy used in the home and elsewhere comes from transforming natural resources of one kind or another. Some of those natural resources are renewable, and some are nonrenewable. A **renewable resource** is one that has a continuing supply, such as sunlight, water, wind, and biomass. To be considered renewable, a resource must be supplied faster than it is used up. A **nonrenewable resource**, such as coal, natural gas, and petroleum, is one that has a limited supply; once it is used up there is no more of it.

CHALLENGE

What are the advantages and disadvantages of the different sources of energy that produce electricity in the United States?

Electricity is brought to communities from power plants through transmission lines.

MATERIALS

For each student

1   Student Sheet 64.1, "Three-Level Reading Guide: Electricity Generation"

READING

Use Student Sheet 64.1, "Three-Level Reading Guide: Electricity Generation," to help you complete the following reading.

Where Does Electricity Come From?

Electrical energy is a convenient and important kind of energy. For over 100 years, people have put it to work in almost every area of human life. Americans use about 3.9 million *million* kilowatt-hours of electricity every year. (One kilowatt-hour is equal to the energy needed to light a 100-watt lightbulb for 10 hours.)

The term **electricity generation** refers to any one of several types of energy that is transformed into electricity. The transformation is usually done at a centralized **power plant**, which then distributes the electricity to the area around the plant. The first power plants burned coal to generate electricity. As well as coal, today's power plants run on other fossil fuels, the force of water, and nuclear energy. The newest ways of generating electricity— often called alternative energy—include solar power, tidal harnesses, wind generators, biomass, and geothermal resources. In fossil fuel, biomass, geothermal, or nuclear power plants, heat is released that boils water. High-pressure steam from the water turns the blades of a turbine. A **turbine** is like a large fan that uses mechanical energy to turn the blades. Then a **generator** transforms the rotating energy of the turbine into electricity.

Electrical power comes mainly from regional power plants. Those power plants are themselves fueled by various energy sources. In the United States, the major sources are coal, nuclear power, and natural gas. The chart on the next page shows the types of electricity generation we use in the United States and in what amounts. The map on the next page shows what parts of the country use what kinds of fuel.

U.S. Electrical Sources in 2005

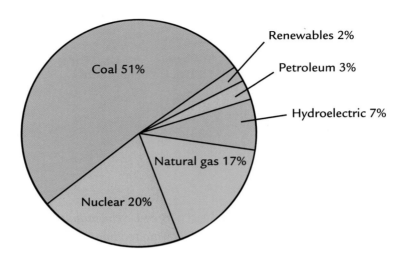

Coal 51%

Renewables 2%

Petroleum 3%

Hydroelectric 7%

Natural gas 17%

Nuclear 20%

Major Power Plants in the Continental United States, by Type

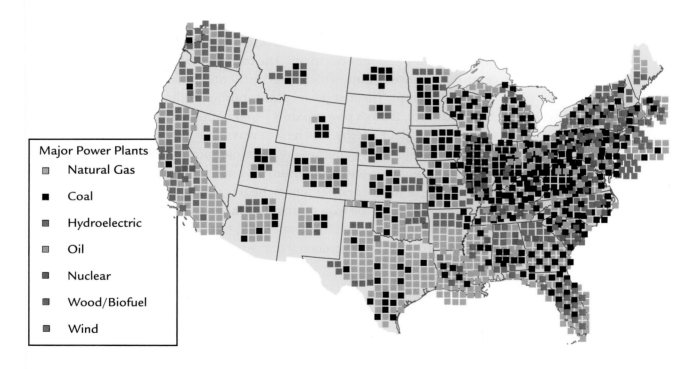

Major Power Plants

- Natural Gas
- Coal
- Hydroelectric
- Oil
- Nuclear
- Wood/Biofuel
- Wind

Nonrenewable Resources

Fossil Fuels—Coal, Petroleum, and Natural Gas

Fossil fuels such as coal, petroleum (crude oil), and natural gas come from plant materials and small animals that have been buried in the earth for millions of years. They are nonrenewable energy sources because it takes millions of years and special conditions for these fuels to form. Fossil fuels are convenient for us because the United States already has the infrastructure (such as railroads near coal mines, pipelines, power plants, and relay stations) to get and transport these fuels and transform their potential energy into electrical energy. Another advantage of fossil fuels is that the amount of energy released per kilogram of fuel burned is much greater than what burning renewable fuels, such as biomass, produces. The efficiency for burning varies, depending on the fuel, but fossil fuel efficiency is about 38–47%.

A big problem with burning any fuel is that it produces carbon dioxide, which contributes to global warming. Coal is the leading fuel source for electricity generation in the United States. When coal burns, however, the gases that are produced are major air pollutants. A growing body of evidence suggests that the carbon dioxide released from burning fossil fuels is the major cause of global warming. Petroleum, which is the raw material for gasoline, diesel, heating oil, and other fuel oils, and natural gas produce less pollution than coal. Natural gas produces the least pollution of the fossil fuels, but releases the least amount of energy per kilogram. There have been some technological advances that can reduce the amount of pollutants released during burning, particularly at coal plants.

Nuclear Energy

When atoms of radioactive elements, such as uranium and plutonium, are split apart, a huge amount of energy is released. Nuclear energy plants do not produce the air pollution of fossil-fuel-burning plants, nor do they produce carbon dioxide. The efficiency of a nuclear power plant, however, is about 35%. Of greater concern, nuclear power plants generate radioactive waste that can cause severe health and environmental problems. As a result, waste from nuclear power plants requires special handling, containers, transportation, and storage facilities so that the waste is safely contained for millions of years.

The danger to nearby communities in the case of an accident is far greater than for other kinds of power plants.

Nuclear fuel is usually categorized as a nonrenewable resource because the uranium mined from the earth cannot be replenished. However, a small amount of uranium can generate huge amounts of electricity. Compared to chemical energy such as fossil fuels, nuclear energy releases the largest amount of energy with the smallest mass.

Renewable Resources

Biomass Energy

Some power plants can burn biomass, such as wood, paper, organic material, or even garbage. The energy released by the burning is transformed into electricity in a similar way as energy is transformed from fossil fuels. Unlike fossil fuels, biofuels are a renewable resource because we will always produce waste products and we can continually grow plants used for biomass. Burning biomass can decrease the amount of waste that ends up in landfills, but it raises some environmental concerns because burning biofuels gives off pollution, although less than that from burning fossil fuels. Burning just about anything, even organic material, releases carbon dioxide that contributes to global warming. Even burning wood releases toxins, such as carbon monoxide, into the air. Sometimes collecting and transporting enough biomass to keep a power plant running is inefficient because the amount of energy per pound of biomass burned is not high. The efficiency varies from 22–40%, depending on the material burned.

Geothermal Energy

Geothermal energy is the product of heat transferring from the interior of the earth (the prefix *"geo-"* means earth) to the surface. Thermal energy in some places inside the earth is so intense that water seeping through the area boils. Energy companies pipe the naturally occurring hot water, steam, and other hot gases to the surface where it will run turbines or heat buildings directly. Once the water is cooled, it is injected back deep into the earth, where it reheats. Some of the steam and other gases are released to the air.

Unfortunately, some of the gases are foul smelling. Generally, however, geothermal power does not pollute the air or release carbon dioxide. Geothermal power plants do not take up much room, and little or no other kind of energy is needed to run them. However, the efficiency of a geothermal power plant is only 15%.

One limitation of geothermal energy is that only certain places on earth have water under the earth's surface hot enough to be used for geothermal plants. Many of these places are near active or recently active volcanoes, and many people do not want to live nearby. The amount of heat in the earth is enough to classify this type of energy as renewable, although some geothermal regions eventually cool down.

Hydroelectric Energy

In a hydroelectric plant, moving water turns the blades of turbines (the prefix "*hydro*"- means water). It does this by transforming the gravitational potential energy of water at the top of a waterfall into kinetic energy and then into electricity. While naturally flowing rivers and streams can be used to produce small amounts of electricity, large hydroelectric plants usually require the construction of a large dam. Hoover Dam, a large dam on the Colorado River, created a waterfall of 122 meters (400 feet), which is more than twice as high as Niagara Falls. Hydroelectric power is a renewable resource because the water cycle continually supplies water to streams and rivers. Building hydroelectric dams also creates lakes and reservoirs that increase the local water supply. This kind of power does not produce any pollution or waste outside of making the dam. Although building a dam is very expensive, once the dam is built, the cost of power is very low. Its efficiency is the highest of all types of electricity-generating plants and can be nearly 95%.

Dams do have negative environmental effects, such as a loss of fish and other aquatic animals and plants in the area. Building a large dam floods the area upstream, in some cases drowning out forests and forcing whole towns to move away. Downstream, the amount and quality of water may also change because the dam will have changed the flow of the water.

Solar Energy

Energy from the Sun can be converted directly into electricity by solar cells—no turbine or generator is necessary. This makes solar energy a convenient way to get electricity. The Sun's energy can also be used to heat water and other liquids to spin turbines, although this is less common than solar cells. Some solar energy is collected on the small scale of individual houses, which can easily power an individual home. Making the equipment for solar power produces some pollution, but using solar power does not. The efficiency of using solar cells to convert energy is about 15%.

There are large-scale solar facilities designed to serve the needs of a whole community. It takes a large number of solar collectors, and therefore large areas of land, to collect enough solar energy to power a community. Although solar energy is a renewable resource, communities relying on it need storage facilities or other sources of electricity for nights and cloudy days. Some parts of the country would have trouble generating enough electricity for their needs because of their climates.

Tidal Harness

Tidal harnessing captures the kinetic energy of ocean water between high and low tides. This kinetic energy turns the blades of a turbine connected to a nearby generator. This type of energy only works in areas where there is at

least 3-meters (10 feet) difference between high and low tides. Because tides are predictable, the energy is reliable. The efficiency is nearly 90%. Once the equipment is built, there is almost no chemical pollution. However, the equipment is so large that it increases the turbidity of the water nearby, and this affects birds and other wildlife. Although not used in the United States, there is hope that it may become a major source of energy here in the future.

Additionally, huge floats that use the waves to turn the blades of a turbine can harness the energy in ocean waves. Since waves are free and the equipment does not cost very much, there is almost no cost for the energy. However, waves are unpredictable, and it takes large waves to produce a significant amount of electricity. Not all areas around the world have consistently big waves. The equipment is noisy, and it is easily damaged by the constant pounding of the waves.

Wind Energy

Wind, which is simply moving air, can turn the blades of turbines. Today, large assemblies of windmills, known as wind farms, have been set up in areas of the country where the wind blows for long periods of time. Because each wind turbine produces a relatively small amount of electricity, vast areas of land are needed to hold all the windmills it takes to produce significant amounts of electrical energy. There are also small wind turbines designed for household electricity production for people who live in windy areas. As with solar energy, wind energy can be a good power source for people who want to power their own homes.

Windmills generate no pollution beyond that produced while making them. They do create some noise, and they can disrupt the environment. In some places certain species of birds and bats have been caught in the blades and killed. Although wind energy is a renewable resource, communities relying on it need large storage facilities or other sources of electricity for times when the wind is not blowing.

ANALYSIS

1. Which energy sources are:

    a. renewable?

    b. nonrenewable?

2. Which type of electrical energy generation do you feel has:

    a. the most important advantage?

    b. the greatest disadvantage?

3. A sunny and windy city near a mountain river currently uses 40% coal, 30% natural gas, 25% hydroelectric, and 5% other renewable methods for generating electricity. The community needs more electricity, and you have been hired to recommend the type(s) of electrical generation to install. Which energy facility(ies) should this city build for the future? Be sure to weigh the advantages and disadvantages of each energy type that you recommend.

4. Look at the information below about the top four electricity-producing countries in the world.

    a. What trends do you see in electricity generation of the major producers?

    b. France generates its 530 billion kilowatt hours (kWh) of electricity, using 10% fossil fuels, 11% hydroelectric, 78% nuclear power, and less than 1% geothermal, wind, and biomass. How is France's energy generation similar to or different from the trends you identified in Analysis Question 4a?

Annual Electricity Generation, by Country					
Country	Total generation (billion kWh)	Method of electricity generation (%)			
		Fossil fuels	Hydroelectric	Nuclear power	Geothermal, wind, and biomass
United States	3,900	71	7	20	2
China	1,800	82	15	2	<1
Japan	980	65	10	23	2
Russia	870	65	18	16	<1

EXTENSION 1

Contact your local electricity company, and find out what percent of their electrical generation comes from each source. They may call this the local "Electricity Generation Portfolio."

EXTENSION 2

Investigate how the use of fossil fuels in the United States compares to other countries. Go to the *Issues and Physical Science* page of the SEPUP website.

LABORATORY

One way of transforming potential energy into electricity is by battery. Batteries do not provide the large amounts of electricity that power plants do, and they don't serve communities in the same way as power plants. They are, however, a source of electricity that is important to everyday life, whether in a car, a phone, a wristwatch, or a hearing aid.

Batteries contain metals and other chemicals that store potential energy. When the chemicals in the battery are connected to a device and allowed to react, they release electrical energy. Once the reactants are used up, the battery no longer can produce electricity and is "dead." In rechargeable batteries, the battery regains potential energy when it is charged—by another source of electricity.

CHALLENGE ⟹ **What combination of metals makes the best battery to power a small motor?**

MATERIALS

For each group of four students

1 dropper bottle of 3% hydrogen peroxide solution

1 small piece of sandpaper

For each pair of students

SEPUP wet cell chamber

strip of each of the following metals:

    copper

    iron

    magnesium

    zinc

5 packages of table salt

1 plastic spoon

1 50-mL graduated cylinder

2 wire leads—one red and one black, with clips

1 clear plastic cup

1 electric motor

  masking tape

  paper towel

For each student

1 pair of safety goggles

SAFETY

Wear safety goggles at all times during this lab. Do not allow the solutions to touch your skin or clothing. Clean up any spills immediately. If accidental contact occurs, tell your teacher and rinse exposed areas. Wash your hands after completing the activity.

PROCEDURE

Part A: Testing the Motor

1. Put 25 ml of water into the plastic cup. Add 5 packages of salt. Add 25 drops of hydrogen peroxide. Stir until all of the salt is dissolved. Carefully pour the mixture into the SEPUP wet cell. This is the battery's **electrolyte**—the material that makes the liquid electrically conductive.

2. Attach a small piece of masking tape to the motor shaft to make a flag. This will allow you to see when the spindle on the motor is turning.

3. Clip one wire lead onto the copper strip and another wire lead onto the magnesium strip. Clip the other ends to the motor.

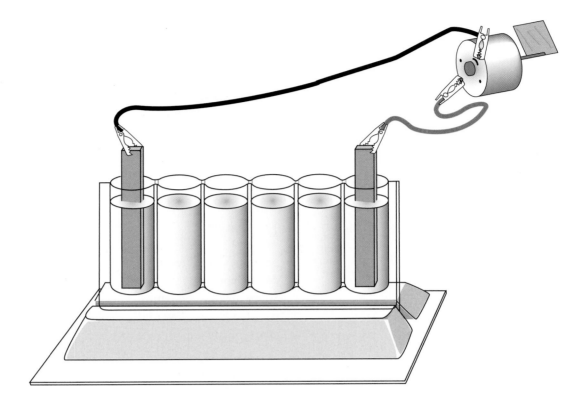

4. Lower the copper and magnesium strips into the outside slots of the SEPUP wet cell as shown. **There should be a small amount of metal sticking out of the cells.**

5. Observe the motor spinning.

   Hint: If the motor doesn't spin, try giving the flag a small push with your finger to start it. If it still does not spin, let your teacher know.

6. Once the motor spins, disconnect the wire leads. Remove the two metal pieces. Dry them, and then shine them with a piece of sandpaper. It is extremely important to completely dry the metals on a paper towel and clean both sides with the sandpaper!

Part B: The Effects of Different Metals

7. You just tested two metals, copper and magnesium, that, along with the electrolyte, transformed chemical energy into electrical energy. The motor transformed the electrical energy into the mechanical energy that caused the shaft to turn. Design an investigation to test other combinations of metals. While you're designing the investigation, think about the following questions:

   What is the purpose of your investigation?

   What will you observe or test?

What materials will you need to conduct your investigation?

How will you record your observations?

How will you use the results to make a conclusion?

8. Obtain your teacher's approval for your investigation.

9. Conduct your investigation, and record the results in your science notebook.

Part C: Other Effects

10. Investigate what happens when you place the metals closer together. Use two strips that caused the motor to turn slowly. Place them in the slots at opposite ends of the SEPUP wet cell. In steps, move one strip from slot to slot so that it gets closer to the other strip. Observe what happens to the motor during each step. Make a table in your science notebook to record the results.

11. Investigate what happens to the direction the shaft turns when you reverse the connections. Use the zinc and copper combination of metals to explore this. Record your observations in your science notebook.

12. Investigate what happens to the motor as you gradually remove both of the metal strips from the electrolyte. Use a combination that caused the motor to spin rapidly to explore this. Record your observation in your science notebook.

ANALYSIS

1. Was there a chemical change when you inserted the strips into the electrolyte? Describe any evidence that supports your answer.

2. Use your results from Part B to rank the metal combinations from 1 to 6, with 1 as the highest-releasing electrical energy rate, and 6 as the least. Describe any evidence that determined the ranking.

Magnesium–copper

Magnesium–iron

Zinc–copper

Zinc–magnesium

Zinc–iron

Copper–iron

3. Look at the table below that describes the reactivity of the metals used in this activity. Compare the table to your response in Analysis Question 2.

Reactivity of Common Metals		
Metal	**Reactivity**	**Tendency to give up electrons**
Magnesium	Most	Most
Zinc		
Iron	↓	↓
Copper	Least	Least

Based on the comparison:

a. Does reactivity alone indicate what combinations of metals will release the most energy?

b. What patterns do you see that could indicate why the most and least energy combinations occurred?

c. Gold is the least reactive metal known and tends not to give up electrons. Which metal from the table would you pair it with to make a strong battery? Explain your choice.

 4. Make a table that summarizes your investigation in Part C. It should identify each effect, summarize the results, and include a brief explanation of why you think each result happened.

5. From the materials in this activity, draw and label a battery that would produce the most energy.

EXTENSION

Design and conduct an investigation that tests the effect of changing the concentration of the electrolyte.

66 Connecting Circuits

INVESTIGATION

The batteries in the previous activity were part of an electrical circuit. A **circuit** is any path along which electrical energy can transfer. A circuit has to be a continuous loop made of electrically conducting material, such as copper. A circuit will work only if all the conductors in the loop are connected. For example, a light switch breaks a circuit when turned off and completes the circuit when turned on.

There are many kinds of circuits that range from simple to complex. With batteries a simple **series circuit** is one where all the components in the circuit are connected in succession with a battery. There is only one path for the electrical energy in the circuit. In a **parallel circuit**, the components are set up in the circuit so that the electrical energy has more than one conducting path from the battery.

CHALLENGE

How is energy transferred and transformed in an electrical circuit?

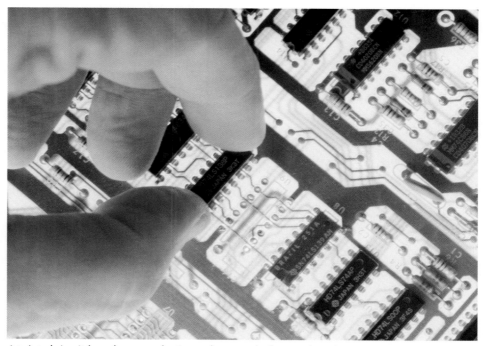

A printed circuit board uses conductive pathways etched onto a board to connect components.

MATERIALS

For each group of four students

1 buzzer
1 motor
1 strip each of:
    aluminum
    copper
    iron
    zinc
    magnesium
    polystyrene plastic
1 small carbon rod
1 glass rod
1 ceramic tile
1 block of wood
1 piece of granite
1 lightbulb in socket
2 wire leads with clips

For each pair of students

2 wire leads with clips
2 D (1.5 V) batteries
2 battery holders
1 lightbulb in socket

PROCEDURE

Electricity Symbols

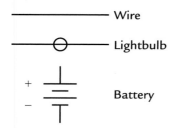

Wire

Lightbulb

Battery

Part A: Conductors in a circuit

1. With your partner, use the equipment to make one of the bulbs light up. In your notebook, draw a diagram of the circuit.

2. Replace the bulb and the socket with the motor. Observe and record what happens when the motor is part of the circuit.

3. Replace the motor in the circuit with the buzzer. Observe and record what happens when the buzzer is part of the circuit.

4. Design an investigation to determine what items from the materials list conduct electricity when placed in the circuit. Describe your design in your science notebook. Be sure to include:

   The purpose of your investigation.

   What you will observe or test.

   What materials you will need for conducting your investigation.

   What materials you predict will be good conductors.

   How you will record your observations.

   How you will use the results to make a conclusion.

5. Obtain your teacher's approval of your investigation.

6. Conduct your investigation, and record your results.

Part B: Series and Parallel Circuits

7. In your group of four, combine all your materials. Connect two batteries, four wire leads, and three lightbulbs in series. Use the diagram below to help you build the series circuit.

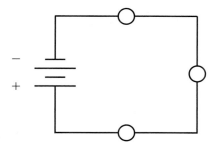

8. Unscrew one of the bulbs from the socket and observe what happens. Secure the lightbulb back into the socket, and record your observations in your science notebook.

9. Remove one of the bulbs and one wire from the circuit, and observe the circuit. Record your observations in your science notebook.

10. Remove another bulb and wire from the circuit, and observe the circuit carefully. Record your observations in your notebook. Make sure to comment on the differences between the 3-, 2-, and single-bulb combinations in series.

11. Disconnect the circuit.

12. Now build a parallel circuit using two batteries, six wire leads, and three lightbulbs. Use the diagram below to help you make the parallel circuit.

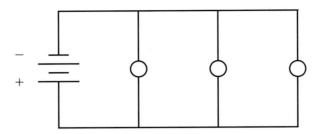

13. Remove one of the bulbs from its socket, and observe what happens. Return the lightbulb to the socket, and record your observations in your science notebook.

14. Replace one of the bulbs with the motor, and observe what happens.

15. Replace the motor with the buzzer, and observe what happens.

16. Remove the motor, and observe the circuit with two bulbs. Record your observations in your science notebook.

17. Remove another bulb and a wire from the circuit, and observe the circuit carefully. Record your observations in your science notebook. Make sure to comment on the differences between the 3-, 2-, and single-bulb combinations in parallel.

ANALYSIS

1. Which materials were the best conductors? Explain how you know these materials conducted electricity better than other materials

2. Describe the transfer and transformation of energy involved in a battery that lights up a bulb and runs a motor in a circuit.

3. Create a larger version of the Venn diagram shown below. Record the similarities of series and parallel circuits in the space that overlaps. In the labeled spaces that do not overlap, record differences between the circuits.

4. Holiday lights are lightbulbs that are wired in a parallel circuit. Why is this a better idea than putting them in series?

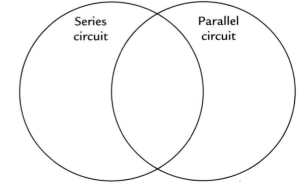

LABORATORY

Yasmin knew the lights in her room transformed electrical energy into light energy as part of an electrical circuit in the house. One time, she accidentally touched a lightbulb of a lamp she had just turned off, and it was quite hot. That means that some of the electrical energy was transformed into heat instead of light. She wondered how much of the bulb's energy was "lost" or given off as heat.

CHALLENGE ➡ **What is the efficiency of a lightbulb?**

MATERIALS

For each group of four students

- 1   9-volt battery
- 1   battery harness and leads
- 1   foam cap with flashlight bulb and socket
- 1   foam cap
- 1   SEPUP tray
- 1   graduated cylinder
- 2   metal-backed thermometers
- 1   timer

For each student

- 1   Student Sheet 53.1, "Anticipation Guide: Ideas About Energy," from Activity 53, "Home Energy Use"

SAFETY

Do not try this investigation with any other kind of battery or electrical energy source without consulting your teacher. Never, under any circumstances, place plugged-in electrical appliances in or near water.

PROCEDURE

Part A: Collecting Data

1. Using the graduated cylinder, carefully measure 12 mL of water into Cup A of the SEPUP tray.

2. Carefully place the foam cap with the bulb over Cup A and insert the thermometer, as shown on the next page.

3. Make a data table in your science notebook like the one on the next page.

4. Measure and record in the table the initial temperature of the water.

5. Use Cup E of the SEPUP tray as a control for this experiment. Decide in your group what should be placed in Cup E and what measurements should be taken.

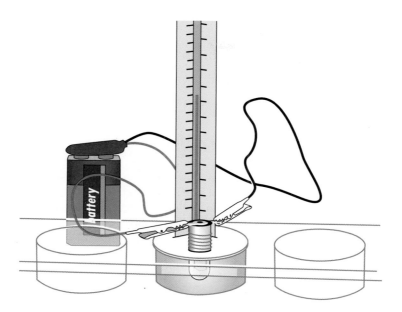

6. Make sure the battery is connected to the harness. Clip one wire to one of the prongs on the brass socket.

7. Clip the other wire to the other prong so that the bulb is lit, as shown above. Keep the lighted bulb in the water in Cup A for exactly 3 minutes. Time this as precisely as you can.

8. After 3 minutes, disconnect the battery from the bulb. Measure and record the temperature of the water.

9. Calculate the temperature changes of the water in Cups A and E, and record them in your table.

Lightbulb Data

Cup	Volume of water (mL)	Time (minutes)	Initial temperature (°C)	Final temperature (°C)	Temperature change (°C)
A					
E					

Part B: Calculating Efficiency

10. Make a table in your science notebook like the one below. Show your work and the calculations done in Procedure Steps 11–14 in this table.

Lightbulb Calculations

Cup	Thermal energy released (calories)	Electrical energy absorbed (calories)	Thermal energy output (%)	Light efficiency (%)
A				
E				

11. Calculate the thermal energy released from the flashlight bulb using the equation:

$$\text{energy released (calories)} = \text{temperature change (°C)} \times \text{mass of water (mL)}$$

Hint: 1 mL of water weighs 1 gram.

12. If the flashlight bulb uses about 27 calories of electrical energy for each minute it is lit, calculate the electrical energy input using the equation:

$$\text{Electrical energy absorbed (calories)} = \text{time bulb is lit (minutes)} \times \text{27 calories per minute}$$

13. Calculate the percent of thermal energy produced by the bulb using the equation:

$$\text{thermal energy output (\%)} = \frac{\text{thermal energy released}}{\text{electrical energy absorbed}} \times 100\%$$

14. Calculate the light efficiency of the bulb using the equation:

$$\text{Light efficiency (\%)} = 100\% - \text{thermal energy output (\%)}$$

ANALYSIS

1. Answer the following questions about the control in Cup E:

   a. Why should you use a control in an experiment?

   b. What did you place in the control cup? Explain why.

   c. What measurements did you take? Explain why.

   d. What did the results of your control tell you?

LABORATORY

Most of the energy types on Earth can be traced back to energy radiating from the Sun. As important as the Sun is to us, only a small fraction of its total radiant energy reaches Earth. Of the energy that does reach Earth, we can use only some of it to directly heat such things as houses, pools, office buildings, and food. In the last activity, you explored how solar energy can be transformed into electricity. In this activity, you will determine how efficient it is to transform the Sun's radiant energy into thermal energy.

CHALLENGE

What is the efficiency of a solar energy collector?

MATERIALS

For each group of four students

1   water pump, with clear tubing and connector
1   piece of black plastic tubing
1   white plastic tubing holder
1   D-cell (1.5 V) battery
1   battery holder
2   wire leads with clips, one red one black
2   metal-backed thermometers
1   50-mL graduated cylinder
1   foam cup
1   plastic cup

SAFETY

Do not try this investigation with any other kind of battery without consulting your teacher. Never, under any circumstances, place plugged-in electrical appliances in or near water. Be careful not to break the thermometers. Be aware that the metal on the thermometers may become quite hot in the sunlight.

PROCEDURE

Part A: Gathering the Data

1. With your group, use the diagram of the completed setup shown on the next page to guide you through the procedure.

2. Adjust the angle of the plastic holder so that it faces the Sun.

3. Attach one end of the black tubing to the pump by pushing it into the cylindrical opening on the side of the pump's base. The pump transports the heated water to and from the cup through the tubing.

4. Attach the red wire to the positive terminal of the pump (look for the small +). Connect the black wire to the negative terminal of the pump (look for the small –).

5. Place the pump upright in the foam cup. Avoid pinching the tubing.

6. Place the other end of the black tubing in the cup. This end of the tube returns the water to the cup. Make sure it is positioned so that it does not pour water onto the pump.

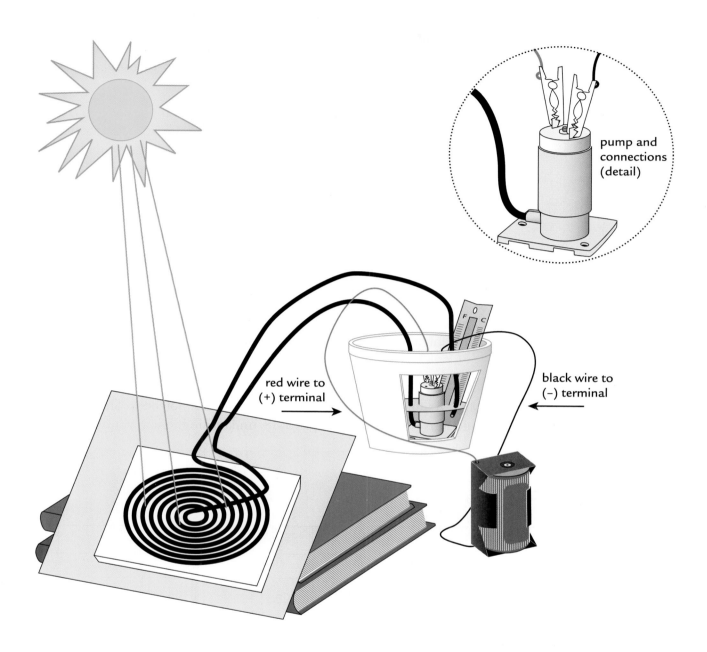

pump and
connections
(detail)

red wire to
(+) terminal

black wire to
(–) terminal

7. Place the battery in the holder so that its tip (positive end) faces the side of the holder that has the red connector. Attach the red wire from the pump to the red wire from the battery.

   Note: Do not attach the black wire at this time!

8. Measure 100 mL of water into the plastic cup. Carefully pour just enough water from the plastic cup into the foam cup, which contains the pump, to cover the base of the pump.

   Note: Do not completely submerge the pump in water.

9. Place a thermometer in the foam cup with the pump. Take the temperature of the water in that cup. Leave the thermometer inside the cup.

10. Make a data table of your own design to record the temperature of the water every minute for 15 minutes. Remember to include a place to record the temperature of the class control.

11. To start the water pump, connect the black wire to the negative terminal of the battery. Begin timing. As water goes from the cup into the tubing, slowly add the rest of your 100mL water. Do not allow the water level in the cup to rise more than 1 cm above the base of the pump.

12. Allow the pump to run for 15 minutes with direct sunlight on the tubing. Measure the temperature of the water every minute. Record this data in your table.

    Note: Check the pump every few minutes to make sure it is still sitting in the water. The pump will be damaged if it runs without water.

13. After 15 minutes, disconnect the wires from the pump. Record the final temperatures of the water in the pump cup and the class control data. Calculate the change in temperatures, and record it in your table.

Part B: Calculating Efficiency

14. Make a table like the one below in your science notebook. Show the calculations for Procedure Steps 15–18, and record them in your table.

Calculating Energy Efficiency

Energy transferred to water (calories)	
Area of solar heater (cm²)	
Energy transferred to the tubing (calories)	
Efficiency of heating system (%)	

15. You put 100 mL of water in the cup. Calculate how many calories of energy were transferred to the water.

    Hint: Look back at Activity 67, "Hot Bulbs," to remember how to calculate the calories transferred to the water.

16. The tubing holder is approximately 20 cm wide.

    a. With your group, decide what method you should use to determine the area of the solar heater.

    b. Estimate the surface area of the solar heater in centimeters. Explain how you came up with this number.

17. If the Sun supplies 1.5 calories of energy per square centimeter per minute to the Earth, calculate how many calories were supplied to your tubing in 15 minutes.

18. Calculate the efficiency of the solar heating system using the following equation:

$$\text{Efficiency (\%)} = \frac{\text{calories transferred to the water}}{\text{calories supplied to the tubing}} \times 100\%$$

ANALYSIS

1. The efficiency of a photovoltaic cell is about 11%. How does the efficiency of your solar heater compare?

2. How could you improve the design of your collector to increase its efficiency?

EXTENSIONS

Run the pump for the solar water-heater system using electricity from two solar cells placed in series rather than the battery. Investigate whether one solar cell will run the pump or if it takes more. Investigate ways to control the speed of the pump using the solar cells.

A woman in China uses a solar collector at her home to warm a tea kettle.

MODELING

When solar energy hits an object, the light can do several things. The light can be **absorbed**, or captured, by the object and transformed into heat. The light might also be **transmitted**, or travel through, the object and remain unaffected. Or, the light could be **reflected**, or bounced off, the surface of the object. In many cases, the light does some of each of these three. An example is when light hits glass: most of the light is transmitted through (since you can see through it), some is reflected (since you can see your own image), and a small amount is absorbed (since the glass heats up). Every object transmits, reflects, and absorbs some amount of solar energy depending on its individual properties.

CHALLENGE

Can you control the solar energy in a model house?

Light hitting this glass is reflected, transmitted and absorbed.

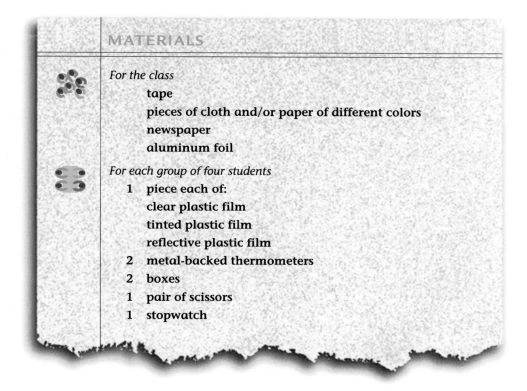

MATERIALS

For the class
- tape
- pieces of cloth and/or paper of different colors
- newspaper
- aluminum foil

For each group of four students
- 1 piece each of:
  - clear plastic film
  - tinted plastic film
  - reflective plastic film
- 2 metal-backed thermometers
- 2 boxes
- 1 pair of scissors
- 1 stopwatch

PROCEDURE

Part A: Build Your Model Houses

1. With your group, and using the materials provided for the class, modify one of your boxes (model house) so that it will absorb as much solar energy that can be transformed into heat as possible. Do not cut into or change the volume of the box.

2. Place one of the metal-backed thermometers in the center of your house.

3. Using the class materials, modify the other box so that it will absorb as little energy as possible. Do not cut into or change the volume of the box.

4. Place the second metal-backed thermometer in the center of your second house.

5. In your science notebook, draw a diagram of the two houses, and explain the choices you made in building it. Label the houses, "Warm House" and "Cool House."

Reflective windows are commonly used on commercial buildings to help control the solar energy going through the windows.

Part B: Testing Your Model Houses

6. Making sure your houses are NOT in sunlight, measure the temperature inside each house, and record it in your science notebook.

7. Place your houses in the sunlight for the time allowed by your teacher.

8. Record the final temperature inside your houses.

9. Calculate the temperature change in each house, and record it in your science notebook.

ANALYSIS

1. What was the change in temperature of each of the two houses you designed? If the changes were different, explain why. In your explanation use the words *absorb*, *reflect*, and *transmit*.

2. Compare your designs to those of your classmates. What materials tended to:

   a. absorb solar energy? Explain.

   b. reflect solar energy? Explain.

   c. transmit solar energy? Explain.

3. Imagine you are living in Texas during the summer. What type of window film would you want on your home's windows? Explain your choice, using evidence from this activity.

   a. clear

   b. tinted grey

   c. reflective

4. Imagine you are living in New York during the winter. What type of window film would you want on your home's windows? Explain your choice, using evidence from this activity.

   a. clear

   b. tinted grey

   c. reflective

READING

It would be simple to design an energy-efficient home if the temperature was always 21°C (70°F), and people did not use appliances. Most people, however, live in areas where the temperature varies a lot, and they depend on their refrigerators, furnaces, air conditioners, televisions, computers, and other appliances and electronic devices. In this activity, you will read about the major factors that determine how much energy is used in a home. You will also read about some actions people can take to use energy more efficiently.

CHALLENGE

How can features in a home affect the energy efficiency of a home?

Use the "Listen, Stop, and Write" strategy to help you with this reading. Listen as your teacher reads aloud. When he or she stops reading, close your book. Write down the main ideas you just heard.

READING

Energy Use in the Home

Every year, the United States consumes more energy than any other country in the world. As shown in the diagram below, about 22% of that energy is used in residential homes. The diagram also shows how residential energy is generally used.

Most people can reduce their costs and consumption of nonrenewable energy by focusing on their transportation and their homes. Just by driving

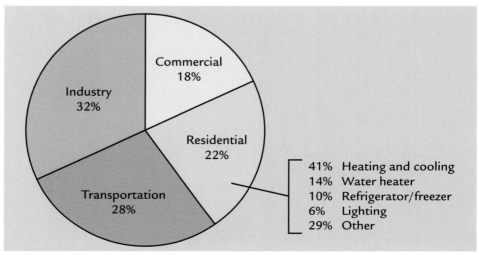

U.S. Energy Use in 2005

a gas-efficient car and driving less, for example, a person will buy less gasoline. Reducing energy use in the home, however, can be a little more challenging, especially for those who live in extreme climates where heating or air conditioning can be essential. Increasing efficiency in the home, however, is an important way to reduce energy use.

How much energy a home uses is affected by the size of the home, the number of people living in it, its location, the climate, and the type of energy available. In any case, however, better energy efficiency costs less and is less harmful for the environment.

Insulation

The biggest energy cost in a home is from maintaining a comfortable temperature. Since energy moves from a warmer to a cooler area, it can be difficult to keep warm air inside the building when it is cold outside and to keep hot air outside when it is very warm outside. The less energy it takes to accomplish that, the more energy-efficient the building. One way of slowing the movement of energy is to use insulating materials, such as concrete brick, and to insulate the walls of the building. In the summer insulation keeps a home cooler, and in the winter it keeps a home warmer. Insulation that is placed between walls and between floors and ceilings is made of various materials and comes in many forms, such as rolls or blankets of fibers, sprayed-in foam, or rigid sheets. It can be anywhere from three to 75 centimeters (1–30 inches) thick. How much insulation a building should have depends on its design, the climate, local energy costs, and the homeowner's budget. While most buildings have insulation in the walls, an energy-efficient home usually has insulation under the floors and above the ceilings as well.

Windows

Windows are a major source of energy transfer in a building. While most windows still have single panes of glass, high-performance windows have dual panes or even triple panes. This means there are two or three pieces of glass with a layer of air or some other gas, such as argon, in between them. That layer of air or gas acts as an insulator, preventing energy transfer. Additionally, high performance windows may have glazes that are similar to the films that you worked with in the last activity. These prevent energy transfer and also protect furniture from sun damage. High-performance windows have frames made of wood or fiberglass that also insulate. The windows are sealed tightly in their frames so air cannot leak in or out. No matter how efficient the window is, however, it does not block energy transfer as well as a solid wall does. Therefore, the more window space a home has, the less energy-efficient it will be overall.

Heating and Cooling Equipment

Heating systems are a significant factor in the total amount of energy used in a home—nearly half of a family's energy bill is spent on heating and cooling it. Most of the time, a home's location determines what type of energy is available for heating and cooling. For example, natural gas is the cleanest-burning fossil fuel, but in many areas of the United States, it is not available. People in those areas must depend on electric heaters, oil, or propane gas for heat. Although renewable sources such as wind, solar, and geothermal energy are environmentally friendly, they are not available in many areas. Even if they are available, the cost to install them can be very high.

Heating and cooling are important not only in homes, but also in large buildings. The heating, ventilation and air conditioning (HVAC) systems in commercial buildings are designed to maintain a safe and healthy climate.

Many heating systems are built around a central furnace that burns a fossil fuel. A duct system or radiator system then distributes hot air or hot water around the house. The most common sources of energy for this type of heat are natural gas, propane, and oil. Sometimes a heater or furnace is located in one room only and energy is not distributed through the home; you might see this is in an old country house with a wood stove or in an apartment with a fireplace or a wall heater in the living room. Houses that do not have some kind of furnace often have baseboard heaters that run on electricity. The electricity comes from a utility company or from a renewable source such as solar.

Buildings can be cooled in several ways, too. A cooling system that includes air conditioning is one way, but passive-energy designs can also be effective. A passive-energy design doesn't depend on external energy to run it, as an air conditioner does. Instead it involves building the house in a way that the physical structure of the house and its outdoor surroundings control the temperature. One effective passive design for keeping a house cool is to plant trees and vegetation close to the house to provide shade, especially by the windows. Overhangs, such as wide roofs and window awnings that block the sunlight, are effective as well. Windows that block or reflect sunlight help keep energy out of a building. Another way to keep a house cool is to take advantage of natural ventilation. Architects often design houses with windows and doors placed in ways that allow air to circulate when there are breezes. Fans—whether ceiling fans, portable fans, or whole house fans—are less expensive to operate than an air-conditioning system.

By changing the amount of solar energy coming into the building, the adjustable blinds on this building use a passive-energy design that controls the inside temperature.

Unfortunately, some climates are too hot for houses to stay cool with these methods only—especially in summer. Many house in hot climates need both passive-energy designs and air conditioning.

Water Heaters

Most water heaters that supply hot water to bathrooms and kitchens consist of a large tank of water and a source of energy, such as gas, fuel oil, electricity, or even solar panels. Cold water runs into the tank at the bottom, and then as it heats up, a pipe takes it from the top of the water heater and through pipes to your faucets. Once the water is heated, it must stay warm and ready for use, and so energy-efficient water heaters are well insulated. Traditional hot water heaters use a significant amount of energy to keep the water in the tank warm so it is ready all the time. Newer water heaters, called "tankless" heaters, heat the water on demand instead of continually warming a tank that experiences energy loss. A tankless water heater system can supply a whole house or just a couple of faucets, such as in a bathroom. Tankless heaters are much more energy-efficient than traditional tank heaters, but sometimes they involve running water for a long time at the tap before hot water comes out.

Lighting and Appliances

Compact fluorescent lightbulbs use about one-third of the energy of typical incandescent bulbs. Additionally, because they do not get as hot, they are safer than other bulbs, especially halogen bulbs. As you discovered in a previous activity, compact fluorescent bulbs cost more to buy initially but save energy over time.

The energy efficiency of household appliances varies greatly. Older appliances, such as gas stoves where pilots for burners and the oven are always burning, tend to be much less energy-efficient than new ones. Even how appliances are used can make a difference in the amount of energy they consume. For example, leaving air space around a refrigerator's coils and keeping them clean makes a refrigerator more efficient. Opening the refrigerator door as little as possible and running a dishwasher on the shortest cycle or without the dry cycle improves energy efficiency. For washing clothes, using a low-water, front-loading machine and cold water save energy.

New appliances have two tags on them. One states the cost of the appliance; the other states how much it costs to operate the appliance for a year. This is called the energy rating because it gives a measure of the appliance's energy usage. Energy Star appliances have a high energy rating because they use energy more efficiently than standard appliances. However, Energy Star appliances are generally more expensive to buy. Like lightbulbs, often the least expensive appliance costs more money to operate.

Making Choices

When home dwellers select the things that make up their homes, such as construction materials, insulators, heaters, air conditioners, windows, and appliances, they are often faced with hard economic choices. On one hand, it takes less money to buy less efficient equipment. The payoff from a fluorescent lightbulb, an Energy Star appliance, or a new kind of water heater is not immediate. Over a few years, however, the extra up-front cost for an energy efficient item pays off, and the consumer starts saving money.

Many state and federal programs help home dwellers get the cash they need to buy more efficient equipment through rebates, tax incentives, and loans. Often, it makes the most sense to improve many things at once. For example, getting a more efficient furnace is not nearly as effective as getting the furnace and then keeping the heat in the home with new windows and insulation. Making an energy efficient home involves planning ahead, spending some money, and then having bit of patience for the savings to start.

This homeowner in Oregon took advantage of a tax incentive to outfit her home with a solar panel hot water system.

ANALYSIS

1. What are three things that people who live in older houses can do to make their houses more energy efficient? Explain why those actions would succeed.

2. Your community is building a new school on a tight budget. The town planners do not want to buy energy-efficient equipment for the school because it will cost more. Do you agree with this idea? Explain why or why not.

3. **Reflection:** What energy-efficient features described in the reading do you have, or could you have, in your own home?

EXTENSION

Find out more about making a home energy-efficient by going to the *Issues and Physical Science* page of the SEPUP website. Then use all the information you have to make an energy-improvement plan specifically for your home.

The winter after Yasmin helped her mom insulate their house was very cold. When the energy bill came, they looked at it together to see the effect of the new insulation. "It is $320 lower than last winter!" said Yasmin triumphantly.

"Yes," said her mom, "But remember, it cost $400 to buy the insulation."

Her mom's remark upset Yasmin. She said, "Well, then why did we do it? We just lost money!"

"Because," her mother explained, "the savings are not a one-time event. We will continue to save every winter from now on. So next year, the insulation cost will be recovered. Every year after that, the money saved goes into our pocket."

"I see," said Yasmin thoughtfully, "It is better to look at energy use over a long time."

In this activity, you are part of a team of energy experts that works with families to reduce energy costs in the home. Your job is to improve energy efficiency and reduce the use of nonrenewable resources. The families each have a budget of $5,000 that they can spend now, and they will have another $5,000 in a few years for more improvements. Some families have also thought about borrowing money now or saving their current funds until later so they can make more improvements at one time.

CHALLENGE

Can you help a family decide what energy improvements they should invest in?

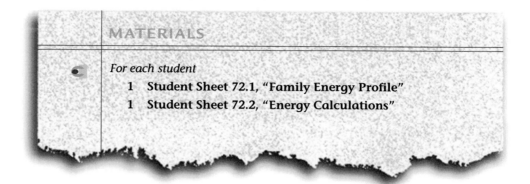

MATERIALS

For each student
1   **Student Sheet 72.1, "Family Energy Profile"**
1   **Student Sheet 72.2, "Energy Calculations"**

PROCEDURE

1. With your group, review the table of Energy Improvements shown below. Discuss what each improvement means. In your science notebook, explain how energy is conserved by each improvement.

Energy Improvements	
Energy use in home	**Ways to improve efficiency**
Heating and cooling	Install a programmable thermostat Add insulation Replace windows Seal windows, doors, ducts Replace source or burner Replace AC system
Water heater	Change type or use more efficient model
Refrigerator/freezer	Buy efficient model such as Energy Star
Lights	Use compact fluorescent
Other	Buy efficient appliances and electronics Add passive-energy devices

2. With the class, review the family profile on the next page.

Family Energy Profile: Buffalo, New York

Annual energy cost: $8,700

Buffalo

Average summer temperature: High: 27°C (80°F) Low: 18°C (63°F)

Average winter temperature: High: 0°C (32°F) Low: –7°C (19°F)

Yasmin, her brother Joe, and their mother live in a small house. Last summer, Yasmin helped her mom insulate the house, for which they got a rebate from the state. They think there must be more ways to save energy in their house. They use electric baseboard heat. They have a very old electric water heater and appliances, including the refrigerator that just broke. The windows are original to the house that was built in the 1960s, but the house has good ventilation and is shaded by trees. Yasmin's mom plans to do a lot of improvement work herself, except for large installations such as furnaces or solar panels.

Approximate Improvement Costs & Savings:

Improvement	Cost of materials (dollars)	Cost to install (dollars)	Annual energy savings (dollars)
Programmable thermostat	70	100	300
Dual-pane wood-frame windows (throughout house)	3,000	600	400
Seal windows, doors, ducts	400	230	300
Solar panels (at the home)	20,000	5,000	2,200
Wind power (at the home)	10,000	6,000	1,900
High-efficiency electric heat pump	1,600	230	1,300
Energy Star gas furnace	3,300	2,400	3,000
Efficient oil furnace	4,000	2,000	2,500
High-efficiency central air conditioning	5,500	2,000	20
Energy Star single-room air conditioner	200	50	10
Energy Star electric water heater, tankless	4,500	1,000	1,800
Energy Star gas water heater (includes gas line)	2,000	1,750	850
Compact fluorescent lightbulbs (high-use lights)	100	20	110
Energy Star refrigerator/freezer	1,800	80	20
Energy Star washing machine	900	80	100
Energy Star dryer	800	80	50
Energy Star dishwasher	330	90	30
Deciduous trees and shading vegetation	400	100	50

3. Your teacher will assign you a family that is profiled on Student Sheet 72.1, "Family Energy Profile." Read the profile carefully.

4. Consider the following for your family:

   • Needs based on the average high and low temperatures in the location

   • Immediate cost of the improvement versus the cost over a longer time

   • Major environmental impact of improvements

   • Other recommendations that are not included in the table of Energy Improvements

5. Use Student Sheet 72.2, "Energy Calculations," to help you calculate the long-term benefits of the improvements.

6. Use your ideas and your "Family Energy Profile" Student Sheet to decide what improvements your family should implement. As you work:

   • Listen to and consider explanations and ideas of other members of your team.

   • If you disagree with your team members about what features to include, explain why you disagree.

ANALYSIS

1. Write a report that gives your energy-improvement recommendation for your family within the budget given. In the report, explain why you recommend the improvement(s). Include a discussion of the trade-offs involved in the choices you made.

2. Would the recommendations you made work for families in other locations? Explain why or why not.

3. If money were not a limiting factor, what else would you recommend for your family?

4. How does reducing energy costs help the environment?

EXTENSION 1

Go to the *Issues and Physical Science* page of the SEPUP website, and investigate what energy saving measures you and your family can take where you live.

EXTENSION 2

Research the electricity costs in your area and compare them to the cities in the table on the next page.

Electricity Costs in Five Cities*			
	Cost of electricity (kWh)	Cost of heating: electric heat per year (dollars)	Cost of cooling: central air conditioning per year (dollars)
Boise	.06	1,900	80
Buffalo	.15	5,400	90
Chicago	.08	2,900	100
Houston	.10	860	470
Palm Springs	.12	830	1,200

* The costs are for homes of a similar size and the same number of people living in each home.

Index

A **bold** page number identifies the page on which the term is defined.

CREDITS